STEWART

18 Pasture Lane
Poughkeepsie, NY
12603

CHEMICAL ENGINEERING KINETICS

THE SERIES

ARIES AND NEWTON—*Chemical Engineering Cost Estimation*
BADGER AND BANCHERO—*Introduction to Chemical Engineering*
CLARKE—*Manual for Process Engineering Calculations*
COMINGS—*High Pressure Technology*
CORCORAN AND LACEY—*Introduction to Chemical Engineering Problems*
DODGE—*Chemical Engineering Thermodynamics*
GRISWOLD—*Fuels, Combustion, and Furnaces*
GROGGINS—*Unit Processes in Organic Synthesis*
HENLEY AND BIEBER—*Chemical Engineering Calculations*
HUNTINGTON—*Natural Gas and Natural Gasoline*
JOHNSTONE AND THRING—*Pilot Plants, Models, and Scale-up Methods in Chemical Engineering*
KATZ, CORNELL, KOBAYASHI, POETTMANN, VARY, ELENBAAS, AND WEINAUG—*Handbook of Natural Gas Engineering*
KIRKBRIDE—*Chemical Engineering Fundamentals*
KNUDSEN AND KATZ—*Fluid Dynamics and Heat Transfer*
KOHL AND RIESENFELD—*Gas Purification*
LEE—*Materials of Construction*
LEVA—*Fluidization*
LEWIS, RADASCH, AND LEWIS—*Industrial Stoichiometry*
MANTELL—*Adsorption*
MANTELL—*Electrochemical Engineering*
McADAMS—*Heat Transmission*
McCABE AND SMITH, J. C.—*Unit Operations of Chemical Engineering*
MICKLEY, SHERWOOD, AND REED—*Applied Mathematics in Chemical Engineering*
NELSON—*Petroleum Refinery Engineering*
PERRY (EDITOR)—*Chemical Business Handbook*
PERRY (EDITOR)—*Chemical Engineers' Handbook*
PETERS—*Elementary Chemical Engineering*
PETERS—*Plant Design and Economics for Chemical Engineers*
PIERCE—*Chemical Engineering for Production Supervision*
REID AND SHERWOOD—*The Properties of Gases and Liquids*
RHODES, F. H.—*Technical Report Writing*
RHODES, T. J.—*Industrial Instruments for Measurement and Control*
ROBINSON AND GILLILAND—*Elements of Fractional Distillation*
SCHMIDT AND MARLIES—*Principles of High-polymer Theory and Practice*
SCHWEYER—*Process Engineering Economics*
SHERWOOD AND PIGFORD—*Absorption and Extraction*
SHREVE—*The Chemical Process Industries*
SMITH, J. M.—*Chemical Engineering Kinetics*
SMITH, J. M., AND VAN NESS—*Introduction to Chemical Engineering Thermodynamics*
TREYBAL—*Liquid Extraction*
TREYBAL—*Mass-transfer Operations*
TYLER AND WINTER—*Chemical Engineering Economics*
VILBRANDT AND DRYDEN—*Chemical Engineering Plant Design*
VOLK—*Applied Statistics for Engineers*
WALAS—*Reaction Kinetics for Chemical Engineers*
WALKER, LEWIS, McADAMS, AND GILLILAND—*Principles of Chemical Engineering*
WILLIAMS AND JOHNSON—*Stoichiometry for Chemical Engineers*
WILSON AND RIES—*Principles of Chemical Engineering Thermodynamics*
WILSON AND WELLS—*Coal, Coke, and Coal Chemicals*
WINDING AND HASCHE—*Plastics, Theory and Practice*

Chemical Engineering Kinetics

J. M. SMITH

Dean of Technology
University of New Hampshire
Durham, New Hampshire

McGRAW-HILL BOOK COMPANY, INC.

New York   Toronto   London

1956

CHEMICAL ENGINEERING KINETICS

Library of Congress Catalog Card Number 56-6971

v

58692

THE MAPLE PRESS COMPANY, YORK, PA.

PREFACE

Industrial operations can be divided into component parts which are primarily physical or chemical. Chemical engineers are concerned with both types. The physical processes of most interest are based upon rates of mass, momentum, and energy transfer. Application of the principles of chemistry and physics to these processes has been successful in developing methods of designing commercial equipment for heat transfer, distillation, crystallization, and many of the other unit operations. On the other hand, progress has been slower in arriving at quantitative design procedures for chemical operations. This is due to the complexity in analyzing and correlating rate data for chemical reactions. The quantitative treatment of chemical processes is further complicated because heat, momentum, and mass transfer frequently occur simultaneously with chemical conversion.

During recent years the science of chemical kinetics has advanced rapidly. The absolute rate theory has stimulated theoretical progress, and new experimental techniques have improved rate data. Catalysis is better understood than heretofore, and progress has been significant in interpreting processes where chemical reactions are accompanied by physical transfer operations. Taken together, these advances make it possible to present sound design methods for several types of reaction equipment and thus bring reactor design closer to the stage of development achieved in the unit operations. This book has as its objective the presentation of these design procedures and their application to practical problems.

As used in this book, the term "design" refers only to process design problems, i.e., the specification of temperatures, pressures, composition, flow variables, size and shape of the equipment, and other properties of the reaction system. Plant design problems, including such questions as location, materials of construction, and mechanical design features, are not treated in detail.

The material is arranged, in general, so as to present the underlying theory and the necessary technical tools in the early chapters. Chapter 2 is devoted to a review of methods of evaluating the energy release of chemical reactions and the equilibrium limitations on the extent of reaction.   After the thermodynamic summary the concepts of chemical kinetics are introduced.   The treatment at this point is concerned not with reaction equipment but rather with the science of kinetics, particularly the newer theoretical developments and methods of interpreting experimental data.

The subject of reactor design is introduced in Chap. 4 by presenting the construction features and general design principles for several types of reactors.   The remaining chapters are devoted to the application of these principles to the design of specific reactors.   An attempt has been made to arrange the material in increasing order of complexity.   Homogeneous reactions are studied first.   This is followed by a treatment of adsorption and catalysis and their application to catalytic reactors.   In preparation for the final chapter, heat- and mass-transfer processes in fixed-bed and fluidized-bed catalytic reactors are considered.   Then the complex problem is treated in which heat- and mass-transfer and chemical-reaction processes all affect the design.

The book has been written at a level suitable for the fourth year of undergraduate work or for the beginning graduate student.   A knowledge of the rudiments of heat- and mass-transfer processes is desirable, and some background in chemical thermodynamics is necessary.

The suggestions of numerous persons have been of value in preparing the book.   All these are gratefully acknowledged.   Professors E. L. Piret and Theodore Vermeulen, and Robert Von Berg, have reviewed portions of the manuscript and offered constructive comments.   The assistance of these colleagues has been most helpful.

J. M. Smith

CONTENTS

CHAPTER 1

INTRODUCTION

For the most part, equipment for carrying out chemical reactions on a commercial scale is now designed empirically. However, in the past two decades significant advances have been made, both in the science of chemical kinetics and, particularly, in the design procedures for treating combinations of chemical and physical rate processes. These developments have made it possible to place the design of reaction equipment on a more rational and predictable basis.

The over-all problem of determining the size of a reactor can be divided logically into two consecutive parts. The first is the study of the rate at which the chemical reaction occurs and the variables which affect this rate. This is the subject of chemical kinetics. The second is the design problem of using rate data to determine how large the equipment should be to obtain the required quantity of product. This is the subject of reactor design. The breakdown into the separate parts is similar to the conventional approach employed to determine the size of heat exchangers. Here the first phase is the evaluation of the heat-transfer coefficient (similar to the rate-of-reaction determination in reaction kinetics), and the second is the use of this coefficient in a design equation for determining the size (heat-transfer area) of the exchanger.

If the principles underlying the reaction of chemical species were fully developed so that the reaction rate could be predicted as a function of the operating variables, it would be possible to proceed directly to the second phase of the problem and design the commercial-scale equipment without kinetic studies on an experimental basis. Actually, the fundamentals governing chemical reactions are not fully understood, and rates cannot be predicted accurately, so that the engineer must be concerned with both the experimental determination of the rate of the reaction and the design of commercial equipment from the rate data. At this point the similarity between the heat-exchanger and reactor-design problems ends. Thus the fundamentals of heat transfer are well enough known and sufficient experimental data exist so that, in most cases, the heat-transfer coefficient can be predicted and then the exchanger sized without the need for experimental work.

1

Because of the necessity for experimental determination of the rate of reaction, chemical engineers have in the past usually solved the design problem as well as the kinetics problem by carrying out experimental investigations on small-scale equipment of progressively larger size until the results can be projected to a commercial-scale plant. In this approach rates of reaction are not measured, but, instead, the total conversion is obtained in the pilot plant. The drawback to this method is that little information is obtained about the fundamentals governing the rate of the reaction or the design problem. Each reactor design must be treated independently and a separate pilot plant built, previous work being of no fundamental value in later investigations. Recently the more logical procedure of first measuring the rate of the reaction (or interpreting pilot-plant results in terms of empirical rate equations) and then attempting to develop design methods has been the subject of considerable work. Fair progress has been made by this method of attack, and the major developments are described in the chapters that follow. The remainder of this chapter is devoted to a more detailed qualitative discussion of the separate problems of reaction kinetics and reactor design, a classification of reaction equipment, and an analysis of the relationship between kinetics and thermodynamics.

1-1. Kinetics. Chemical kinetics, or reaction kinetics, is the quantitative study of the rate at which chemical reactions occur. This rate can vary from a very large value to essentially zero. In the production of photographic film the ionic reaction between potassium bromide and silver nitrate is so rapid as to appear to be instantaneous. On the other hand, the rate of combination of hydrogen and oxygen at room temperature is immeasurably slow. However, most industrially important reactions occur at rates between these extremes, and it is in these cases that the chemical engineer must apply a knowledge of kinetics in order to determine the size of plant equipment.

The rate of a chemical reaction is influenced by a large number of variables describing the condition of the reaction system. Temperature, pressure, composition of reaction mixture, presence or absence of a catalyst, age of catalyst—all may have an important effect on the rate of the reaction. Hence the subject of kinetics must include the study of the effect of these variables upon the rate of chemical transformation.

The field of kinetics is a relatively new one. The first quantitative measurement of reaction rates was made in the middle of the nineteenth century by Wilhelmy,[1] Berthelot and St. Gilles,[2] and Harcourt and Esson.[3] The first attempt to develop a theory explaining the manner in which

[1] L. Wilhelmy, *Pogg. Ann.*, **81**:413, 499 (1850).
[2] M. Berthelot and L. P. St. Gilles, *Ann. chim. et phys.* (3), **63**:385 (1862).
[3] A. V. Harcourt and W. Esson, *Proc. Roy. Soc. (London)*, **14**:470 (1865).

molecules of a substance react was that of Arrhenius[1] in 1889. He postulated the existence of inert and active molecules of the reactants and that
only the active ones possessed sufficient energy to take part in the reaction. Since these early developments there have been a great many
experimental studies of reaction rates for a wide variety of reactions,
but few noteworthy advances in theory until the work of Eyring and
Polanyi[2] beginning in 1920. Using only such fundamental information
as the configurations, dimensions, and interatomic forces of the reacting
molecules, these investigators postulated an activated-complex theory for
predicting the rate of reaction. Because of the lack of exact knowledge
of the interatomic forces, etc., for any but the most simple molecules the
activated-complex theory is not now useful for computing reaction-rate
data accurate enough for engineering work. While these theoretical
developments have been of great value in the search for an understanding of how and why a chemical reaction takes place, the quantitative
evaluation of the rate of reaction requires an experimental investigation.

In comparison with a field such as thermodynamics, where the fundamentals of the science are well established, reaction kinetics is not clearly
understood. As a consequence much more attention must be given to
experimental methods of obtaining solutions to problems, and frequently
results must be treated in an empirical fashion.

After the kinetics of the reaction are known, the size of reactor for any
set of operating conditions should be able to be computed, just as the
heat exchanger area can be calculated once the heat-transfer coefficient
is known. Actually the reactor-design problem is much more complex.
This is due mainly to two factors: (1) the complex relationship between
the rate of reaction and the variables which affect it; (2) the possibility
that physical processes such as mass transfer and heat transfer, as well
as the chemical-reaction step, may have to be taken into account in
evaluating the over-all rate of transformation of the reactant into the
desired product.

An example of this second factor is evident from an analysis of the
rate of hydrogenation of coal in batch equipment.[3] It has been found
that agitation (rocking the bomb) results in greatly increased rates of
hydrogenation. This can be explained only if it is postulated that the
over-all rate of hydrogenation is affected by the rate of diffusion of the
hydrogen gas to the surface of the coal and through the porous structure
into the interior, as well as by the chemical-reaction rate at the surface.
The rate of diffusion of reactants to a catalyst surface, and products from

[1] S. Arrhenius, *Z. physik. Chem.*, **4**:226 (1889).

[2] H. Eyring and M. Polanyi, *Z. physik. Chem. B*, **12**:279 (1931).

[3] J. L. Bray and C. H. Stockman, *Purdue Univ. Eng. Bull.* 111, *Research Ser.*,
November, 1950.

the surface, may also have an effect on the design of *continuous* catalytic reactors. One of many examples of this is the study of Olson and coworkers,[1] who found that the rate of oxidation of sulfur dioxide with a platinum-on-alumina catalyst increases as the rate of flow of gas past the surface of the catalyst increases. This increase in rate is explained by the greater turbulence, and hence increased diffusion rates, accompanying the higher gas velocities past the catalyst.

The difficulties introduced because of the complex relationship between rate of reaction and operating variables are illustrated by considering the effect of temperature. A commercial reactor may be operated adiabatically (no heat transfer to the surroundings), or energy as heat may be transferred to or from the reaction equipment. A different temperature distribution will result for each type of operation, and, accordingly, the rate of reaction will be different. This in turn means that the size of the reactor will depend upon the heat-transfer conditions.

1-2. Classification of Reactors. Reaction equipment can be classified according to the properties of the chemical system. A distinction is drawn by this means between homogeneous and heterogeneous reactions. Heterogeneous systems are frequently catalytic, but not necessarily so. Thus the important class in which the reactants and products are gases and the catalyst is a solid falls within the heterogeneous category. However, noncatalytic reactions between a gas and a solid are also heterogeneous. Some reaction mixtures exist in two or more liquid phases. Organic nitrations and sulfonations, for example, are frequently heterogeneous in this way. Homogeneous reactions may be gaseous, liquid, and also either noncatalytic or catalytic.

The division between homogeneous and heterogeneous is more important from a reactor-design viewpoint than a classification according to whether or not a catalyst is used. This is because the physical processes of heat and mass transfer, which may influence the design procedures, are affected by the phase condition of the reaction system. For example, in a heterogeneous mixture additional diffusional resistances may be introduced at the phase boundary. On the other hand, whereas catalysis influences the numerical value of the rate, generally the same variables are involved as in a noncatalytic case.

A further subdivision according to type of equipment and operating conditions is helpful. Reactors are usually in the form of (1) a cylindrical or spherical tank in which the entire reaction mixture is concentrated in one space or (2) a tube in which the mixture flows from one end to the other with little or no mixing. In fact the differences between these two kinds of reactors are best described in terms of the degree of mixing. In the tank form it is possible to obtain a uniform concentration with

---

[1] R. W. Olson, R. W. Schuler, and J. M. Smith, *Chem. Eng. Progr.*, **46**:614 (1950).

adequate agitation, while in a tubular reactor little mixing of the reaction mixture is possible.   These differences profoundly affect the importance of the physical processes of heat and mass transfer, and hence entirely different design procedures are employed for tank and tubular reactors.   Tank systems may be operated either continuously or batchwise, while tubular reactors are always run on a continuous flow basis.   The effects of geometry and operating procedure on the behavior of reaction mixtures are discussed in more detail in Chap. 4.

Owing to the great variety in the physical and chemical properties of reaction mixtures, reactors frequently take special form.   A lime kiln is an example of a noncatalytic heterogeneous reactor in which the reactant and products constitute two solid phases and one gas phase.   Energy for the reaction is provided by passing hot combustion gases over the solid limestone.   The horizontal rotary type is supplied with internal baffles to provide better contact between the combustion gases and limestone. The blast furnace is a similar heterogeneous case involving solid and gas phases, but more complex because of the numerous reactions taking place. The oxidation of ethanol to acetaldehyde and nitric oxide to nitrogen dioxide is commonly accomplished by passing the gaseous reactants over a thin gauze of platinum which acts as a catalyst.   In this case the reactor is the platinum gauze, a circular or rectangular section, several feet in diameter, and an inch or more in thickness.   The chamber process for the manufacture of sulfuric acid is another example of a specialized reactor.   While some reaction occurs elsewhere in the system, the reaction chambers themselves are boxlike vessels lined with lead.   No attempt will be made to treat the design of these unusual cases.   Instead the emphasis will be placed on the tank and tubular types, where the geometry is simple enough to develop quantitative design procedures.

1-3. Kinetics and Thermodynamics.   From the principles of thermodynamics and certain thermodynamic data the maximum extent to which a chemical reaction can proceed may be calculated.   For example, at 1 atm pressure, 680°C, and starting with one mole of sulfur dioxide and one-half mole of oxygen, 50 per cent of the sulfur dioxide can be converted to sulfur trioxide.   Such thermodynamic calculations result in maximum values for the conversion, or extent, of a chemical reaction, since they are correct only for conditions such that there is no further tendency for change with respect to time, i.e., equilibrium conditions. It follows from this that the net rate of a chemical reaction must be zero at this equilibrium point; otherwise the composition of the reaction system would change with respect to time.   Thus a plot of reaction rate (for example, in units of gram moles of product per second per unit volume of reaction mixture) vs. time would always approach zero as the time approached infinity.

Such a situation is depicted in Fig. 1-1, curve A, where the rate approaches zero asymptotically. Of course, for some cases equilibrium may be reached more rapidly so that the rate becomes almost zero at a finite time, as illustrated by curve B.

Similarly, the conversion of a chemical reaction calculated from thermodynamic data would be the end point on a curve of conversion vs. time such as shown in Fig. 1-2. Again curve A represents the case where the time required to reach equilibrium conditions is great, while in case B the equilibrium conversion is approached more rapidly and is attained essentially at a finite time. Curves A and B in Fig. 1-2 could apply to

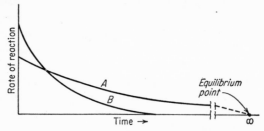

FIG. 1-1. Rate of reaction vs. time.

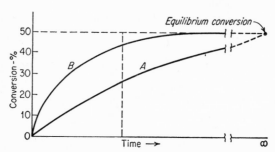

FIG. 1-2. Conversion vs. time.

exactly the same reaction, the difference between them arising because the rate in case B has been increased, for example, by using a catalyst. In fact Figs. 1-1 and 1-2 clearly show the influence of a catalyst in reaction kinetics. The rate of the reaction is initially increased over that for the uncatalyzed reaction, but the equilibrium conversion shown in Fig. 1-2 is the same for both cases.

The time available for carrying out a chemical reaction commercially is limited if the process is to be economically feasible.[1] Hence the important range of the curves of Figs. 1-1 and 1-2 from a practical viewpoint is at the lower time values. It is apparent that equilibrium calculations (giving only the end points of the curves) are not of direct value in designing equipment for commercial use. On the other hand, a knowledge of

[1] For continuous flow reactors the size or volume of the equipment replaces time as the variable.

the equilibrium conversion is of importance as a goal with which the actual performance of the reaction equipment can be compared. For example, suppose a reactor operates at a time (or volume for a flow case) corresponding to the dotted vertical line shown in Fig. 1-2. At this point the conversion for the noncatalytic reaction is about 25 per cent (curve A). A comparison with the equilibrium value of 50 per cent indicates that the noncatalytic rate is rather low and that a search for a catalyst is advisable. Curve B giving a conversion of 45 per cent shows the benefit of using a catalyst and also indicates that additional effort seeking a more effective catalyst is probably unwarranted. Without a prior knowledge of the equilibrium conversion erroneous conclusions well might be drawn from the kinetic studies yielding curves A and B. For example, it might be reasoned that the catalyst giving curve B is only moderately effective, and considerable time might be spent in attempting to discover a catalyst which would give a conversion of 70 or 80 per cent. It is for this comparison of the kinetic results with the equilibrium conversions that the thermodynamic calculations are particularly valuable. However, the actual design of the reaction equipment usually depends upon the location of the curves shown in Figs. 1-1 and 1-2 and, therefore, must be determined by kinetic studies. An exception is the case where the rate is so fast that equilibrium is attained almost instantaneously. In this event the reaction equipment can be designed on the basis of the equilibrium conversion.

A knowledge of the equilibrium conversion, or, more directly, the equilibrium constant, of a chemical reaction is important in another way. Under certain circumstances (particularly high concentrations of products and low equilibrium constant) the rate of a reaction in the reverse direction may be significant. In these cases the net rate of reaction in the forward direction is equal to the rate in the forward direction minus the rate in the reverse direction. It will be seen in Chap. 3 that this net rate can also be formulated solely in terms of the rate in the forward direction, provided the equilibrium constant is known. In other words, it is not necessary to make separate experimental determinations of the forward and reverse rates of reaction.

Although the body of data is growing, it is still not possible to estimate the equilibrium conversion for all reactions. The calculations and data for gaseous systems are the most reliable. A brief review of the application of thermodynamics to such calculations is given in Chap. 2.

The importance of heat transfer in reactor design was mentioned in Sec. 1-1. It will be found that the energy absorbed or evolved as a result of reaction nearly always requires attention in design problems. For this reason procedures for estimating heats of reaction are also reviewed in Chap. 2.

CHAPTER 2

THERMODYNAMICS REVIEW

HEAT OF REACTION

Chemical reactions are generally accompanied by the evolution or absorption of energy, due to the differences in structure of the products and the reactants. For example, when methane is burned with oxygen to form carbon dioxide and water vapor, the carbon-to-hydrogen bonds in methane are replaced with carbon-to-oxygen bonds in carbon dioxide and the oxygen-to-oxygen bond in the oxygen molecule replaced by oxygen-to-hydrogen bonds in the water molecule. Since the energy associated with such bonds varies with the kind of bond, the methane reaction results in a net evolution of energy. The exact amount of net energy associated with any reaction depends upon the temperatures of the reactants and products. If the reactants enter the reaction zone at a higher temperature than the products leave, energy will be evolved due to the excess sensible heat of the reactants, in addition to any energy change associated with the reaction itself. Therefore, in order to have a consistent basis for comparing different reactions, it is desirable to define the heat of reaction as the heat *absorbed* by the system for the over-all process when the products are restored to the same temperature as the reactants.

The pressure also must be specified to define completely the states of the products and reactants from a thermodynamic viewpoint. Furthermore, if the same pressure is chosen for both, the heat of reaction will be equal to the change in enthalpy, or simply ΔH_R. This is of considerable value since the heat of reaction then becomes a property of the system and can be evaluated by any series of processes that are convenient, just as long as the over-all change is from the same initial to the same final state. This point may be illustrated by considering the flow-calorimeter method for evaluating the heat of combustion of gases. The fuel is mixed with air at room temperature and ignited; then the products of combustion are cooled to the temperature of the reactant by contact with the cooling jacket through which water is flowing. The process is complicated. The rate of burning of the fuel is rapid with respect to the rate of heat transfer to the cooling jacket. The actual operation comes close to a two-step process, an adiabatic reaction, followed by sensible cooling of the combustion gases to room temperature. However, this is not entirely true, for there is some heat transferred to the jacket during the reaction stage. These difficulties regarding the actual mechanism of the process need not be considered in evaluating the heat of reaction, since this has been defined as the change in enthalpy between a definite initial and final state. The means by which the change is accomplished are of no significance. In the flow calorimeter the pressure is essentially constant so that any heat effects are equal to changes in enthalpy. Therefore the heat transferred to the *water*, measured by its rise in temperature, is equal to $-\Delta H_R$.

2-1. The Standard Heat of Reaction. Since ΔH_R is dependent upon the temperature, it is customary to define a standard heat of reaction, based on 18°C (or 25°C†) and 1 atm pressure. With this basis the *standard* heat of reaction ΔH_R can be formally defined as the change in enthalpy starting with reactants at 18°C and 1 atm pressure and ending with products at 18°C and 1 atm. If ΔH_R is negative, heat is evolved and the reaction is exothermic. If ΔH_R is positive, heat is absorbed (endothermic reaction).

2-2. Heats of Reaction from Heats of Formation and Heats of Combustion. Since enthalpy is a state function, ΔH_R for any reaction may be evaluated by adding the ΔH_R values for the individual reactions whose sum gives the desired over-all change. Consider the combustion of ethylene,

$$C_2H_4(g) + 3O_2(g) \rightarrow 2CO_2(g) + 2H_2O(l)\ddagger \qquad \Delta H_R$$

This reaction can be considered as the sum of the individual steps,

$$
\begin{array}{ll}
C_2H_4(g) \rightarrow 2C(s) + 2H_2(g) & \Delta H_2 \\
2C(s) + 2O_2(g) \rightarrow 2CO_2(g) & \Delta H_3 \\
\underline{2H_2(g) + O_2(g) \rightarrow 2H_2O(l)} & \underline{\Delta H_4} \\
C_2H_4(g) + 3O_2(g) \rightarrow 2CO_2(g) + 2H_2O(l) & \Delta H_R
\end{array}
$$

$$\Delta H_R = \Delta H_2 + \Delta H_3 + \Delta H_4 \qquad (2\text{-}1)$$

Each of the three individual reactions represents the formation (or decomposition) of the compound from its elements. The heats of such

---

† The 25°C value has become widely used in recent reports of thermodynamic data for organic systems. However, the earlier tabulations such as that of Bichowsky and Rossini have been based upon 18°C. In most engineering applications this difference in base temperature is unimportant.

‡ Since the water produced is indicated to be in the liquid phase, the heat of the reaction is termed the *gross* heat of combustion. The corresponding value when the water is in the vapor phase is the *net* heat of combustion. The difference between the two corresponds to the heat of vaporization of the moles of water involved.

reactions are called heats of formation and will be designated ΔH_f. Hence Eq. (2-1) in terms of heats of formation may be written

$$\Delta H_R = -\Delta H_{f,C_2H_4} + 2\Delta H_{f,CO_2} + 2\Delta H_{f,H_2O} \qquad (2\text{-}2)$$

since
$$\Delta H_2 = -\Delta H_{f,C_2H_4}$$
$$\Delta H_3 = 2\Delta H_{f,CO_2}$$
$$\Delta H_4 = 2\Delta H_{f,H_2O}$$

This example illustrates the principle that any heat of reaction can be evaluated from the heats of formation of the reactants and products. In general form Eq. (2-2) may be written

$$\Delta H_R = \sum_P N \, \Delta H_f - \sum_R N \, \Delta H_f \qquad (2\text{-}3)$$

where the first term on the right side refers to the summation for the products and the second to that for the reactants.

The heat effect accompanying burning a substance with oxygen to water and carbon dioxide is termed the heat of combustion ΔH_c of the substance. Heats of reaction can be obtained by combining heats of combustion for the reactants and products in a manner similar to that expressed by Eq. (2-3) in terms of heats of formation. Consider the reaction

$$C_2H_4(g) + H_2(g) \rightarrow C_2H_6(g) \qquad \Delta H_R$$

This reaction can be obtained by summing the following three combustion reactions:

$$C_2H_4(g) + 3O_2(g) \rightarrow 2CO_2(g) + 2H_2O(g) \qquad \Delta H_{c,C_2H_4}$$
$$H_2(g) + \tfrac{1}{2}O_2(g) \rightarrow H_2O(g) \qquad \Delta H_{c,H_2}$$
$$\underline{2CO_2(g) + 3H_2O(g) \rightarrow C_2H_6(g) + 3\tfrac{1}{2}O_2(g) \qquad -\Delta H_{c,C_2H_6}}$$
$$C_2H_4(g) + H_2(g) \rightarrow C_2H_6(g)$$
$$\Delta H_R = \Delta H_{c,C_2H_4} + \Delta H_{c,H_2} - \Delta H_{c,C_2H_6} \qquad (2\text{-}4)$$

In general form Eq. (2-4) may be written,

$$\Delta H_R = \sum_R N \, \Delta H_c - \sum_P N \, \Delta H_c \qquad (2\text{-}5)$$

which differs from Eq. (2-3) in that the heats of combustion are substituted for the formation values and the signs are reversed.

2-3. Sources of Data for Heats of Reaction. The principle illustrated by Eqs. (2-3) and (2-5) greatly simplifies the experimental work necessary to amass useful tables of data for heats of reaction. Generally such information is tabulated in terms of heats of formation which can be used with Eq. (2-3) to compute heats of any reaction. Most of the experimental measurements have been on heats of combustion, because combustion reactions are usually simple to carry out to completion. These heats of combustion can be employed to determine heats of reaction, including formation reactions, by applying Eq. (2-5). For example, suppose it desired to determine the heat of formation of ethylene

$$2H_2(g) + 2C(s) \rightarrow C_2H_4(g) \qquad \Delta H_{f,C_2H_4}$$

The direct measurement of this quantity is impractical. However, by Eq. (2-5),

$$\Delta H_R = \Delta H_{f,C_2H_4} = 2\Delta H_{c,H_2} + 2\Delta H_{c,C} - \Delta H_{c,C_2H_4} \qquad (2\text{-}6)$$

Since ethylene, hydrogen, and carbon can all be burned to carbon dioxide and water vapor rather easily, Eq. (2-6) can be used to evaluate the heat of formation of ethylene. It may be noted that Eq. (2-6) is the same as Eq. (2-2) solved for $\Delta H_{f,C_2H_4}$, since $\Delta H_{c,H_2}$ is the same as $\Delta H_{f,H_2O}$ and $\Delta H_{c,C}$ the same as $\Delta H_{f,CO_2}$.

Extensive values of heats of formation are available.[1-4] A few values for common substances taken from these sources are given in Table 2-1.

In some instances tabulations are given in terms of the enthalpy of the substance rather than as a heat of formation. This quantity is based upon assuming the enthalpy of each element (or molecule in the case of gases) in the substance to be zero. If the temperature at which this assumption is made is the same as that for which the enthalpy of the substance is given, the latter value is equal to the heat of formation. However, in recent years many enthalpies have been reported on the basis of zero values for the elements at absolute-zero temperature. Under these conditions, such enthalpy values are not equal to heats of formation.

While ΔH_f data are available for many inorganic and organic compounds, it is sometimes necessary to estimate such information for new substances. Several schemes[5-8] have been suggested for this purpose. All are based upon predicting the effect of differences in the chemical structure of the reactants and products. Perhaps the most successful one from an engineering viewpoint is that proposed by Watson et al.[5] and

[1] F. L. Bichowsky and F. D. Rossini, "Thermochemistry of Chemical Substances," Reinhold Publishing Corporation, New York, 1936.

[2] "Selected Values of Chemical Thermodynamic Properties," ser. I to III, U.S. Bureau of Standards, Washington, D.C., 1947–.

[3] M. S. Kharasch, Bur. Standards J. Research, 2:359 (1929).

[4] American Petroleum Institute, Research Project 44, U.S. Bureau of Standards, Washington, D.C., 1946.

[5] J. W. Andersen, G. H. Beyer, and K. M. Watson, Natl. Petroleum News, Tech. Sec., 36(R476) (July 5, 1944).

[6] R. H. Ewell, Ind. Eng. Chem., 32:778 (1940).

[7] F. D. Rossini, Ind. Eng. Chem., 29:1424 (1937).

[8] Mott Souders, Jr., C. S. Matthews, and C. O. Hurd, Ind. Eng. Chem., 41:1037, 1048 (1949).

TABLE 2-1. HEATS OF FORMATION

Compound or element	Formula	ΔH_f, cal/g mole†
Aluminum (s)‡...............	Al	0
Aluminum chloride (s).........	$AlCl_3$	−38,000
Barium (s).................	Ba	0
Barium chloride (s)...........	$BaCl_2$	−205,520
Barium chloride (aq).........	$BaCl_2$	−207,920
Calcium carbonate (s)........	$CaCO_3$	−289,540
Calcium sulfate (s)...........	$CaSO_4$	−336,580
Carbon (s) (graphite).........	C	0
Carbon monoxide (g).........	CO	−26,416
Carbon dioxide (g)...........	CO_2	−94,052
Methane (g).................	CH_4	−17,889
Ethane (g).................	C_2H_6	−20,236
Propane (g).................	C_3H_8	−24,820
n-Butane (g)................	C_4H_{10}	−29,812
i-Butane (g)................	C_4H_{10}	−31,452
n-Pentane (g)................	C_5H_{12}	−35,000
n-Hexane (g)................	C_6H_{14}	−39,960
n-Heptane (g)...............	C_7H_{16}	−44,890
n-Heptane (l)...............	C_7H_{16}	−53,630
n-Octane (g)................	C_8H_{18}	−49,820
n-Octane (l)................	C_8H_{18}	−59,740
Ethylene (g)................	C_2H_4	12,496
Propylene (g)...............	C_3H_6	4,879
1-Butene (g)................	C_4H_8	280
1-Pentene (g)...............	C_5H_{10}	−5,000
Acetylene (g)...............	C_2H_2	54,194
Butyne (g).................	C_4H_6	39,700
Benzene (g).................	C_6H_6	19,820
Toluene (g).................	$C_6H_5CH_3$	11,718
Cyclopentane (g)............	C_5H_{10}	−18,460
Cyclohexane (g).............	C_6H_{12}	−29,430
Methanol (g)................	CH_3OH	−48,080
Methanol (l)................	CH_3OH	−57,040
Ethanol (g).................	C_2H_5OH	−52,230
Ethanol (l).................	C_2H_5OH	−66,350
Propanol (g)................	C_3H_7OH	−61,170
Propanol (l)................	C_3H_7OH	−71,870
n-Butanol (g)...............	C_4H_9OH	−67,810
n-Butanol (l)...............	C_4H_9OH	−79,610
Ethylene glycol (g)..........	$(CH_2OH)_2$	−92,530
Ethylene glycol (l)..........	$(CH_2OH)_2$	−107,910
Glycerol (l).................	$C_3H_8O_3$	−159,160
Phenol (g).................	C_6H_5OH	−21,710
Phenol (l).................	C_6H_5OH	−37,800
Ethylene oxide (g)...........	C_2H_4O	−16,100
Diethyl ether (l).............	$C_4H_{10}O$	−65,200

TABLE 2-1. HEATS OF FORMATION (*Continued*)

Compound or element	Formula	ΔH_f, cal/g mole†
Formaldehyde (*g*).............	HCHO	−28,290
Acetaldehyde (*g*).............	CH₃CHO	−39,720
Benzaldehyde (*g*).............	C₆H₅CHO	−9,570
Acetone (*g*).................	(CH₃)₂CO	−51,790
Acetone (*l*).................	(CH₃)₂CO	−59,370
Formic acid (*g*)..............	HCOOH	−86,670
Formic acid (*l*)..............	HCOOH	−97,800
Acetic acid (*g*)..............	CH₃COOH	−104,720
Acetic acid (*l*)..............	CH₃COOH	−116,200
Carbon disulfide (*g*)..........	CS₂	28,100
Hydrogen cyanide (*g*).........	HCN	31,100
Hydrogen cyanide (*l*).........	HCN	25,200
Ethyl acetate (*l*).............	CH₃COOC₂H₅	−110,720
Copper (*s*)...................	Cu	0
Copper chloride (*s*)...........	CuCl₂	−48,830
Cuprous oxide (*s*)............	Cu₂O	−38,500
Cupric oxide (*s*).............	CuO	−43,000
Copper sulfide (*s*)...........	CuS	−11,600
Copper sulfate (*s*)...........	CuSO₄	−184,700
Hydrogen (*g*)................	H₂	0
Hydrogen chloride (*g*)........	HCl	−22,063
Hydrogen bromide (*g*)........	HBr	−8,660
Hydrogen fluoride (*g*)........	HF	−64,200
Water (*g*)..................	H₂O	−57,798
Water (*l*)...................	H₂O	−63,317
Hydrogen peroxide (*l*)........	H₂O₂	−45,160
Nitrogen (*g*)................	N₂	0
Ammonia (*g*)................	NH₃	−10,960
Ammonia (*l*)................	NH₃	−19,270
Hydrazine (*l*)................	N₂H₄	12,060
Nitrous oxide (*g*)............	N₂O	19,550
Nitric oxide (*g*).............	NO	21,600
Nitrogen dioxide (*g*)..........	NO₂	7,960
Sodium carbonate (*s*).........	Na₂CO₃	−269,460
Sodium chloride (*s*)...........	NaCl	−98,321
Sulfur (*s*)(rhombic)...........	S	0
Sulfur (*g*)..................	S	53,250
Sulfur (*g*)..................	S₂	31,020
Sulfur (*g*)..................	S₆	27,780
Sulfur (*g*)..................	S₈	27,090
Sulfur dioxide (*g*)............	SO₂	−70,940
Sulfur trioxide (*g*)...........	SO₃	−94,396
Sulfur trioxide (*l*)...........	SO₃	−103,030

† The heats of formation refer to the heat absorbed when the compound is formed from the elements at the conditions of 18°C and 1 atm pressure.

‡ *s* = solid, *l* = liquid, *g* = gas, aq = aqueous solution.

described by Hougen and Watson.[1] It is applicable to compounds involving carbon, hydrogen, oxygen, nitrogen, and the halogens.

2-4. Effect of Temperature upon the Heat of Reaction. The heat of reaction depends upon the temperature at which the reaction occurs since the enthalpies of the products and reactants depend upon this temperature. These enthalpies may be related to the temperature by the equation $\Delta H = Nc_p \, \Delta T$ at constant pressure. Therefore it is possible to evaluate the effect of temperature upon ΔH_R from a knowledge of the heat capacities of the reactants and products. For example, if ΔH_R is known at a base temperature T_0 and is desired at a temperature T, it can be computed by imagining the following three-step process:

1. Cool the reactants from T to T_0, $\Delta H = \sum_R N\bar{c}_p(T_0 - T)$.

2. Carry out the reaction at T_0, $\Delta H = (\Delta H_R)_{T_0}$.

3. Heat the products from T_0 to T, $\Delta H = \sum_P N\bar{c}_p(T - T_0)$.

The sum of these steps is equivalent to the reaction at T. Hence the heat of reaction at T is given by the sum

$$(\Delta H_R)_T = \sum_R N\bar{c}_p(T_0 - T) + (\Delta H_R)_{T_0} + \sum_P N\bar{c}_p(T - T_0)$$

This may be written in the shorter form

$$(\Delta H_R)_T = (\Delta H_R)_{T_0} + [\Sigma(N\bar{c}_p)_P - \Sigma(N\bar{c}_p)_R](T - T_0) \qquad (2\text{-}7)$$

In these equations the subscripts R and P refer to reactants and products. Also the heat capacities $\bar{c}_p$ are the average values between T_0 and T. Such results for simple gases are shown in Fig. 2-1, where $T_0 = 60 + 460 = 520°R$, or about 16°C. When such average values are not available, point heat-capacity equations may be integrated from T_0 to T to obtain the required enthalpy change.

Equation (2-7) is concerned only with temperature changes. Since ΔH_{T_0} is generally known at atmospheric pressure, the expression is useful for computing heats of reaction at elevated temperatures but still at atmospheric pressure. The effect of pressure for gaseous reactions is small unless the gases deviate widely from perfect-gas behavior. For liquid and solid reactants, pressure has no significant effect except at high pressures. The effect of pressure on ΔH_R for gaseous reactions is considered in Sec. 2-5.

The applications of heat-of-reaction information for predicting energy requirements in reactors are illustrated in the following examples:

[1] O. A. Hougen and K. M. Watson, "Chemical Process Principles," pt. 2, p. 758, John Wiley & Sons, Inc., New York, 1947.

Example 2-1. Ethylene oxide is to be produced by direct oxidation with air using a fixed bed of silver catalyst on a suitable carrier. Suppose that the stream enters the flow reactor at 200°C and contains 5 mole per cent ethylene and 95 per cent air. If the exit temperature does not exceed 260°C, it is possible to convert 50 per cent of the ethylene to the oxide, although 40 per cent is also completely burned to carbon dioxide. How much heat must be removed from the reaction per mole of ethylene fed, in order not to exceed this limiting temperature? The average molal heat capacity of ethylene may be taken as 18 Btu/(lb mole)(°R)

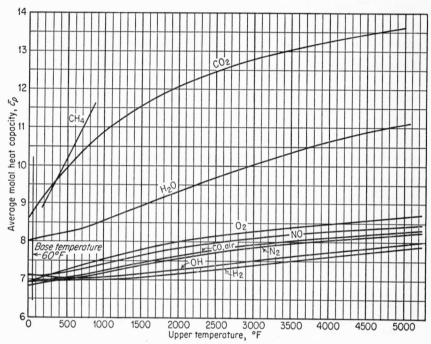

FIG. 2-1. Average molal heat capacity of gases at constant pressure ($\bar{c}_p$) between 60°F and upper temperature.

between 18 and 200°C and as 19 between 18 and 260°C. Similar values for ethylene oxide are 20 and 21 Btu/(lb mole)(°R). The pressure is essentially atmospheric.

Solution. Since heat effects at constant pressure are equal to enthalpy changes, the actual process may be replaced by one that utilizes the available heat of reaction data at 18°C (Table 2-1). This process divided into steps will be:

1. Cool the reactants and air from 200 to 18°C.
2. Carry out the reactions at 18°C.
3. Heat the products and the air from 18 to 260°C.

The sum of the enthalpy changes for each step will be the total heat absorbed by the reaction system.

STEP 1. The mean-heat-capacity chart (Fig. 2-1) may be used without significant error even though its base temperature is 60°F rather than 18°C (64.4°F).

Using a basis of 1 mole of ethylene, there will be 95/5 × 1 = 19 moles of air fed to the reactor.

From Fig. 2-1 the average heat capacity of air from 60°F to 200°C is 7.0. Hence the enthalpy change for step 1 is

$$\Delta H_1 = 1 \times 18(64 - 392) + 19 \times 7.0(64 - 392)$$
$$= -5,900 - 43,700$$
$$= -49,600 \text{ Btu/lb mole}$$

STEP 2. The only heat effect is due to the two reactions

$$C_2H_4 + \tfrac{1}{2}O_2 \rightarrow C_2H_4O(g)$$
$$C_2H_4 + 3O_2 \rightarrow 2CO_2 + 2H_2O(g)$$

Using the heat-of-formation data in Table 2-1, for the first reaction

$$\Delta H_{R_1} = -16,100 - 12,496 - 0$$
$$= -28,596 \text{ cal/g mole, or } -51,500 \text{ Btu/lb mole}$$

for the second

$$\Delta H_{R_2} = 2 \times -57,798 + 2 \times -94,052 - 12,496 - 0$$
$$= -316,196 \text{ cal/g mole, or } -569,000 \text{ Btu/lb mole}$$

Since, per mole of ethylene, there will be 0.5 mole to react to form ethylene oxide and 0.4 mole to be completely burned,

$$\Delta H_2 = 0.5 \times -51,500 + 0.4 \times -569,000$$
$$= -253,000 \text{ Btu/lb mole}$$

STEP 3. The products will consist of the following quantities:

Ethylene = 1 − 0.5 − 0.4 = 0.1 mole
Ethylene oxide = 0.5 mole
Water vapor = 2 × 0.4 = 0.8 mole
Carbon dioxide = 2 × 0.4 = 0.8 mole
Nitrogen = 19 × 0.79 = 15.0 moles
Oxygen = 19 × 0.21 − $\tfrac{1}{2}$ × 0.5 − 3 × 0.4 = 2.6 moles

Using the heat-capacity data in Fig 2-1, read from the chart at 500°F (260°C)

$$\Delta H_3 = (0.1 \times 19 + 0.5 \times 21 + 0.8 \times 8.25 + 0.8 \times 9.4 + 15 \times 7.0$$
$$+ 2.6 \times 7.25)(500 - 64)$$
$$\Delta H_3 = 150(500 - 64)$$
$$= 64,700 \text{ Btu/lb mole}$$

Then the net heat absorbed will be

$$Q = -49,600 - 253,000 + 64,700$$
$$= -238,000 \text{ Btu/lb mole of ethylene}$$

Hence the heat that must be removed is 238,000 Btu/lb mole of ethylene fed to the reactor.

Example 2-2. A hydrogen plant using the Bosch process produces 10 tons of hydrogen per day. The process involves the following reaction,

$$CO + H_2O(g) \rightarrow CO_2 + H_2$$

and is carried out by passing the carbon monoxide and steam through a catalyst bed at close to atmospheric pressure. The entire reactor is surrounded by a water jacket. The carbon monoxide and steam enter at 300°F, and the products leave the reactor at 900°F.

Steam, 50 per cent in excess of stoichiometric requirements, is used to improve the kinetics of the reaction so that 100 per cent conversion of the carbon monoxide is obtained. If the temperature rise of the cooling water is not to exceed 20°F, calculate the pounds per hour of water required.

Solution. As in Example 2-1 the data for the heat of reaction at 18°C can be utilized by carrying out the three steps:

1. Cool the reactants from 300 to 64°F.
2. Carry out the reaction at 64°F.
3. Heat the products from 64 to 900°F.

A rate of 10 tons of hydrogen per day corresponds to 9,920 lb moles. Hence the material fed to the reactor will be 9,920 moles of carbon monoxide and 9,920 × 1.5 moles of steam.

For step 1

1:
$$\Delta H_1 = (9,920 \times 7.0 + 9,920 \times 1.5 \times 8.16)(64 - 300)$$
$$= -44,300,000 \text{ Btu/(hr)(day)}$$

From Table 2-1 the heat of reaction is

2:
$$\Delta H_R = 0 + (-94,052) - (-26,416) - (-57,798)$$
$$= -9838 \text{ cal/g mole, or } -17,700 \text{ Btu/lb mole}$$

For 9,920 moles of hydrogen

$$\Delta H_2 = -175,000,000 \text{ Btu/day}$$

3:
$$\Delta H_3 = 9,920(1 \times 7.0 + 1 \times 10.7 + 0.5 \times 8.5)(900 - 64)$$
$$= 181,000,000 \text{ Btu/day}$$

The heat absorbed by the reaction mixture will be

$$Q = (-44.3 - 175 + 181) \times 10^6$$
$$= -38.3 \times 10^6 \text{ Btu/day}$$

If the temperature rise of the water in the jacket is to be 20°F, the water rate to remove this much heat will be

$$w = \frac{38.3 \times 10^6}{1 \times 20}$$
$$= 1,900,000 \text{ lb/day, or } 80,000 \text{ lb/hr}$$

2-5. Effect of Pressure on ΔH_R in Gaseous Reactions. The change in enthalpy with pressure at constant temperature for a single-phase single-component system is given by the expression

$$\left(\frac{\partial H}{\partial P}\right)_T = V - T\left(\frac{\partial V}{\partial T}\right)_p \tag{2-8}$$

Integrating between the pressure p_0 and p in a formal way,

$$H_p - H_{p_0} = \int_{p_0}^{p}\left[V - T\left(\frac{\partial V}{\partial T}\right)_p\right]dp \tag{2-9}$$

The magnitude of the term in brackets in Eq. (2-9) depends, in the case of gases, upon the deviation from perfect-gas behavior. For perfect gases

$$\left(\frac{\partial V}{\partial T}\right)_p = \frac{R}{p}$$

and hence

$$V - T\left(\frac{\partial V}{\partial T}\right)_p = V - \frac{RT}{p} = 0$$

From this result it is evident that the enthalpy of a gas is independent of the pressure up to the pressure where deviations from perfect-gas behavior become significant. Applying this conclusion to each reactant and product in a gaseous reaction, it is clear that the heat of reaction is essentially independent of pressure as long as the gases involved do not deviate greatly from ideal behavior.

Equation (2-9) suggests that the effect of pressure on the enthalpy of imperfect gases can be evaluated from pressure-volume-temperature (pVT) data or an equation of state. For most practical purposes a simple generalized equation of state, such as that based upon the compressibility factor

$$pV = CRT \qquad \text{for 1 mole}$$

$$C = f(T_R, P_R) \qquad T_R = \frac{T}{T_c}, \; p_R = \frac{p}{p_c} \tag{2-10}$$

is sufficient to evaluate reasonably accurate changes of enthalpy with pressure.[1]

Using Eq. (2-10) to integrate Eq. (2-9), values of $H_p - H_{p_0}$ can be computed for any temperature and over any pressure range. Figure 2-2 shows the results plotted as $(H_{p_0} - H_p)/T_c$ vs. the reduced pressure $p_R = p/p_c$. The value p_0 refers to zero pressure. Hence the ordinate

---

[1] For polar substances, such as methanol, acetone, and acetaldehyde, enthalpy calculations based upon Eq. (2-10) may lead to large errors. For more information about thermodynamic properties computed from the compressibility-factor equation of state, reference may be made to A. L. Lydersen, R. A. Greenkorn, and O. A. Hougen, *Univ. Wis. Eng. Expt. Sta. Rept. 4*, October, 1955.

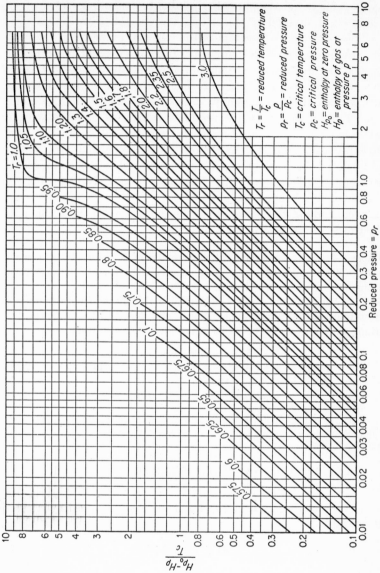

FIG. 2-2. Effect of pressure upon the enthalpy of gases. (*Reproduced by permission from "Chemical Process Principles," pt. 2, O. A. Hougen and K. M. Watson, John Wiley & Sons, Inc., New York, 1947.*)

$T_r = \dfrac{T}{T_c} =$ reduced temperature

$p_r = \dfrac{p}{p_c} =$ reduced pressure

$T_c =$ critical temperature

$p_c =$ critical pressure

$H_{p_0} =$ enthalpy at zero pressure

$H_p =$ enthalpy of gas at pressure p

gives values for the change in enthalpy due to expanding the gas from p to zero pressure, divided by the critical temperature T_c.

To employ this chart to compute the effect of pressure on the heat of reaction, the procedure is as follows: (1) If ΔH_R is desired at a pressure p, first reduce the pressure to zero and obtain separate values for $H_{p_0} - H_p$ for each reactant from Fig. 2-2.   (2) Then carry out the reaction at zero pressure where ΔH_R is available by the methods outlined in Secs. 2-3 and 2-4.   (3) Finally, compress the products from zero pressure to p, and obtain the change in enthalpy for each from Fig. 2-2.   (4) The sum of the enthalpy values for the three steps gives the desired ΔH_R at p.   It should be noted that the entire process is imagined to occur at a constant temperature T, and, indeed, Fig. 2-2 can be used only to evaluate isothermal enthalpy changes.

The magnitude of the pressure effects and the methods of calculation are illustrated in Example 3.

Example 2-3.   Calculate the heat of cracking of propane (to ethylene and methane) at 900°F and 1,000 psia, conditions within the range of thermal cracking operations in the petroleum industry.

Solution.   The problem requires determining the effect of both temperature and pressure upon the value obtained from Table 2-1 at 18°C and 1 atm.

Working with the temperature effect first, and using Eq. (2-7),

$$C_3H_8 \rightarrow C_2H_4 + CH_4$$

$$\Delta H_{900°} = \Delta H_{64} + [\Sigma(N_i\bar{c}_{p_i})_P - \Sigma(N_i\bar{c}_{p_i})_R](900 - 64) \qquad (A)$$

$$\Delta H_{64°} = 12{,}496 - 17{,}889 - (-24{,}820)$$

$$= 19{,}427 \text{ cal/g mole} = 35{,}000 \text{ Btu/lb mole}$$

Heat-capacity equations for propane and ethylene are necessary since they are not included on the average-heat-capacity chart (Fig. 2-1).   Such equations are as follows:

C_3H_8: $\bar{c}_p = 0.41 + 35.95 \times 10^{-3}T + 6.97 \times 10^{-6}T^2$ $T = °R$

C_2H_4: $\bar{c}_p = 2.71 + 16.20 \times 10^{-3}T + 2.80 \times 10^{-6}T^2$ $T = °R$

The average molal values between 64 and 900°F are obtained by integrating these equations.

$$C_3H_8:\quad (900 - 64)\bar{c}_p = \int_{524°}^{1360°} (0.41 + 35.95 \times 10^{-3}T + 6.97 \times 10^{-6}T^2)\, dT$$

$$\bar{c}_p = \frac{34{,}240}{900 - 64}$$

$$= 41.0 \text{ Btu/(lb mole)(°R)}$$

$$C_2H_4:\quad (900 - 64)\bar{c}_p = \int_{524°}^{1360°} (2.71 + 16.20 \times 10^{-3}T + 2.80 \times 10^{-6}T^2)\, dT$$

$$\bar{c}_p = \frac{17{,}240}{900 - 64} = 20.9$$

CH_4: $\bar{c}_p = 11.7$ from Fig. 2-1

Substituting these quantities in Eq. (A),

$$\Delta H_{900} = 35{,}000 + (20.9 + 11.7 - 41.0)(900 - 64)$$
$$= 35{,}000 - 7{,}020$$
$$= 27{,}980 \text{ Btu/lb mole}$$

This value is the heat of cracking at 900°F and 1 atm pressure.

To determine ΔH_R at 1,000 psia, the procedure is as follows:

1. Start with reactant C_3H_8 at 1,000 psia and 900°F, and reduce the pressure to atmospheric.

$$T_R = \frac{T}{T_c} = \frac{900 + 460}{666} = 2.04$$

At 1 atm

$$p_R = \frac{p}{p_c} = \frac{1}{42} = 0.024$$

At 1,000 psia

$$p_R = \frac{1{,}000}{14.7 \times 42} = 1.62$$

From Fig. 2-2,

$$\frac{H_0 - H_{1,000}}{T_c} - \frac{H_0 - H_{14.7}}{T_c} = 0.95 - 0.01\dagger = 0.94$$

$$H_{14.7} - H_{1,000} = 0.94 T_c = 0.94 \times 666$$
$$= 630 \text{ Btu/lb mole}$$

2. Carry out the reaction at 900°F and 1 atm.

$$\Delta H_R = 27{,}980 \text{ Btu/lb mole}$$

3. Compress the products from 1 atm to 1,000 psia.

C_2H_4:
$$T_R = \frac{1{,}360}{509} = 2.67$$

At 1 atm

$$p_R = \frac{1}{50.9} = 0.02$$

At 1,000 psia

$$p_R = \frac{1{,}000}{14.7 \times 50.9} = 1.34$$

$$\frac{H_0 - H_{14.7}}{T_c} - \frac{H_0 - H_{1,000}}{T_c} = \frac{H_{1,000} - H_{14.7}}{T_c} = 0.0 - 0.45$$
$$H_{1,000} - H_{14.7} = -0.45 \times 509$$
$$= -230 \text{ Btu/lb mole}$$

CH_4:
$$T_R = \frac{1{,}360}{344} = 3.06$$

† Estimated value. It is nearly zero; so an approximate result is satisfactory.

At 1 atm

$$p_R = \frac{1}{45.8} = 0.022$$

At 1,000 psia

$$p_R = \frac{1,000}{14.7 \times 45.8} = 1.48$$

$$\frac{H_0 - H_{14.7}}{T_c} - \frac{H_0 - H_{1,000}}{T_c} = \frac{H_{1,000} - H_{14.7}}{T_c} = 0.0 - 0.35$$

$$H_{1,000} - H_0 = -0.35 \times 344$$
$$= -120 \text{ Btu/lb mole}$$

For the third step

$$\Delta H = -230 - 120$$
$$= -350 \text{ Btu/lb mole}$$

If the three steps are added, the over-all process is equivalent to the reaction at 900°F and 1,000 psia. The heat of reaction at these conditions is, then,

$$\Delta H_R = 27,980 + 630 - 350 = 27,980 + 280$$
$$= 28,260 \text{ Btu/lb mole}$$

It is apparent that the effect of pressure is not large in this case. If the temperature were lower, or if higher-molecular-weight compounds were considered, the effect would increase. For example, the effect of pressure on the cracking of a hydrocarbon oil of molecular weight 200 in comparison with propane (molecular weight 44) is of the order of 500 to 1,000 Btu/lb mole.

CHEMICAL-REACTION EQUILIBRIA

The importance of the equilibrium conversion of a chemical reaction has been discussed in Chap. 1. The chief objective here is not to study reaction equilibria from a thermodynamic viewpoint but to review briefly the method of computing the equilibrium constant and equilibrium conversion. For this purpose certain thermodynamic equations will be presented and used, but not developed. For a more fundamental approach to reaction equilibria reference should be made to standard texts on thermodynamics.[1-3]

2-6. Thermodynamics Equations. When a reaction occurs at equilibrium, the temperature and pressure in the system remain constant and the change in free energy (free energy of products minus that of the

---

[1] B. F. Dodge, "Chemical Engineering Thermodynamics," McGraw-Hill Book Company, Inc., New York, 1944.

[2] S. Glasstone, "Thermodynamics for Chemists," D. Van Nostrand Company, Inc., New York, 1947.

[3] J. M. Smith, "Introduction to Chemical Engineering Thermodynamics," McGraw-Hill Book Company, Inc., New York, 1949.

reactants) is zero. Mathematically these conditions may be written

$$\Delta F = 0 \qquad \text{at constant } T \text{ and } P \qquad (2\text{-}11)$$

This result can be used along with the standard free-energy change ΔF^0 to develop the following expression for the equilibrium constant of a chemical reaction:

$$\Delta F^0 = -RT \ln K \qquad (2\text{-}12)$$

The standard free-energy change ΔF^0 refers to the difference between the free energies of the products and reactants when each is in a chosen standard state. Since these standard states do not correspond to the equilibrium states, ΔF^0 is generally not zero but has a finite value. ΔF^0 is similar to the standard heat of reaction in that it can frequently be obtained from tabular values of the free energy, or entropy and enthalpy of formation, of each of the products and reactants. Sources and uses of such data are discussed in Sec. 2-7. If ΔF^0 is a large negative value, Eq. (2-12) shows that K, and hence the equilibrium conversion, will be high. However, if ΔF^0 is large and positive, K is small and the reaction not commercially feasible unless there is an opportunity to increase the equilibrium conversion by other means, such as increasing the pressure or adding a large excess of one reactant. For example, the value of ΔF^0 for the ammonia synthesis at elevated temperatures is positive (see Example 2-4) so that K is a small value. However, by operating at high pressures a reasonable conversion of nitrogen to ammonia is possible.

The equilibrium constant K in Eq. (2-12) is defined in terms of the equilibrium activities a_i of the reactants and products. For a general reaction

$$aA + bB = cC + dD$$

the equilibrium constant is

$$K = \frac{a_C^c a_D^d}{a_A^a a_B^b} \qquad (2\text{-}13)$$

The activities refer to equilibrium conditions in the reaction mixture and are defined as the ratio of the fugacity of the reactant or product in the equilibrium mixture to that in the standard state; i.e.,

$$a = \frac{f}{f^0} \qquad (2\text{-}14)$$

The standard state at which f^0 applies is the same state as that for which the free energy for obtaining ΔF^0 is evaluated.

Gaseous Reactions. Consider the ammonia synthesis

$$\tfrac{1}{2}N_2(g) + \tfrac{3}{2}H_2(g) \rightarrow NH_3(g)$$

At equilibrium at a given pressure and temperature each component will have a fugacity f corresponding to the numerator in Eq. (2-14). For gaseous reactions it is customary to choose as the standard state the pure gas at 1 atm fugacity, i.e., unit fugacity. Hence the free energy of each component will be evaluated at 1 atm fugacity and T in order to obtain ΔF^0. The fugacity f^0 in the denominator of Eq. (2-14) will be unity. For most gases the deviation from perfect-gas behavior at 1 atm pressure is insignificant, so that the standard state of unit fugacity corresponds to 1 atm pressure.

With the standard state of unit fugacity, Eqs. (2-13) and (2-14) become

$$a = f \tag{2-15}$$

and

$$K = \frac{f_C^c f_D^d}{f_A^a f_B^b} \tag{2-16}$$

If in addition the gases follow the ideal-gas law at the pressure of the equilibrium gas mixture, $f = p$ and Eq. (2-16) becomes

$$K = \frac{p_C^c p_D^d}{p_A^a p_B^b} \tag{2-17}$$

Here p, the partial pressure, is the total pressure times the mole fraction of the component in the mixture.

$$p = p_t y \tag{2-18}$$

This second assumption is frequently not justified. For example, the operating pressures for the ammonia-synthesis reaction range from 150 to 1,000 atm. Under these conditions the gases in the mixture will not behave ideally, and Eqs. (2-17) and (2-18) are not correct. For such cases it is convenient to use the fugacity chart (Fig. 2-3), based upon the compressibility-factor equation of state [(Eq. 2-10)]. Then the fugacities f at the equilibrium state can be related to the composition, provided it is assumed that the fugacity of a gas in a mixture is proportional to its mole fraction, i.e., that the mixture forms an ideal solution. With this assumption

$$f_i = f_i' y_i \tag{2-19}$$

where f_i' is the fugacity of the pure component and y_i its composition.[1]

The fugacities f_i' can be determined from Fig. 2-3. Substituting Eq. (2-19) in (2-16) gives

$$K = \frac{(f_C')^c (f_D')^d}{(f_A')^a (f_B')^b} K_y \tag{2-20}$$

where

$$K_y = \frac{y_C^c y_D^d}{y_A^a y_B^b} \tag{2-21}$$

[1] Note that f^0 and f' are not the same quantity, in general. The superscript zero denotes the standard state, and f' refers to the fugacity of the pure substance.

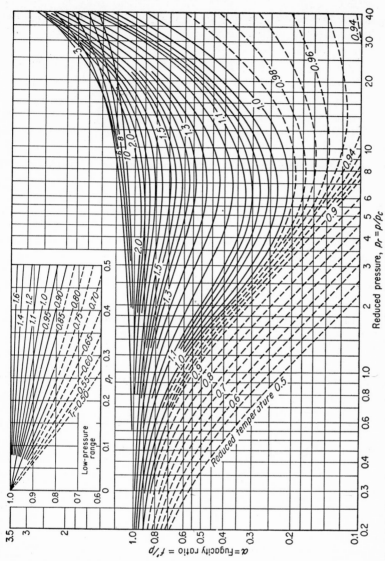

FIG. 2-3. Fugacity-pressure ratio for gases. (*Reproduced by permission from "Chemical Process Principles,"* *pt. 2, O. A. Hougen and K. M. Watson, John Wiley & Sons, Inc., New York, 1947.*)

Since Fig. 2-3 gives values of $\alpha = f'/p_t$, it is convenient to modify Eq. (2-20) to read directly in terms of α,

$$K = p_t^{c+d-(a+b)} K_\alpha K_y \tag{2-22}$$

where

$$K_\alpha = \frac{\left[\dfrac{f'}{p_t}\right]_C^c \left[\dfrac{f}{p_t}\right]_D^d}{\left[\dfrac{f'}{p_t}\right]_A^a \left[\dfrac{f'}{p_t}\right]_B^b} \tag{2-23}$$

In gaseous reactions a quantity K_p is frequently used. This is defined as follows:

$$K_p = \frac{(y_C p_t)^c (y_D p_t)^d}{(y_A p_t)^a (y_B p_t)^b} = K_y p_t^{c+d-(a+b)}$$

In terms of K_p Eq. (2-22) may be written

$$K = K_p K_\alpha$$

Equation (2-22) permits the evaluation of the composition ratio K_y in terms of the equilibrium constant. This is, of course, a necessary step along the path toward computing the equilibrium conversion from free-energy data. The steps along that path are (1) evaluate ΔF^0, (2) determine the equilibrium constant K from ΔF^0 using Eq. (2-12), (3) obtain K_y, and finally (4) calculate the conversion from K_y. The last step is described in Sec. 2-8. Example 2-4 illustrates steps 2 and 3.

Example 2-4. If the standard free-energy change for the synthesis of ammonia is 8700 cal/g mole of NH_3 at 500°C, compute the values of K, K_p, and K_y at 10 atm and 600 atm total pressure.
Solution. From Eq. (2-12)

$$\ln K = -\frac{\Delta F^0}{RT} = -\frac{8{,}700}{1.985 \times 773} = -5.7$$
$$K = 3.4 \times 10^{-3} \text{ atm}^{-1}$$

This result is applicable for the reaction written as follows:

$$\tfrac{1}{2}N_2 + \tfrac{3}{2}H_2 \rightarrow NH_3$$

The value of K is the same at 10 and 600 atm reaction pressures. The values of K_p, and particularly K_y, will vary with pressure, and the degree of variation may be established from Eq. (2-22) and the fugacity chart (Fig. 2-3).

	10 atm	600 atm
N_2:		
$T_R = 773/126$	6.1	6.1
$p_R = p/33.5$	0.30	17.9
f'/p_t (from Fig. 2-3)	1.05	1.37
H_2:†		
$T_R = 773/(33.1 + 8)$	18.8	18.8
$p_R = p/(12.8 + 8)$	0.48	28.9
f'/p_t	1.05	1.20
NH_3:		
$T_R = 773/405$	1.91	1.91
$p_R = p/111$	0.090	5.41
f'/p_t	1.0	0.90

† For hydrogen and helium the reduced correlations of volume, fugacity, etc., are more accurate if 8 is added to T_c in degrees absolute (°K) and p_c in atmospheres.

From these data

$$K_\alpha = \frac{1.0}{(1.05)^{\frac{3}{2}}(1.05)^{\frac{1}{2}}} = 0.91 \qquad \text{at 10 atm}$$

$$K_\alpha = \frac{0.90}{(1.37)^{\frac{1}{2}}(1.20)^{\frac{3}{2}}} = 0.59 \qquad \text{at 600 atm}$$

Then, substituting in Eq. (2-22),

$$K = K_\alpha p_t^{c+d-(a+b)} K_y = 0.91 \times 10^{-1} K_y \qquad \text{at 10 atm}$$

$$K_y = \frac{0.0034}{0.91} \times 10 = 0.037 \qquad \text{at 10 atm}$$

$$K_y = \frac{0.0034}{0.59} \times 600 = 0.35 \qquad \text{at 600 atm}$$

The K_p values do not vary as much with pressure and are given by the relationship

$$K = K_p K_\alpha$$

or

$$K_p = \frac{0.0034}{0.91} = 0.0037$$

$$K_p = \frac{0.0034}{0.59} = 0.0058$$

Liquid-phase Reactions. For liquids a standard state of unit fugacity is not convenient, and in some cases may be impossible. For substances that are normally liquid in the pure state (i.e., solvents) the standard state is chosen as the pure liquid at its vapor pressure at the temperature of the reaction. Thus f^0 in Eq. (2-14) is the fugacity of the saturated liquid, or, what is the equivalent, the fugacity of the saturated vapor in equilibrium with the liquid. If the liquid solution in the reaction mixture is ideal, this definition leads to a simple relationship between the activity and composition, x. Thus at equilibrium in the mixture, according to the concept of ideal solutions,

$$f = f'x \tag{2-24}$$

If the effect of pressure upon the fugacity of pure liquids is neglected, $f^0 = f'$ and according to Eq. (2-14)

$$a = \frac{f'x}{f^0} = x \tag{2-25}$$

Then Eq. (2-13) becomes

$$K = \frac{x_C^c x_D^d}{x_A^a x_B^b} = K_x \tag{2-26}$$

If the reaction mixture is not an ideal solution, the activity coefficient γ can be introduced in Eq. (2-24),

$$f = f'\gamma x \tag{2-27}$$

Then $a = \gamma x$, and Eq. (2-13) is

$$K = \frac{\gamma_C^c \gamma_D^d}{\gamma_A^a \gamma_B^b} K_x \tag{2-28}$$

When the component in a liquid-phase-reaction mixture behaves as a solute, the standard state is usually chosen as a 1-molal solution of the solute.[1] If the 1-molal solution obeys Henry's law,

$$f^0 = HC = H(1) \tag{2-29}$$

where C = molal concentration
H = Henry's-law constant
Under these conditions

$$a = \frac{\gamma HC}{H} = \gamma C \tag{2-30}$$

with γ the activity coefficient of the component in a solution of concentration C.

If Henry's law is not valid at 1-molal concentration,

$$a = \frac{\gamma HC}{\gamma_0 H} = \frac{\gamma}{\gamma_0} C \tag{2-31}$$

where γ_0 is the activity coefficient at 1-molal concentration.

[1] If a 1-molal concentration is not possible, the standard state chosen is such that, as $C \to 0$, $a \to C$. With this standard state $a = \gamma C$, where γ is the activity coefficient at the concentration C.

Just as Eq. (2-22) could be used for gaseous reactions to relate K, and hence ΔF^0, to the equilibrium composition, so Eq. (2-28) can be used for the same purpose for liquid-phase reactions where all components have standard states chosen as the pure liquid state.

Heterogeneous Reactions. The concepts just presented for different standard states can be illustrated by the following case: Suppose that gas A reacts with liquid B under conditions of temperature and pressure such that a liquid solution of product C, in unreacted B, is formed. Specifically, this might be the reaction between ethylene gas and water liquid to form an aqueous solution of ethanol:

$$C_2H_4(g) + H_2O(l) \rightarrow C_2H_5OH(aq)$$

The standard states may be chosen as follows:
C_2H_4, pure gas at unit fugacity.
H_2O, pure liquid at its vapor pressure at the reaction temperature T.
C_2H_5OH, 1-molal aqueous solution.
For ethylene, from Eqs. (2-15) and (2-19),

$$a_E = f_E = f' y_E = p_t \alpha_E y_E \tag{2-32}$$

For water, from Eq. (2-27),

$$a_W = \gamma_W x_W \tag{2-33}$$

For ethanol, from Eq. (2-30),

$$a_A = \gamma_A C_A \tag{2-34}$$

Then the expression relating the equilibrium composition to the equilibrium constant is

$$K = \frac{a_A}{a_E a_W} = \frac{p_t \alpha_E y_E}{(\gamma_W x_W)(\gamma_A C_A)} = \frac{p_t \alpha_E}{\gamma_W \gamma_A} \frac{y_E}{x_W C_A} \tag{2-35}$$

The equilibrium constant is related to ΔF^0 by Eq. (2-12), so that Eq. (2-35) may be written

$$-\frac{\Delta F^0}{RT} = \ln\left(\frac{p_t \alpha_E}{\gamma_W \gamma_A} \frac{y_E}{x_W C_A}\right) \tag{2-36}$$

where ΔF^0 is defined in terms of the chosen standard states as follows:
ΔF^0 = (free energy of ethanol in a 1-molal aqueous solution)
  − (free energy of pure liquid water at its vapor pressure)
  − (free energy of ethylene gas at unit fugacity)
It is understood that all the quantities in ΔF^0 are evaluated at the reaction temperature T.

2-7. Calculation of the Equilibrium Constant. *From Entropy Data.* Equation (2-12) shows that K can be computed, provided ΔF^0 is known. The standard free-energy change can sometimes be determined from the expression

$$\Delta F^0 = \Delta H^0 - T \,\Delta S^0 \qquad (2\text{-}37)$$

The difficulty in this approach is in evaluating the entropy change, ΔS^0, for the products minus the reactants in their standard states. From the third law of thermodynamics it is possible to obtain the absolute entropy from calorimetric data measured at temperatures down to near absolute zero. It is also possible to determine the entropy from spectroscopic data using the principles of statistical mechanics. Tables of entropy values evaluated in these ways are available[1-3] and may be used to obtain ΔS^0 for some reactions. When no information is at hand for the substance, the entropy can be estimated for some types of compounds from their structure. Perhaps the most useful method is that previously mentioned for obtaining the heat of formation, ΔH_f, that is, the group-contribution approach proposed by Andersen, Beyer, and Watson.[4]

Once the standard entropy change is available, Eq. (2-37) is applicable at any temperature. However, the values for ΔH^0 and ΔS^0, obtained from the tables of data, generally apply at 18 or 25°C. Therefore if ΔF^0 is desired at an elevated temperature T, it is necessary to correct the values of ΔH^0 and ΔS^0 to this temperature. This can be accomplished using data for the heat capacities of the reactants and products with the following equations:

$$\Delta H_T^0 = \Delta H_{T_0}^0 + \int_{T_0}^{T} \Delta c_p \, dT \qquad (2\text{-}38)$$

$$\Delta S_T = \Delta S_{T_0}^0 + \int_{T_0}^{T} \frac{\Delta c_p}{T} \, dT \qquad (2\text{-}39)$$

The quantity Δc_p refers to the heat capacities of the products minus those of the reactants.

For a limited number of compounds standard free energies of formation have been tabulated.[5] These data may be used directly to evaluate the equilibrium constant through Eq. (2-12).

[1] "Selected Values of Chemical Thermodynamic Properties," ser. I–III, U.S. Bureau of Standards, Washington, D.C., 1947–.

[2] R. R. Wenner, "Thermochemical Calculations," McGraw-Hill Book Company, Inc., New York, 1941.

[3] K. K. Kelley, *U.S. Bur. Mines, Tech. Paper* 350 (1932).

[4] *Loc. cit.*

[5] G. S. Parks and H. M. Huffman, "The Free Energies of Some Organic Compounds," Reinhold Publishing Corporation, New York, 1932.

Example 2-5. Calculate the equilibrium constant for the vapor-phase hydration of ethylene at 320°C from the following data:

1. $\Delta H^0(298°K) = -10,960$ cal/g mole
2. Entropy values at 298°K and unit fugacity, i.e., at the standard state for gases:

$$\text{Ethanol } (g) = 67.26 \text{ cal/(g mole)}(°K)$$
$$\text{Water vapor } (g) = 45.10$$
$$\text{Ethylene } (g) = 52.47$$

3. Molal-heat-capacity equations:

Ethanol (g):　　$c_p = 3.578 + 0.04985T - 169.9 \times 10^{-7}T^2$　　$T°K$
Water vapor (g): $c_p = 6.890 + 0.00328T - 3.43 \times 10^{-7}T^2$　　$T°K$
Ethylene (g):　　$c_p = 2.706 + 0.029T - 90.6 \times 10^{-7}T^2$　　$T°K$

Solution. From the data

$$\Delta S^0(298°K) = 67.26 - (45.10 + 52.47) = -30.31 \text{ cal/(g mole)}(°K)$$

The quantity Δc_p, from the equations, is

$$\Delta c_p = -6.018 + 0.01757T - 75.9 \times 10^{-7}T^2$$

Then the value of ΔH^0 at 320°C will be

$$\Delta H^0(320°C) = -10,960 + \int_{298°K}^{593°K} (-6.018 + 0.01757T - 75.9 \times 10^{-7}T^2)\, dT$$
$$\Delta H^0(320°C) = -10,960 - 1,773 + 2,309 - 546$$
$$= -10,970 \text{ cal/g mole}$$

Similarly

$$\Delta S^0(320°C) = -30.31 + \int_{298°}^{593°} \left(-\frac{6.018}{T} + 0.0157 - 75.9 \times 10^{-7}T\right) dT$$
$$\Delta S^0(320°C) = -30.31 - 4.15 + 5.18 - 1.19$$
$$= -30.47 \text{ cal/(g mole)}(°K)$$

From Eq. (2-37), at 320°C

$$\Delta F^0 = -10,970 - 593 \times -30.47 = 7120 \text{ cal/g mole}$$

Finally K can be obtained from Eq. (2-12),

$$\ln K = -\frac{\Delta F^0}{RT} = -\frac{7,120}{1.98 \times 593} = -6.06$$
$$K = 2.3 \times 10^{-3}$$

From Experimental Measurements. Applying the thermodynamic relationship

$$\frac{\partial F}{\partial T}\bigg|_p = -S$$

to a chemical reaction carried out at constant total pressure and temperature, one may write

$$\frac{\partial(\Delta F^0)}{\partial T} = -\Delta S^0 \tag{2-40}$$

This equation can be combined with Eq. (2-37) to eliminate ΔS^0 and integrated to give

$$\frac{\Delta F^0}{T} = -\int \frac{\Delta H^0}{T^2} dT \tag{2-41}[1]$$

The variation of ΔH^0 with temperature is expressed by the relation

$$\Delta H^0 = \Delta H^0_{T_0} + \int_{T_0}^{T} \Delta c_p \, dT = \Delta H^0_{T_0} + \int_{T_0}^{T} (\Delta a + \Delta bT + \Delta cT^2) \, dT$$

If T_0 is chosen equal to 0, this may be integrated to the form

$$\Delta H^0 = \Delta H^0_0 + \Delta aT + \frac{\Delta b}{2} T^2 + \frac{\Delta c}{3} T^3 \tag{2-42}$$

where ΔH^0_0 is the constant of integration.

Combining this result with Eq. (2-41), and integrating, yields

$$\Delta F^0 = \Delta H^0_0 - \Delta aT \ln T - \frac{\Delta b}{2} T^2 - \frac{\Delta c}{6} T^3 - IT \tag{2-43}$$

where I is the integration constant.

Finally Eq. (2-43) may be combined with Eq. (2-12) to show how the equilibrium constant varies with temperature,

$$\ln K = -\frac{\Delta H^0_0}{RT} + \frac{\Delta a}{R} \ln T + \frac{\Delta b}{2R} T + \frac{\Delta c}{6R} T^2 + A \tag{2-44}$$

where A is a new constant equal to I/R.

Equation (2-44) indicates that the equilibrium constant can be calculated at any temperature provided the constants ΔH^0_0 and A can be deter-

---

[1] This equation shows an important result when written in terms of the equilibrium constant.

$$\frac{\Delta F^0}{T} = -R \ln K = -\int \frac{\Delta H^0}{T^2} dT$$

Differentiating,

$$\frac{d \ln K}{dT} = \frac{\Delta H^0}{RT^2}$$

If the reaction is exothermic, ΔH^0 is negative. For such cases the equilibrium constant will decrease as the temperature is raised. Hence for exothermic reactions an increase in temperature reduces the equilibrium conversion. For an endothermic reaction the conversion increases with the temperature.

mined. If the equilibrium constant K is measured experimentally[1] at two temperatures, these constants can be evaluated. ΔH_0^0 can be found also from the value of the heat of reaction ΔH^0 at any one temperature, using Eq. (2-42). In this case there remains only the constant A to determine from experimental equilibrium-constant data and Eq. (2-44). Hence where ΔH^0 is known at one temperature, K need be determined experimentally at but one temperature in order to be able to use Eq. (2-44) to compute K at any temperature.

Of course, in both methods it is necessary to have heat-capacity data for reactants and products in order to evaluate Δa, Δb, and Δc.

2-8. The Equilibrium Conversion. The equilibrium conversion in a chemical reaction depends, in general, upon the temperature, pressure, and the initial composition of the reaction mixture. The importance of temperature enters through its effect upon the equilibrium constant, as in Eq. (2-44), or as illustrated in Example 2-5.

Pressure has no effect on the true equilibrium constant K but may influence the composition ratio K_y and hence the equilibrium conversion. This is illustrated by Eq. (2-22) for gaseous reactions. It is apparent that there will be little effect if there is no change in the number of moles as a result of reaction (corresponding to $c + d = a + b$), for then the pressure term in Eq. (2-22) drops out. For liquid-phase reactions, K_x or K_c is little influenced by pressure unless the critical value is approached. For these reasons pressure has a significant effect on the equilibrium conversion only for gaseous reactions where there is a change in the number of moles as a result of the reaction.

The initial composition of the reaction mixture affects neither K nor the composition ratios K_y, K_x, K_c.

The application of material balances and the equilibrium constant to the evaluation of the equilibrium conversion is illustrated by the following examples:

Example 2-6. The water-gas reaction

$$CO(g) + H_2O(g) \rightarrow CO_2(g) + H_2(g)$$

is carried out under several different conditions. Calculate the fraction of the steam decomposed in each case. Assume that the mixture behaves as a perfect gas.

1. The reactants consist of 1 mole of water vapor and 1 mole of CO. The temperature is 1530°F ($K = 1.0$) and the total pressure 1 atm.
2. Same as (1) except that the pressure is 10 atm.
3. Same as (2) except that 2 moles of N_2 are included in the initial reactants.

[1] This requires carrying out the reaction experimentally in such a way that equilibrium conditions are obtained. Then the composition of the reaction mixture is measured and K_y (for a gas-phase reaction) evaluated. Finally K is computed from K_y through Eq. (2-22).

4. The reactants are 2 moles of H_2O and 1 mole of CO. Other conditions are the same as in (1).

5. The initial mixture consists of 1 mole of H_2O, 1 mole of CO, and 1 mole of CO_2. Other conditions are the same as in (1).

Solution. 1. Since the perfect-gas law is valid, $f'/p_t = 1.0$ in all cases and $K_\alpha = 1.0$. Hence Eq. (2-22) becomes

$$K = 1.0 = p_t^{1+1-(1+1)}(1.0)K_y = K_y = \frac{y_{CO_2}y_{H_2}}{y_{CO}y_{H_2O}}$$

If the moles of H_2 at equilibrium are supposed to be z, the moles of the other components at equilibrium will be

$$H_2 = z \qquad\qquad y_{H_2} = \frac{z}{2}$$

$$CO_2 = z \qquad\qquad y_{CO_2} = \frac{z}{2}$$

$$CO = 1 - z \qquad\qquad y_{CO} = \frac{1-z}{2}$$

$$H_2O = 1 - z \qquad\qquad y_{H_2O} = \frac{1-z}{2}$$

$$\text{Total moles} = \overline{2} \qquad\qquad \text{Total} = \overline{1}$$

Substituting in Eq. (A),

$$1.0 = \frac{z^2}{(1-z)^2}$$

$$z = 0.50$$

Fraction of steam decomposed $= 0.50$

2. Since the mixture is assumed to be a perfect gas, K_α still is 1.0 at 10 atm pressure and $K_y = 1.0$ as before. Hence the solution is the same as (1), and the fraction of steam decomposed $= 0.50$.

3. In this case the moles at equilibrium tabulated for each component in (1) will remain unchanged, but the total moles will increase to 4, because of the nitrogen. Since there is no change in number of moles during the reaction, the total number of moles does not affect the result.

Fraction of steam decomposed $= 0.50$

4. At equilibrium, moles of.

$$H_2 = z$$
$$CO_2 = z$$
$$H_2O = 2 - z$$
$$CO = 1 - z$$
$$\text{Total moles} = \overline{3}$$

$$K_y = 1.0 = \frac{z^2}{(1-z)(2-z)}$$

$$z = 0.0667$$

Fraction of steam decomposed $= \frac{0.667}{2} = 0.333$

5. In this case the moles of CO_2 at equilibrium become $1 + z$, and Eq. (A) is

$$1.0 = \frac{z(1 + z)}{(1 - z)^2}$$
$$z = 0.333$$

Fraction of steam decomposed $= 0.333$

Example 2-7. Estimate the maximum (or equilibrium) conversion of ethylene to alcohol by vapor-phase hydration at 250°C and 500 psia. The initial steam-to-ethylene ratio is to be 5.0. The equilibrium constant K is 5.8×10^{-3}.
Solution

$$C_2H_4(g) + H_2O(g) \rightarrow C_2H_5OH(g)$$

For this gaseous reaction Eq. (2-22) becomes

$$K = 0.0058 = p_t^{-1}K_\alpha K_y \qquad \text{(A)}$$

K_α is evaluated by finding the f'/p_t ratios for each component from Fig. 2-3. For ethanol

$$T_R = \frac{T}{T_c} = \frac{273 + 250}{516} = 1.01\dagger$$

$$p_R = \frac{p}{p_c} = \frac{500}{63.1 \times 14.7} = 0.54\dagger$$

$$\frac{f'}{p_t} = 0.81$$

For ethylene

$$T_R = \tfrac{5\,2\,3}{2\,8\,3} = 1.85$$

$$p_R = \frac{500}{50.9 \times 14.7} = 0.67$$

$$\frac{f'}{p_t} = 0.98$$

For water vapor

$$T_R = \tfrac{5\,2\,3}{6\,4\,7} = 0.81$$

$$p_R = \frac{500}{218 \times 14.7} = 0.16$$

$$\frac{f'}{p_t} = 0.88$$

With these data

$$K_\alpha = \frac{0.81}{0.98 \times 0.88} = 0.94$$

† Critical temperatures and pressures may be obtained from J. H. Perry, "Chemical Engineers' Handbook," 3d ed., McGraw-Hill Book Company, Inc., New York, 1950.

Therefore, from Eq. (A),

$$K_y = \frac{y_A}{y_W y_E} = \frac{0.0058(500/14.7)}{0.94} = 0.21 \tag{B}$$

If the initial steam-to-ethylene ratio is 5 and a basis of 1 mole ethylene is chosen, a material balance gives the following results:

$$\begin{aligned}
\text{Moles ethanol at equilibrium} &= z \\
\text{Moles ethylene at equilibrium} &= 1 - z \\
\text{Moles water at equilibrium} &= \underline{5 - z} \\
\text{Total moles} &= 6 - z
\end{aligned}$$

Then $\qquad y_A = \dfrac{z}{6-z} \qquad y_E = \dfrac{1-z}{6-z} \qquad y_W = \dfrac{5-z}{6-z}$

Substituting these results in Eq. (B),

$$\frac{z(6-z)}{(1-z)(5-z)} = 0.21$$
$$z^2 - 6.0z + 0.868 = 0$$
$$z = 3.0 \pm 2.85 = 5.85 \text{ or } 0.15$$

The first solution is greater than unity, which is impossible. Therefore $z = 0.15$ is correct and corresponds to a 15 per cent conversion of ethylene to alcohol at equilibrium.

NOMENCLATURE

a Activity, defined as f/f^0
C Concentration
c_p Specific heat at constant pressure ($\bar{c}_p$ denotes average value over temperature range T_0 to T)
F Free energy
ΔF^0 Free-energy change for products minus reactants in their standard states
F_A Fugacity of component A in a mixture
f^0 Fugacity at a chosen standard state
f' Fugacity of a pure component at the temperature and pressure of the mixture
H Enthalpy
H Henry's-law constant, $p = HC$
H_0 Enthalpy at a pressure p_0, where p_0 approaches zero
ΔH_R Heat of reaction or enthalpy change of reaction
ΔH_f Heat of formation
ΔH_c Heat of combustion
ΔH^0 Heat of reaction for reactants and products at their standard states
ΔH_0^0 Constant of integration in Eq. (2-42)
K True-equilibrium constant defined in terms of activities (K_p, K_y, K_x, K_c are special forms defined in terms of partial pressures, mole fractions, or concentrations)
N_i Number of moles of component i

p_A Partial pressure of component A in a mixture
p Pressure of a pure component
p_t Total pressure
p_0 Pressure approaching zero
R Gas constant per mole
T Absolute temperature
S Entropy
V Volume
x Mole fraction in a liquid phase
y Mole fraction in a gas phase

Subscripts

c Critical state
R Reduced state, that is, $T_R = T/T_c$
α Fugacity-to-pressure ratio f'/p_t
γ Activity coefficient

PROBLEMS

1. (a) Assuming that the only reaction involved is the dehydrogenation to vinyl alcohol, estimate the equilibrium constant and equilibrium yield of vinyl alcohol from ethanol at 400°F and 1 atm pressure.   (b) Determine the composition of the gases at equilibrium obtained by dehydrogenating ethanol at 400°F and 1 atm pressure, this time considering the formation of both vinyl alcohol and acetaldehyde.

The group-contribution method may be helpful in estimating thermodynamic properties.

2. One mechanism that has been proposed for the conversion of ethyl alcohol to butadiene, in the vapor phase, consists of the three steps: (a) dehydration of the ethyl alcohol; (b) dehydrogenation of the ethyl alcohol; (c) condensation of the ethylene and acetaldehyde found in (a) and (b) to give butadiene, C_4H_6.

At 400°C the following information is available:

ΔF^0 for (a) $= -10,850$ cal/g mole
ΔF^0 for (b) $= -3610$ cal/g mole
ΔF^0 for (c) $= -1380$ cal/g mole

Determine the conversion of alcohol to butadiene at 400°C and 1 atm total pressure. For uniformity let α be the extent of reaction (a), β the extent of reaction (b), and γ be the moles of butadiene at equilibrium.

3. Another mechanism which has been proposed for the over-all reaction in Prob. 2 is the following:

a. $C_2H_5OH \rightarrow C_2H_4 + H_2O$.
b. $C_2H_5OH \rightarrow CH_2{=}CHOH + H_2$.
c. $CH_2{=}CHOH + C_2H_4 \rightarrow C_4H_6 + H_2O$.

Is there any simple relationship between (1) the equilibrium constants for the reactions in Probs. 2 and 3, (2), the conversion to butadiene for the reactions in Probs. 2 and 3?

4. Assuming the value of K_p for the methanol-synthesis reaction is 9.28×10^{-3} at 1 atm pressure and 300°C, what are the numerical values of the following quantities at this temperature?

a. K at $p_t = 1$ atm.
b. K_p at $p_t = 10$ atm.

c. K_p at $p_t = 50$ atm.

d. K at 10 and 50 atm total pressure.

e. K_y at 1, 10, and 50 atm total pressure.

5. Newton and Dodge[1] and von Wettberg and Dodge[2] experimentally measured the composition of equilibrium mixtures of CO, H_2, and CH_3OH in the methanol synthesis.

Compute the value of K and ΔF^0 at 309°C from the following data taken from their work:

$t = 309$°C

$p_t = 170$ atm.

Equilibrium gas analysis, mole per cent,

$$
\begin{aligned}
\text{Hydrogen} &= 60.9 \\
\text{Carbon monoxide} &= 13.5 \\
\text{Methanol} &= 21.3 \\
\text{Inerts} &= \underline{4.3} \\
\text{Total} &= 100.0
\end{aligned}
$$

6. The complete results of Dodge and coworkers, referred to in Prob. 5, are given in Table 2-2.

TABLE 2-2

$1{,}000/T$, °K^{-1}	log K
1.66	−4.15
1.73	−3.75
1.72	−3.65
1.75	−3.30
1.82	−3.10
1.81	−3.20
1.82	−3.00
1.82	−2.90
1.83	−2.95
1.88	−2.60
1.91	−2.70
1.91	−3.00
1.92	−2.30
2.05	−2.30
2.05	−2.15
2.05	−2.35

From this information determine the best relationship between K and T in the form of

$$ \ln K = A \frac{1}{T} + B $$

[1] *J. Am. Chem. Soc.*, **56**:1287 (1934).

[2] *Ind. Eng. Chem.*, **22**:1040 (1930).

7. The method of determining K in Prob. 5 was based upon direct measurement of equilibrium compositions. In the present instance use the listed calorimetric data and the third law to prepare a plot of log K vs. $1/T$ for the methanol synthesis. Include a temperature range of 298 to 800°K. Compare the graph with the result obtained in Prob. 6.

1. Entropy of CO gas at 298.16°K in the ideal-gas state at 1 atm is 47.30 cal/(g mole)(°K).
2. A similar value for hydrogen is 31.21.
3. Data for methanol are:
   a. Heat of vaporization at 298.16°K = 8943.7 cal/g mole.
   b. Vapor pressure at 298.16°K = 0.1632 atm.
   c. Heat of formation of CH_3OH in the ideal-gas state at 1 atm is −48,490 cal/g mole.
   d. Low-temperature specific-heat and heat-of-transition data are given in Table 2-3.

TABLE 2-3

T, °K	c_p, cal/(g mole)(°C)	T, °K	c_p, cal/(g mole)(°C)
18.80	1.109	118.79	11.64
21.55	1.512	121.44	11.75
24.43	1.959	125.07	12.18
27.25	2.292	129.38	12.28
30.72	2.829	133.71	12.64
34.33	3.437	147.86	12.97
57.64	3.962	152.29	13.69
40.87	4.427	153.98	14.12
43.93	4.840	164.14	11.29
48.07	5.404	166.23	11.63
56.03	6.425	167.75	11.68
59.53	6.845	181.09	16.60
63.29	7.252	185.10	16.67
69.95	8.001	189.06	16.77
73.95	8.392	196.77	16.78
77.61	8.735	210.34	16.97
81.48	9.001	235.84	17.41
85.52	9.295	256.34	17.70
89.29	9.693	273.58	18.30
93.18	9.939	285.15	18.70
97.22	10.23	292.01	19.11
111.14	11.23		
111.82	11.48		
117.97	11.64		

Methanol crystals undergo a phase transition at 157.4°K for which ΔH = 154.3 cal/g mole. The melting point is 175.22°K, and the heat of fusion is 757.0 cal/g mole.

4. Specific-heat information at temperatures above 298.16°K is given in Table 2-4.

TABLE 2-4

T, °K	c_{p,CH_3OH}, cal/(g mole)(°C)
298.16	10.8
300	10.8
400	12.7
500	14.5
600	16.3
700	17.8
800	19.2

Temp, °C	c_p, cal/(g)(°C)	
	CO	H_2
25	0.249	3.42
100	0.250	3.45
200	0.253	3.47
300	0.258	3.47
400	0.264	3.48
500	0.271	3.50
600	0.276	3.53

CHAPTER 3

KINETICS

The objective of this chapter is the understanding of the concepts of the rate of a chemical reaction. To accomplish this, it will be necessary to consider the variables which affect the rate, experimental methods, interpretation of rate data in terms of mathematical equations, and the present-day theories of just how a chemical reaction occurs. Only when this objective has been reached can rate-of-reaction data and design principles be intelligently utilized in reactor-design problems.

3-1. Rate of Reaction. The rate of a chemical reaction is expressed quantitatively as the mass or moles of a product produced, or reactant consumed, per unit time. Since this is an extensive property,[1] it is desirable to eliminate the magnitude factor and define the rate as the amount of product formed per unit time, per unit volume of reaction mixture.

In rate studies it is helpful to make a distinction between two types of systems. In one the physical processes of diffusion are important in the sequence of chemical and physical steps which determine the over-all rate. In the second such processes are unimportant. An illustration of the first type is the work on the hydrogenation of coal mentioned in Chap. 1. In general, whenever the reaction involves more than one phase (either as one of the reactants or products or as a catalyst) or a single-phase reaction mixture is not well enough mixed to be essentially homogeneous, diffusion may be important.[2] This more complex group of systems will not be considered here but instead will be taken up in the later chapters on reactor design. In this chapter consideration will be limited to the rate of the chemical reaction itself, regardless of the significance of diffusional processes.

It is also important to make a distinction between the static (batch) and dynamic (flow) methods of obtaining rate data. The early investigations of the speed of chemical reactions were invariably made by the

---

[1] That is, it would be proportional to the amount of reaction mixture.

[2] The importance of the diffusion effect depends also upon the level of the rate of the chemical-reaction step itself. If the chemical step is very fast, as in some ionic and combustion reactions, diffusion is more likely to be significant in determining the rate of the over-all process. Quantitative treatment of this point is considered in Chap. 9.

static method, in which the reactants are enclosed in a vessel with no provision made for flow in or out during the course of the reaction. Under such conditions the restraint of constant volume is frequently satisfied. In the case of gaseous systems the vessel will always be completely filled so that the constant-volume restraint is exactly met. In liquid systems changes in density during the course of the reaction may cause changes in volume, but these are generally small. Under constant-volume conditions the concentration (moles per unit volume) of a component in the system can change only because of the reaction. Hence the rate of reaction, defined as moles of a component produced or consumed per unit time per unit volume, is equal to the rate of change of concentration of the component with time.

This conclusion may be developed mathematically in the following manner: If dN represents the moles of a product produced in an element of time $d\theta$ and r is the rate of reaction,

$$r = \frac{1}{V}\frac{dN}{d\theta} \tag{3-1}$$

where V is the volume of the reaction mixture. The concentration of the component is given by the equation

$$C = \frac{N}{V} \tag{3-2}$$

or in differential form

$$dC = d\left(\frac{N}{V}\right) \tag{3-3}$$

Equations (3-2) and (3-3) are entirely general, applying equally well to both batch- and flow-type reaction systems. However, if the volume V is constant during the reaction, as in the case of a batch system of constant density, Eq. (3-3) may be written,

$$dC = \frac{dN}{V} \tag{3-4}$$

If this is substituted in Eq. (3-1) to eliminate dN,

$$\frac{dC}{d\theta} = r \tag{3-5}$$

This verifies the previous conclusion; that is, the rate is equal to the rate of change of concentration with time.

In contrast to the batch case consider the dynamic system where the reactants flow continuously into the reaction vessel and products are continuously removed. Under steady-state conditions there is no change in any of the properties of the system with time; i.e., time is not a variable in the flow method of studying reaction rates. Instead the amount of reaction varies as the mixture flows through the reaction vessel. In other words, the volume of the reaction vessel is the measurable variable in the dynamic system. If the change in flow rate of a product (in moles per unit time) produced in an element of reactor volume dV_R is dN', the rate of reaction will be dN' divided by dV_R. Hence, the defining equation for the rate of reaction in a flow system, in contrast to Eq. (3-1) for a batch system, is

$$r = \frac{dN'}{dV_R} = \frac{F\,dx'}{dV_R} \qquad (3\text{-}6)[1]$$

It should be noted that N' is a product flow rate and as such is a steady-state quantity independent of time. This is emphasized in the right-hand side of Eq. (3-6), where dN' is replaced by the product of the total feed rate F and the conversion dx' (dx' is the fraction of the total feed that reacts in a volume dV_R).

The rate r occurring in Eqs. (3-1) and (3-6) is exactly the same quantity, as long as the physical process of diffusion is not involved. For example, if a study is made of the rate of a certain reaction in both a batch and a flow apparatus, the results will be identical at the same values of the variables which affect the rate, for example, temperature and concentrations. However, in obtaining the rates from the observed measurements of time and conversion in the one case, and volume of reactor and conversion in the other, different expressions for r must be employed, Eq. (3-1) in the batch case and Eq. (3-6) for the flow data.

3-2. Variables Affecting the Rate of Reaction. The rate of a chemical reaction is a function of the concentrations of the components existing in the reaction mixture, temperature, pressure, and variables associated with the catalyst, if one is present. In gaseous reactions the concentrations and the pressure are not independent of each other. Nevertheless, the pressure may exert an independent effect on the reaction rate. In order to evaluate the importance of these variables, it is desirable to carry out the experimental investigations in such a manner that a minimum number of factors are changing simultaneously. For example, the effects of concentrations are best determined by experiments in which the temperature, catalyst variables, and pressure are maintained constant. Methods of interpreting such experimental data are described in Sec. 3-4.

3-3. Effect of Concentration: Order of Reaction. Both direct evidence and theoretical deductions (see Sec. 3-6) show that the rate may be a

---

[1] It is important to understand the difference between dN' in Eq. (3-6) and dN in Eq. (3-1). The former represents the change in rate of production, moles per unit time, due to a change in reactor volume dV_R. On the other hand dN is the change in moles of product due to a change in time $d\theta$.

function of the concentrations of one or more of the components involved in the reaction. For example, in the decomposition of dilute aqueous solutions of acetic anhydride the rate has been found to be proportional to the concentration of the undecomposed anhydride. This may be expressed mathematically as follows:

$$r = k_1 C_A \tag{3-7}$$

where r = rate, g moles anhydride decomposed/(sec)(liter)

$\quad C_A$ = concentration of anhydride, g moles/liter

The constant k is called the specific reaction rate (that is, $k = r$ when $C_A = 1$) or reaction-velocity constant. The second term is somewhat misleading in that k is not a constant but a function of all the variables listed in Sec. 3-2, except concentration. An equation such as (3-7) is termed first-order since the rate is proportional to the first power of the concentration. If the decomposition experiments are carried out in concentrated solutions of acetic anhydride, it is found that the rate is proportional to the product of the anhydride and water concentrations:

$$r = k_2 C_A C_W \tag{3-8}$$

Equation (3-8) is termed a second-order rate expression since the rate, from an over-all viewpoint, is proportional to the second power of the concentration. It is first-order with respect to anhydride concentration and also first-order with respect to water concentration. It is concluded that the reaction

$$(CH_3CO)_2O + H_2O \rightarrow 2CH_3COOH$$

is truly second order as indicated by Eq. (3-8). The only reason the first-order expression applies at dilute solutions is that the water concentration is so large that it remains essentially constant during the course of the reaction. If this constant water concentration is C_{w_0}, it is clear from Eqs. (3-7) and (3-8) that the two specific reaction rates are related by the expression

$$k_1 = k_2 C_{w_0}$$

In general, if the order of a reaction is α with respect to reactant A, β with respect to reactant B, and γ with respect to reactant C, the rate equation may be written

$$r = k_{\alpha+\beta+\gamma} C_A^\alpha C_B^\beta C_C^\gamma \tag{3-9}$$

It will be observed that the units of the specific reaction rate will vary depending upon the order. In the general case cited in Eq. (3-9) the units of k, in the metric system, would be

$$(g \text{ moles})^{1-\gamma-\beta-\alpha}(\text{liters})^{\alpha+\beta+\gamma-1}(\text{sec})^{-1}$$

This would reduce to simply sec^{-1} for a first-order reaction and to (liters) (g moles)$^{-1}$ (sec)$^{-1}$ for a second-order case.

3-4. Interpretation of Kinetic Data in Batch Systems. The chief importance of rate equations such as Eq. (3-9) is that they can be used satisfactorily to interpret experimental kinetic data. For example, if a kinetic study is carried out in the laboratory and it is found that the rate varies with the concentration according to a form of Eq. (3-9), this expression will be valuable in designing a commercial-scale reactor to carry out the reaction. Hence, it is important for the chemical engineer to be able to interpret laboratory kinetic data in terms of a rate equation, i.e., to determine the apparent order of the reaction, the specific-rate constant, and its variation with temperature.

The use of the rate equation in designing reactors is the subject of later chapters. Here the objective is the interpretation of laboratory kinetic data. Sometimes the data are obtained in constant-volume batch experiments, sometimes in flow apparatus. The batch data are usually in the form of observed concentrations at various time intervals, while the flow data are usually available as concentrations (or conversion leaving the reactor) for various feed rates F. Also the system may consist of reversible, consecutive, or simultaneous reactions so that combinations of equations like (3-9) are necessary to obtain the net rate of reaction.

The analysis of experimental data to determine the reaction order and the value of k can follow two methods of attack. An assumed rate equation can be combined with the appropriate defining expression for the rate, Eq. (3-5) for a batch system and Eq. (3-6) for a flow system, and then integrated to give a relationship between concentration and time (for a batch system). This theoretical relationship can be compared with the experimental concentration vs. time data to give k and the order. It is clear that if the proposed rate equation is to fit the data, the value of k so determined should be a constant. This approach is known as the integration method.

The second, or differential, method is to differentiate the data rather than integrate the equations. For example, if the concentration of a reactant or product is plotted vs. the time of reaction θ in a batch system, the slope of the curve is the rate of reaction, as seen by Eq. (3-5). The variation of this slope with concentration can then be compared with different forms of Eq. (3-9) to determine the order and numerical value of k.

Distinction between Rate Equation and Reaction Mechanism. At this point a careful distinction should be made between the determination of the mechanism of a reaction and a satisfactory rate equation. A satisfactory rate equation is one which may be used with confidence to design commercial-scale equipment for carrying out the reaction. The mechanism refers to the exact sequence of steps involved in the reaction and as such requires a knowledge of any intermediate substances that may exist between the reactants and final products. This difference between mechanism and rate equation is clearly illustrated by Daniels,[1] using the decomposition of nitrogen pentoxide as an example. Data from a number of investigators show conclusively that the decomposition occurs according to a first-order equation. This reproducibility of data suggests that the reaction is a simple one, involving a single molecule of N_2O_5 reacting at a time, according to the reaction

$$N_2O_5 \rightarrow 2NO_2 + \tfrac{1}{2}O_2$$

However, this equation is not feasible kinetically because the formation of one-half molecule of oxygen cannot be explained. An atom of oxygen would be possible, but the activation energy involved in the reaction is not sufficient to produce atomic oxygen. The reaction must be written with two molecules of N_2O_5. Then the problem is faced of explaining first-order kinetics with two molecules of N_2O_5 reacting at a time. After fifty years of study it appears that the solution is available. It postulates consecutive and parallel steps, involving NO, NO_2, NO_3, and N_2O_3, which taken together result in two molecules of N_2O_5 reacting according to an over-all first-order rate equation.

In another example, Watson and Myers[2] from experimental rate data on the thermal cracking of n-butane have obtained the following rate equation:

$$r = k p_{C_4H_{10}}$$

The product analysis indicated that the over-all reaction would be written as follows:

$$C_4H_{10} \rightarrow 0.12H_2 + 0.49CH_4 + 0.39C_2H_4$$
$$+ 0.38C_2H_6 + 0.49C_3H_6 + 0.01C_3H_8 + 0.12C_4H_8$$

It is clear that the rate equation, while it is first-order with respect to butane, makes no attempt to describe the mechanism by which butane is decomposed to the final products. A study of the mechanism would require determination of the intermediate chemical species that exist and, according to the best information now available, would indicate free radical formation as one of the first reactions taking place in the cracking process.

From the examples chosen it is apparent that the evaluation of the mechanism of a reaction is a much more complicated problem than the

[1] Farrington Daniels, *Chem. Eng. News*, **33**(No. 23): 2371 (1955).

[2] P. S. Myers and K. M. Watson, *Natl. Petroleum News, Tech. Sec.*, May 1 and June 5, 1946.

development of a satisfactory rate equation. Since it is generally necessary, for economic reasons, to proceed with the commercial production of a product without taking the time to determine the mechanism by which it is produced, the chemical engineer must be contented with a satisfactory rate equation. Hence in this text emphasis will be placed on using kinetic data to determine a satisfactory rate equation. This approach will usually not lead to an understanding of the reaction mechanism.

Single Irreversible Reactions. This simple case is illustrated in Example 3-1, where both the integration and the differential method are used to analyze batch data. More complicated batch cases and flow systems are considered in Examples 3-2 to 3-5.

Example 3-1. The liquid-phase reaction between trimethylamine and n-propyl bromide has been studied by Winkler and Hinshelwood[1] by immersing sealed glass tubes containing the reactants in a constant-temperature bath. The results at 139.4°C are shown in Table 3-1. Initial solutions of trimethylamine and n-propyl bromide in benzene, 0.2-molal, are mixed, sealed in glass tubes, and placed in the constant-temperature bath.

After various time intervals the tubes were removed, cooled to stop the reaction, and the contents analyzed. The analysis depended upon the fact that the product, a quaternary ammonium salt, is completely ionized. Hence the concentration of bromide ions could be estimated by titration.

TABLE 3-1

Run	Time, min	Conversion, %
1	13	11.2
2	34	25.7
3	59	36.7
4	120	55.2

From this information determine the first-order and second-order specific reaction rates, k_1 and k_2, assuming that the reaction is irreversible over the conversion range covered by the data. Use both the integration and the differential method, and compare the results. Which rate equation best fits the experimental data?

Solution. The reaction may be written

$$N(CH_3)_3 + CH_3CH_2CH_2Br \rightarrow (CH_3)_3(CH_2CH_2CH_3)N^+ + Br^-$$

Since the concentrations of reactants and products are small and the temperature is constant, the density may be assumed constant without serious error. Then the rate equations for first- and second-order mechanisms, in terms of the

[1] C. A. Winkler and C. N. Hinshelwood, *J. Chem. Soc. (London)*, 1147 (1935).

concentration of bromide ions C_B, can be written as follows:

$$\frac{dC_B}{d\theta} = k_1 C_T$$

$$\frac{dC_B}{d\theta} = k_2 C_T C_P$$

where C_T = concentration of trimethylamine, g moles/liter

C_P = concentration of n-propyl bromide, g moles/liter

INTEGRATION METHOD.   To integrate the rate equations, the concentration of trimethylamine at any time can be expressed in terms of its initial concentration C_{T_0} and the concentration of bromide ions as follows:

$$C_T = C_{T_0} - C_B$$

Similarly,

$$C_P = C_{P_0} - C_B$$

For the first-order case

$$\frac{dC_B}{d\theta} = k_1(C_{T_0} - C_B)$$

Integrating, and noting that, at $\theta = 0$, $C_B = 0$,

$$\ln \frac{C_{T_0}}{C_{T_0} - C_B} = k_1\theta \tag{A}$$

For the second-order case

$$\frac{dC_B}{d\theta} = k_2(C_{T_0} - C_B)(C_{P_0} - C_B)$$

Integrating,

$$\frac{1}{C_{T_0} - C_{P_0}} \ln \frac{(C_{T_0} - C_B)C_{P_0}}{(C_{P_0} - C_B)C_{T_0}} = k_2\theta \tag{B}$$

Equations (A) and (B) give expressions for the bromide-ion concentration at any time θ and are suitable for any first- and second-order irreversible batch reactions, provided the product concentrations are initially zero.   The second-order expression has another restriction, that the initial reactant concentrations are not equal, for under these circumstances Eq. (B) becomes indeterminate.   In the reaction of this example, $C_{T_0} = C_{P_0} = 0.1$ so that (B) is not applicable. However, the differential equation may be written

$$\frac{dC_B}{d\theta} = k_2(C_0 - C_B)^2 \qquad C_{T_0} = C_{P_0} = C_0$$

Integrating this form gives a suitable expression for C_B in terms of θ.   It is

$$\frac{C_B}{C_0(C_0 - C_B)} = k_2\theta \tag{C}$$

The conversion may be expressed in terms of the bromide-ion concentration as $C_B = 0.1x$, since the maximum concentration of bromide ions, corresponding to complete reaction, is 0.1-molal.

Illustrating the evaluation of k_1 and k_2 with the first run,

$$C_B = 0.1 \times 0.112 = 0.0112$$
$$\theta = 13 \times 60$$
$$= 780 \text{ sec}$$

Substituting in Eq. (A),

$$k_1 = \frac{1}{\theta} \ln \frac{C_{T_0}}{C_{T_0} - C_B} = \frac{1}{780} \ln \frac{0.1}{0.1 - 0.0112}$$
$$= 1.54 \times 10^{-4} \text{ sec}^{-1}$$

Similarly, from Eq. (C)

$$k_2 = \frac{1}{\theta} \frac{C_B}{C_0(C_0 - C_B)} = \frac{1}{780} \frac{0.0112}{0.1(0.1 - 0.0112)}$$
$$= 1.63 \times 10^{-3} \text{ liter/(g mole)(sec)}$$
$$= 1.63 \text{ cc/(g mole)(sec)}$$

Table 3-2 summarizes the results obtained in a similar way for the four runs.

TABLE 3-2. SPECIFIC REACTION RATES FOR TRIMETHYLAMINE AND
n-PROPYL BROMIDE

Run	Time, sec	Concentration, C_B, g moles/liter	$k_1 \times 10^4$, sec^{-1}	$k_2 \times 10^3$, liters/(g mole)(sec)
1	780	0.0112	1.54	1.63
2	2,040	0.0257	1.46	1.70
3	3,540	0.0367	1.30	1.64
4	7,200	0.0552	1.12	1.71
				(1.67, av)

The k_1 values show a definite trend with time, and therefore the first-order mechanism does not satisfactorily explain the kinetic data. The k_2 values not only are more nearly identical, but the variations show no definite trend.

DIFFERENTIAL METHOD. A plot of the concentration of bromide ions vs. time of reaction is shown in Fig. 3-1. The slope of the curve at any point, $dC_B/d\theta$, is equal to r in accordance with the equation

$$r = -\frac{dC_T}{d\theta} = \frac{dC_B}{d\theta}$$

Geometric evaluation of the slope at a series of concentrations can be made by drawing tangents to the curve. The results are shown in Table 3-3.

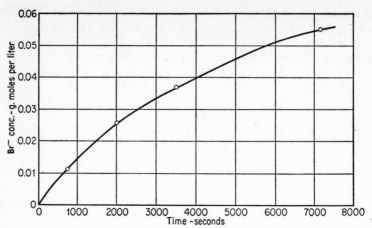

FIG. 3-1. Concentration vs. time, reaction between $(CH_3)_3N$ and $CH_3CH_2CH_2Br$.

TABLE 3-3

Concentration, g moles/liter		Rate, $-\dfrac{dC_T}{d\theta}$,
Br^-	Trimethylamine	g moles/(liter)(sec)
0.0	0.10	1.58×10^{-5}
0.01	0.09	1.38×10^{-5}
0.02	0.08	1.14×10^{-5}
0.03	0.07	0.79×10^{-5}
0.04	0.06	0.64×10^{-5}
0.05	0.05	0.45×10^{-5}

If the reaction is first-order, the rate is given by the expression

$$r = -\frac{dC_T}{d\theta} = k_1 C_T$$

or

$$\log r = \log k_1 + \log C_T \qquad\qquad (D)$$

Similarly, if the reaction is second-order,

$$\log r = \log k_2 + \log C_T C_P$$

Since the concentrations of trimethylamine and n-propyl bromide are identical, this last expression may be written

$$\log r = \log k_2 + \log C_T^2 = \log k_2 + 2 \log C_T \qquad\qquad (E)$$

For the first-order mechanism to be true, according to Eq. (D), $\log r$ plotted vs. $\log C_T$ should yield a straight line with a slope of 1.0. For the second-order mechanism to be correct, a straight line of slope of 2.0 should result, in accordance with Eq. (E). A plot of the data in Table 3-3 is shown in Fig. 3-2. While there is some scattering, the points do suggest a straight line of a slope approximately equal to 2.0.   For comparison purposes lines with slopes of both 2.0 and 1.0 have been set down on the plot.   The equation of the solid line (slope = 2.0) is

$$\log r = -2.76 + 2.0 \log C_T$$

By comparison with Eq. (E)

$$\log k_2 = -2.76$$
$$k_2 = 1.73 \times 10^{-3} \text{ liter/(g mole)(sec)}$$

This value agrees well with the average result, 1.67×10^{-3}, obtained by the integration method.

In summary, both methods show that the second-order mechanism is preferred. However, the unsuitability of the first-order assumption is perhaps more clearly

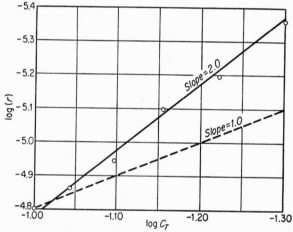

FIG. 3-2. Rate vs. concentration of trimethylamine, Example 3-1.

shown by the differential method than the integration approach.   Thus, the data in Fig. 3-2 do not approach a slope of 1.0 at all closely, but the k_1 values in Table 3-2 are of the same magnitude, differing from an average value by not more than 17 per cent.   This is because the integration process tends to mask small variations.

Reversible Reactions.   It was mentioned in Chap. 1 that for reactions with a low equilibrium constant (for example, some esterifications) the reverse reaction may be important in formulating an expression for the net rate.   It is now pertinent to inquire what the mathematical equation for the net rate will be.   Consider a general reaction between A and B to form products C and D in a single phase at constant volume,

$$A + B \rightarrow C + D$$

From Sec. 3-3, if the forward reaction is second-order, the rate of combination of A and B is

$$\text{Rate in forward direction} = kC_A C_B$$

Similarly, the rate of combination of C and D to re-form the reactants will be

$$\text{Rate in reverse direction} = k'C_C C_D$$

where k' represents the specific reaction rate in the reverse direction from the way the equation is written.[1]

The net rate of production of C or consumption of A is given by the difference between the forward and reverse rates, or

$$r = kC_A C_B - k'C_C C_D \tag{3-10}$$

It is evident that the expression for the net rate involves two rate constants. Actually one of these constants can be expressed in terms of the equilibrium constant and the other rate constant. This may be seen by noting that for equilibrium the net rate would be zero. At equilibrium Eq. (3-10) may be written

$$0 = kC_A C_B - k'C_C C_D$$

or
$$\frac{k}{k'} = \left(\frac{C_C C_D}{C_A C_B} \right)_{\text{equil}} = K_c \tag{3-11}$$

The ratio of the concentrations at equilibrium is the equilibrium constant K_c. Hence Eq. (3-10) may be expressed in terms of k and K_c,

$$r = kC_A C_B - \frac{k}{K_c} C_C C_D = k \left(C_A C_B - \frac{1}{K_c} C_C C_D \right) \tag{3-12}$$

For reactions that have high equilibrium constants (large values of K) the second term of the right side of Eq. (3-12) is negligible, and the simple expression for the rate developed in Sec. 3-3 is applicable. Even for reversible reactions where K is small the second term in (3-12) is zero provided the concentrations of products are zero. Thus the *initial* rate (rate at zero time) of reversible reactions can be expressed by the simple form. The initial-rate approach, as a modification of the integration method, is frequently used to simplify the kinetic study. Besides being able to eliminate consideration of the reverse reaction, the composition of the reaction system is usually known more definitely at the initial state than at any subsequent time. Compositions at later times are generally computed on the basis of a limited analysis plus the assumption that cer-

---

[1] It should be observed that it is an assumption here that the reverse rate is second-order. If the reverse rate is not of the same order as suggested by the stoichiometry of the reaction, Eq. (3-12) resulting from this development is not true.

tain reactions have occurred. If more reactions or different ones have taken place, the composition will not be known correctly.

Examples 3-2 and 3-3 illustrate the kinetic interpretation of experimental data for a reversible system.

Example 3-2. The reaction between methyl iodide and dimethyl-p-toluidine in nitrobenzene solution forms an ionized quaternary ammonium salt.[1] It can be studied kinetically in the same manner as the trimethylamine reaction considered in Example 3-1. Starting with an initial solution containing methyl iodide and dimethyl-p-toluidine in 0.05 g mole/liter concentrations, the data of Table 3-4 were obtained.

TABLE 3-4

Run	Time, min	Fraction of the toluidine reacted
1	10.2	0.175
2	26.5	0.343
3	36.0	0.402
4	78.0	0.523

In view of the results for Example 3-1, and assuming that the equilibrium constant for this reaction is 1.43, what rate equation best fits the experimental data?

Solution. The reaction may be written as follows:

$$CH_3I + N\!\!-\!\!R \rightarrow CH_3 - N^+\!\!-\!\!R + I^-$$

If it is supposed to be second-order and the rate is followed in terms of the concentration of iodide ion, Eq. (3-12) becomes

$$\frac{dC_I}{d\theta} = k_2\left(C_M C_T - \frac{1}{K_c} C_I C_{N^+}\right)$$

Since the initial concentrations, C_0, of reactants are equal, the concentrations at any time are

$$C_M = C_T = C_0 - C_I$$
$$C_{N^+} = C_I$$

Hence the rate expression can be simplified to read

$$\frac{dC_I}{d\theta} = k_2\left[(C_0 - C_I)^2 - \frac{1}{K_c} C_I^2\right] \tag{A}$$

INTEGRATION METHOD. Integrating Eq. (A),

$$k_2(\theta - 0) = \int_0^{C_I} \frac{dC_I}{(C_0 - C_I)^2 - \frac{1}{K_c} C_I^2}$$

[1] Taken from K. J. Laidler, "Chemical Kinetics," McGraw-Hill Book Company, Inc., New York, 1950.

Carrying out the integration of the right-hand side and simplifying,

$$k_2\theta = \frac{K_c^{\frac{1}{2}}}{2C_0}\left[\ln\frac{C_0 + (\alpha - 1)C_I}{C_0 - (\alpha + 1)C_I}\right] \tag{B}$$

where $\alpha^2 = 1/K_c$.

The experimental data are given in terms of conversion x, which is related to the iodide concentration by the relationship

$$C_I = C_0 x$$

Converting Eq. (B) to a form involving the conversion yields the result

$$k_2 = \frac{K_c^{\frac{1}{2}}}{2C_0\theta}\left[\ln\frac{1 + (\alpha - 1)x}{1 - (\alpha + 1)x}\right] \tag{C}$$

Equation (C) can now be used to test the proposed second-order mechanism,

$$\alpha^2 = \frac{1}{1.43} \qquad \alpha = 0.835$$

$$k_2 = \frac{1.20}{2 \times 0.05 \times \theta}\left(\ln\frac{1 - 0.165x}{1 - 1.835x}\right) \tag{D}$$

Substituting the corresponding values of θ and x in (D) gives the results of Table 3-5.

TABLE 3-5

Run	θ, sec	k_2, liters/(g mole)(sec)	k_2 (neglecting reverse reaction)
1	612	7.05×10^{-3}	6.93×10^{-3}
2	1,590	7.06×10^{-3}	6.57×10^{-3}
3	2,160	7.06×10^{-3}	6.23×10^{-3}
4	4,680	7.97×10^{-3}	4.68×10^{-3}

As a matter of interest the values of k_2 computed assuming that the reaction is irreversible are shown in the fourth column of the preceding table. They were computed from the expression [Eq. (C)] developed in Example 3-1, i.e.,

$$k_2\theta = \frac{C_I}{C_0(C_0 - C_I)}$$

The steady trend in values of k_2 so computed indicates that the irreversible assumption is a poor one. On the other hand, the specific-velocity constants evaluated from Eq. (D) are nearly constant except for the fourth run.

In studying rate data, trends in the computed values of k are of more significance than random variations. The former suggest that the assumed order is open to question, while the latter suggest errors in the experimental data. Of course, if the precision of the data is too poor, random variations will mask any trends in computed k values that might otherwise be noticeable.

DIFFERENTIAL METHOD. Replacing $1/K_c$ and C_0 with their numerical values, and taking logarithms of the rate equation (A), yields

$$\log r = \log \frac{dC_I}{d\theta} = \log k_2 + \log [(0.05 - C_I)^2 - 0.70C_I^2] \qquad \text{(E)}$$

According to Eq. (E) a plot, on logarithmic coordinates, of the rate vs. $[(0.05 - C_I)^2 - 0.70C_I^2]$ should yield a straight line of slope equal to unity.

Figure 3-3 shows on one part a plot of C_I vs. θ. Slopes of this curve give the rate values shown in Table 3-6.

TABLE 3-6

Time, sec	C_I	$\dfrac{dC_I}{d\theta}$	$\log \dfrac{dC_I}{d\theta}$	$(0.05 - C_I)^2$ $- 0.70C_I^2$	$\log [(0.05 - C_I)^2$ $- 0.70C_I^2]$
0	0	1.93×10^{-5}	-4.71	25.0×10^{-4}	-2.60
612	0.00875	1.12×10^{-5}	-4.95	16.5×10^{-4}	-2.78
1,590	0.0171	0.62×10^{-5}	-5.20	8.75×10^{-4}	-3.05
2,160	0.0201	0.42×10^{-5}	-5.37	6.13×10^{-4}	-3.21
4,680	0.0261	0.13×10^{-5}	-5.89	0.96×10^{-4}	-4.01

Also on Fig. 3-3 is shown a plot of Eq. (E). It is observed that the first four points establish a line with a slope close to unity, as required by the second-order

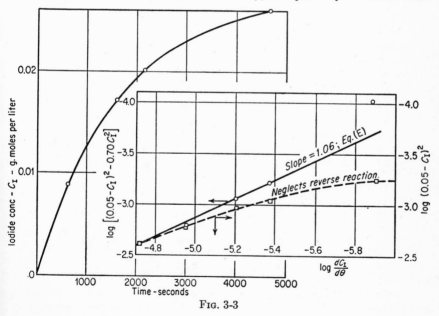

FIG. 3-3

mechanism. The last point deviates from the line, just as the k value for this point obtained by the integration method was not in agreement with the other values.

Example 3-3. The interpretation of kinetic data for gaseous reactions is similar to that for liquid systems. The analysis for a reversible case is well illustrated by the vapor-phase decomposition of hydrogen iodide,

$$2HI \rightarrow H_2 + I_2$$

This reaction has been carefully studied by a number of investigators, for example, Bodenstein,[1] Taylor,[2] and Kistiakowsky.[3] It is generally considered one of the most certain examples of a second-order reaction, at least at low pressures. The equilibrium values of the fraction, x, of HI decomposed can be accurately represented by Bodenstein's equation,

$$x_e = 0.1376 + 7.22 \times 10^{-5}t + 2.576 \times 10^{-7}t^2 \qquad t = °C$$

Kistiakowsky[3] used a static experimental method to study the reaction. Pure hydrogen iodide was sealed in glass bulbs, immersed in a constant-temperature bath for various time intervals, then removed, cooled, and the contents analyzed for all three chemical species. The initial pressure of HI (and hence the initial concentration) and the size of the reaction bulb were varied over a wide range. The data obtained at an average temperature of 321.4°C are given in Table 3-7.

TABLE 3-7

Run	Time, sec	% of HI decomposed	Vol. of reaction bulb, cc	Initial HI conc., g moles/liter
1	82,800	0.826	51.38	0.02339
2	172,800	2.567	59.80	0.03838
3	180,000	3.286	51.38	0.04333
4	173,100	3.208	51.38	0.04474
5	81,000	2.942	7.899	0.1027
6	57,560	2.670	7.899	0.1126
7	61,320	4.499	7.899	0.1912
8	19,200	2.308	7.899	0.3115
9	18,000	2.202	7.899	0.3199
10	16,800	2.071	7.899	0.3279
11	17,400	2.342	7.899	0.3464
12	17,700	2.636	7.899	0.4075
13	18,000	2.587	7.899	0.4228
14	23,400	4.343	7.899	0.4736
15	6,000	2.224	3.28	0.9344
16	5,400	1.903	0.778	0.9381
17	8,160	3.326	0.781	1.138
19	5,400	2.741	0.713	1.231

[1] M. Bodenstein, *Z. physik. Chem.*, **13**:56 (1894), **22**:1 (1897), **29**:295 (1898).
[2] H. A. Taylor, *J. Phys. Chem.*, **28**:984 (1924).
[3] G. B. Kistiakowsky, *J. Am. Chem. Soc.*, **50**:2315 (1928).

1. From this information estimate the specific-reaction-rate constants [liters/ (g mole)(sec)] for the forward and reverse reactions, both of which may be taken as second-order.

2. Could the differential method be used to interpret the data?

3. What would be the values of the specific-reaction-rate constants in units of g moles/(liter)(sec)(atm)^2?

4. Could the course of this reaction be followed by measuring the total pressure on the reaction vessel at various times?

Solution. 1. The net rate of reaction in the forward direction may be written

$$\frac{dC_I}{d\theta} = k_2 C_{HI}^2 - k_2' C_H C_I = k_2 \left(C_{HI}^2 - \frac{1}{K_c} C_I^2 \right)$$

The concentration of HI at any time, in terms of its initial value C_0, is given by the relationship

$$C_{HI} = C_0 - 2C_I$$

Substituting in the rate equation and integrating,

$$\frac{dC_I}{d\theta} = k_2 \left[(C_0 - 2C_I)^2 - \frac{1}{K_c} C_I^2 \right]$$

$$\int_0^C \frac{dC_I}{(C_0 - 2C_I)^2 - (1/K_c)C_I^2} = k_2(\theta - 0)$$

The lower limit of integration is based upon the fact that $C_I = 0$ at $\theta = 0$. Carrying out the indicated integration yields

$$\frac{1}{2\beta C_0} \left[\ln \frac{C_0 + C_I(\beta - 2)}{C_0 - C_I(\beta + 2)} \right] = k_2\theta \tag{A}$$

where $\beta^2 = 1/K_c$.

The equilibrium constant is related to the concentrations at equilibrium by the expression

$$K_c = \left(\frac{C_I C_H}{C_{HI}^2} \right)_{equil}$$

If x = the fraction of the HI decomposed,

$$C_I = C_H = \tfrac{1}{2}C_0 x$$
$$C_{HI} = C_0(1 - x)$$

Hence

$$K_c = \frac{(C_0 x_e/2)^2}{C_0^2(1 - x_e)^2} = \frac{1}{4} \frac{x_e^2}{(1 - x_e)^2}$$

From the given equation for x_e at 321.4°C,

$$x_e = 0.1376 + 7.221 \times 10^{-5} \times 321.4 + 2.576 \times 10^{-7} \times 321.4^2 = 0.1873$$

Hence

$$\beta = \left(\frac{1}{K_c} \right)^{\frac{1}{2}} = \frac{2(1 - 0.1873)}{0.1873} = 8.67$$

Substituting this value of β in Eq. (A) and introducing the fraction decomposed,

$$k_2 = \frac{1}{2 \times 8.67 \times C_0\theta}\left[\ln\frac{C_0 + \frac{1}{2}C_0x(8.67 - 2)}{C_0 - \frac{1}{2}C_0x(8.67 + 2)}\right]$$

or
$$k_2 = \frac{1}{2 \times 8.67 \times C_0\theta}\ln\frac{1 + 3.335x}{1 - 5.335x} \tag{B}$$

The experimental data for x can be used directly in Eq. (B) to compute values of the specific reaction rate k_2. However, another form of the expression is more useful when the x values are very low, as in the present case (maximum value of x is 0.04499 for run 7). Equation (B) may be written in the form

$$k_2 = \frac{1}{2 \times 8.67 \times C_0\theta}\ln\left(1 + \frac{8.67x}{1 - 5.335x}\right)$$

Expanding the logarithmic term in a power series and retaining the first two terms,

$$k_2 = \frac{1}{2 \times 8.67 \times C_0\theta}\left[\frac{8.67x}{1 - 5.335x} - \frac{1}{2}\left(\frac{8.67x}{1 - 5.335x}\right)^2\right] \tag{C}$$

The use of Eq. (C) may be illustrated with run 1,

$$k_2 = \frac{1}{2 \times 8.67 \times 0.02339 \times 82{,}800}$$
$$\left[\frac{8.67 \times 0.00826}{1 - 5.335 \times 0.00826} - \frac{1}{2}\frac{(8.67 \times 0.00826)^2}{(1 - 5.335 \times 0.00826)^2}\right]$$
$$k_2 = 2.97 \times 10^{-5}(0.0749 - 0.0028)$$
$$= 2.14 \times 10^{-6} \text{ liter/(g mole)(sec)}$$

The results for the other runs are summarized in Table 3-8.
The mean value of k_2 is 1.99×10^{-6}.
For the reverse reaction

$$k_2' = \frac{k_2}{K_c} = (1.99 \times 10^{-6}) \times 8.67^2$$
$$= 1.50 \times 10^{-4} \text{ liter/(g mole)(sec)}$$

2. The differential method could not be applied with the information given, because conversion vs. time data are not available for any one run. These data would be necessary in order to plot C_I vs. time and determine the rate by the slope of the curve. From the data given only one point could be established on each of 18 different curves, since each initial concentration would give a different curve.

It is evident that the differential method cannot be applied to what is called initial-rate data, that is, to data obtained at conditions of such low conversion that the concentration is essentially constant at the initial value. As previously mentioned, such initial-rate data may be of considerable value in a kinetic study, because the exact concentrations of the chemical species present are known. At a later time, after a significant amount of reaction has occurred, the complete composition is based upon suppositions regarding the reactions that occur. These may be doubtful assumptions in some systems.

TABLE 3-8

Run	x	$k_2 \times 10^6$, liters/(sec)(g mole)
1	0.00826	2.14
2	0.02567	2.01
3	0.03286	2.20
4	0.03208	2.17
5	0.02942	1.92
6	0.02670	2.08
7	0.04499	2.04
8	0.02308	1.99
9	0.0202	1.80
10	0.02971	1.77
11	0.02342	2.00
12	0.02636	1.90
13	0.02587	1.75
14	0.04343	2.08
15	0.02224	2.05
16	0.01903	1.93
17	0.03326	1.87
19	0.02741	2.15

3. The rate equations could also have been written in terms of partial pressures. These are proportional to the concentrations in a gas-phase reaction, provided the gas mixture follows perfect-gas behavior. In terms of pressures the net rate may be written

$$\frac{dC_\mathrm{I}}{d\theta} = k_p p_\mathrm{HI}^2 - k_p' p_\mathrm{I} p_\mathrm{H}$$

According to the perfect-gas law the partial pressure is given by the expression

$$p_i = \frac{N_i RT}{V} = C_i RT$$

Substituting partial-pressure relationships in the rate equation,

$$\frac{dC_\mathrm{I}}{d\theta} = k_p (RT)^2 C_\mathrm{HI}^2 - k_p' (RT)^2 C_\mathrm{I} C_\mathrm{H}$$

Comparison with the original equation employed in (1) shows that k_p is related to k_2 as follows:

$$k_p = \frac{k_2}{(RT)^2} = \frac{1.99 \times 10^{-6}}{0.082^2(273.1 + 321.4)^2}$$
$$= 0.84 \times 10^{-9} \text{ g mole/(liter)(atm)(sec)}^2$$

and
$$k_p' = \frac{k_2'}{(RT)^2}$$
$$= 6.40 \times 10^{-8} \text{ g mole/(liter)(atm)(sec)}^2$$

While no pressures are given in the tabulated data, approximate values can be computed from the perfect-gas law. Thus the total pressure will be given by

$$p_t = \frac{N_t RT}{V}$$

Initially the only substance present is HI, so that N_t/V represents the initial concentration of HI. For run 1

$$p_t = C_0 RT = 0.02339 \times 0.082 \times 594.5$$
$$= 1.14 \text{ atm}$$

The highest pressure will be for run 19, where the initial concentration is the greatest. In this case

$$p_t = 1.2310 \times 0.082 \times 594.5$$
$$= 60 \text{ atm}$$

4. In reactions where the number of moles of products is different from the moles of reactants, the progress of the reaction can be computed from measurements of the total pressure as a function of time. However, in the present case the change in moles as a result of reaction is zero, so that the total pressure does not change with the extent of the reaction.[1]

Total-pressure Method of Following Kinetic Data. To illustrate the method of studying the kinetics of constant-volume gaseous reactions by total pressure measurements, consider the example

$$2NO_2 \rightarrow N_2O_4$$

There is a change in moles, and the total pressure change will depend upon the extent of the reaction. If the initial moles of NO_2 is N_0 and no N_2O_4 is present, the total moles at any time will be

$$N_t = N_{N_2O_4} + N_{NO_2} = N_{N_2O_4} + N_0 - 2N_{N_2O_4} = N_0 - N_{N_2O_4}$$

The total pressure at any time will be

$$p_t = \frac{N_t RT}{V} = \frac{N_0 - N_{N_2O_4}}{V} RT \tag{3-13}$$

[1] If the perfect-gas law is not followed, the total pressure can vary without a change in number of moles of reaction mixture. However, this variation is not large enough to use with confidence in analyzing kinetic data.

If the initial total pressure is p_0,

$$p_0 = \frac{N_0 RT}{V}$$

Hence the expression for p_t may be written in terms of p_0 as follows:

$$p_t = p_0 - \frac{N_{N_2O_4}}{V} RT = p_0 - C_{N_2O_4}RT \qquad (3\text{-}14)$$

If the conversion x is defined as the fraction of the NO_2 reacted,

$$x = \frac{N_0 - N_{NO_2}}{N_0} = \frac{N_0 - (N_0 - 2N_{N_2O_4})}{N_0} = \frac{2N_{N_2O_4}}{N_0}$$

or
$$N_{N_2O_4} = \frac{N_0 x}{2}$$

Substituting this expression for $N_{N_2O_4}$ in Eq. (3-14) yields the relationship between the total pressure p_t and the conversion x.

$$p_t = p_0 - \frac{x}{2} \frac{N_0 RT}{V} = p_0 \left(1 - \frac{x}{2}\right) \qquad (3\text{-}15)$$

This is similar to Eq. (3-14) but is in terms of conversion instead of concentration.

To compute the reaction-velocity constant from total-pressure measurements, the rate equation is first written in the usual way,

$$\frac{dC_{N_2O_4}}{d\theta} = k_2(C_{NO_2})^2 = k(C_0 - 2C_{NO_2O_4})^2 \qquad (3\text{-}16)$$

Then Eq. (3-14) can be employed to replace the concentration of N_2O_4 with the total pressure. For example, differentiation of Eq. (3-14) yields

$$\frac{dC_{N_2O_4}}{d\theta} = -\frac{1}{RT} \frac{dp_t}{d\theta}$$

Also
$$C_0 = \frac{p_0}{RT}$$

$$C_{N_2O_4} = \frac{p_0 - p_t}{RT}$$

Substituting these equalities in Eq. (3-16),

$$\frac{dC_{N_2O_4}}{d\theta} = -\frac{1}{RT} \frac{dp_t}{d\theta} = k_2 \left(\frac{p_0}{RT} - 2\frac{p_0 - p_t}{RT}\right)^2$$

$$-\frac{dp_t}{d\theta} = \frac{k_2}{RT} (2p_t - p_0)^2 \qquad (3\text{-}17)$$

Eq. (3-17) can be integrated and the measured p_t data used directly to determine k_2.

Successive and Simultaneous Reactions. The net rate of formation or consumption of a substance as a result of simultaneous or successive reactions can be developed by combining rate expressions of the form of Eq. (3-9). An example is the successive chlorination of benzene, where three reactions are involved. One of the products of the first reacts with an original reactant to give the second reaction, and a product from the second reacts with the same original reactant to give the third reaction,

1:          $C_6H_6 + Cl_2 \rightarrow C_6H_5Cl + HCl$
2:          $C_6H_5Cl + Cl_2 \rightarrow C_6H_4Cl_2 + HCl$
3:          $C_6H_4Cl_2 + Cl_2 \rightarrow C_6H_3Cl_3 + HCl$

This particular problem is illustrated with a numerical solution in Example 3-4.

Example 3-4. Benzene is to be chlorinated in the liquid phase in a kettle-type reactor operated on a semibatch basis; i.e., the reactor is initially charged with liquid benzene and then chlorine gas bubbled into the well-agitated solution. The reactor is to be equipped with a reflux condenser which will condense the benzene and chlorinated products but not interfere with the removal of hydrogen chloride.

Assume that the chlorine is added slowly enough so that the chlorine and hydrogen chloride concentrations in the liquid phase are small and so that there is no loss of chlorine.

At the constant operating temperature of 55°C the significant reactions are the three substitution ones leading to mono-, di-, and trichlorobenzene.

k_1: $C_6H_6 + Cl_2 \rightarrow C_6H_5Cl + HCl$
k_2: $C_6H_5Cl + Cl_2 \rightarrow C_6H_4Cl_2 + HCl$
k_3: $C_6H_4Cl_2 + Cl_2 \rightarrow C_6H_3Cl_3 + HCl$

In an investigation of these reactions MacMullin[1] found the ratios of the constants to have the following values at 55°C:

$$\frac{k_1}{k_2} = 8.0$$

$$\frac{k_2}{k_3} = 30$$

Find values of the composition of the reaction mixture vs. the moles of chlorine (x) added per mole of benzene charged to the reactor.[2] Include a range of x of 0 to 2.1. The holdup in the reflux condenser is negligible.

[1] R. B. MacMullin, *Chem. Eng. Progr.*, **44**:183 (1948).
[2] From the viewpoint of determining rate equations from experimental data, it would be more appropriate to reverse this example, i.e., to require the evaluation of the ratios of the rate constants from given composition curves. Actually the calculations involved are essentially the same for this arrangement as in the example as stated.

Solution.[1] The process described is actually neither flow nor batch, but of a semibatch type. However, by making assumptions which are reasonably valid, the problem can be reduced to a constant-volume batch system for which Eq. (3-5) is applicable. If it is assumed that the density of the solution remains constant and that the hydrogen chloride vaporizes and leaves the solution, the volume of the liquid-phase reaction will be constant. Then the relationship between the composition of the substances in the liquid phase is governed by rate expressions of the constant-volume batch type. For example, the rate of disappearance of benzene is determined entirely by the first reaction, so that

$$-\frac{dC_B}{d\theta} = r_1 = k_1 C_B C_{Cl_2}$$

where the subscripts B and Cl_2 refer to benzene and chlorine (dissolved).

Monochlorobenzene is formed by the first reaction and consumed by the second; hence its net rate of formation is the difference between the rates of these two reactions,

$$\frac{dC_M}{d\theta} = k_1 C_B C_{Cl_2} - k_2 C_M C_{Cl_2}$$

where the subscript M refers to monochlorobenzene.

Similarly, the net rate of formation of dichlorobenzene is

$$\frac{dC_D}{d\theta} = k_2 C_M C_{Cl_2} - k_3 C_D C_{Cl_2}$$

where the subscript D refers to dichlorobenzene.

Finally, the rate of formation of the trichlorinated benzene is governed by the third reaction only, so that

$$\frac{dC_T}{d\theta} = k_3 C_D C_{Cl_2}$$

where the subscript T refers to trichlorobenzene.

These four rate equations, with the material balance, could be solved for the concentrations of each of the five substances as a function of time, provided the individual specific-reaction-velocity constants were known. Actually the problem requires only the composition of the mixture in terms of the amount of chlorine reacted; i.e., the time required to obtain a given composition is not sought. Hence the rates may be eliminated from the four equations and the resultant expressions solved for the relative amounts of each substance present. It will be simpler to work with moles of a component present rather than concentration. These quantities are related as follows:

$$N = VC$$

Also
$$dN = V\,dC$$

since V is constant.

---

[1] This problem was originally solved by MacMullin, *loc. cit.*, in a somewhat different manner.

Using these expressions, the four rate equations may be rewritten in terms of moles.

$$V \frac{dN_B}{d\theta} = -k_1 N_B N_{Cl_2} \tag{A}$$

$$V \frac{dN_M}{d\theta} = k_1 N_B N_{Cl_2} - k_2 N_M N_{Cl_2} \tag{B}$$

$$V \frac{dN_D}{d\theta} = k_2 N_M N_{Cl_2} - k_3 N_D N_{Cl_2} \tag{C}$$

$$V \frac{dN_T}{d\theta} = k_3 N_D N_{Cl_2} \tag{D}$$

If the original number of moles of benzene is taken as unity, the total moles of reaction mixture at any time will also be unity (neglecting the small amount of dissolved chlorine). On this basis, any N value will also equal the mole fraction, and a material-balance equation may be written as follows:

$$1 = N_B + N_M + N_D + N_T \tag{E}$$

In addition, the number of moles of chlorine x reacted per mole of original benzene is related, by the stoichiometry of the reactions, to the other mole fractions in this way:

$$x = N_M + 2N_D + 3N_T \tag{F}$$

The six equations (A to F) may be solved for the composition as a function of x. One way of accomplishing this is to divide Eq. (B) by Eq. (A), giving

$$\frac{dN_M}{dN_B} = \frac{k_1 N_B N_{Cl_2} - k_2 N_M N_{Cl_2}}{-k_1 N_B N_{Cl_2}} = -1 + \frac{k_2}{k_1} \frac{N_M}{N_B}$$

This expression is a linear first-order differential equation and may be solved directly to yield

$$N_M N_B^{-\alpha} = - \int B^{-\alpha} \, dB = - \frac{N_B^{1-\alpha}}{1 - \alpha} + C$$

where $\alpha = k_2/k_1$.

Noting that initially there is no monochlorobenzene ($N_M = 0$) and 1 mole of benzene ($N_B = 1$), the constant of integration C is equal to $1/(1 - \alpha)$. Hence

$$N_M = \frac{1}{1 - \alpha} (1 - N_B^{1-\alpha}) N_B^{+\alpha} = \frac{1}{1 - \alpha} (N_B^{\alpha} - N_B) \tag{G}$$

and

$$\frac{N_M}{N_B} = \frac{1}{1 - \alpha} (N_B^{\alpha-1} - 1) \tag{H}$$

This expression gives a relationship for N_M in terms of N_B. Equations (C) and (A) may be employed to obtain a similar relationship between N_D and N_B. Thus, if Eq. (C) is divided by Eq. (A),

$$\frac{dN_D}{dN_B} = -\alpha \frac{N_M}{N_B} + \beta \frac{N_D}{N_B} \qquad \beta = \frac{k_3}{k_1}$$

Using Eq. (H) for N_M/N_B,

$$\frac{dN_D}{dN_B} = - \frac{\alpha}{1 - \alpha} (N_B^{\alpha-1} - 1) + \beta \frac{N_D}{N_B}$$

This expression likewise is a first-order linear differential equation. Integrating, and noting that $N_D = 0$ when $N_B = 1$, yields

$$N_D = \frac{\alpha}{1 - \alpha} \left(\frac{N_B}{1 - \beta} - \frac{N_B^\alpha}{\alpha - \beta} \right) + \frac{\alpha N_B^\beta}{(\alpha - \beta)(1 - \beta)} \tag{I}$$

The mole fraction di- and monochlorobenzene for any value of N_B can be found from Eqs. (G) and (I). Then N_T is obtained from Eq. (E), and finally x from Eq. (F).

First take $N_B = 0.5$ (corresponding to the time when one-half of the benzene has been reacted), and note that $\alpha = 1/8.0 = 0.125$ and

$$\beta = \frac{k_3}{k_1} = \frac{k_3}{k_2} \frac{k_2}{k_1} = \frac{1}{30} \frac{1}{8} = 0.00417$$

Under these circumstances Eq. (G) gives

$$N_M = \frac{1}{1 - 0.125} [(0.5)^{0.125} - 0.5] = 0.477$$

Equation (I) yields

$$N_D = \frac{0.125}{1 - 0.125} \left[\frac{0.50}{1 - 0.00417} - \frac{(0.50)^{0.125}}{0.125 - 0.00417} \right]$$
$$+ \frac{(0.125)(0.50)^{0.00417}}{(0.125 - 0.00417)(1 - 0.00417)} = 0.022$$

From Eq. (E)

$$N_T = 1 - N_B - N_M - N_D = 1 - 0.50 - 0.477 - 0.022 = 0.001$$

Finally from Eq. (F)

$$x = N_M + 2N_D + 3N_T = 0.477 + 2 \times 0.022 + 3 \times 0.001$$
$$= 0.524$$

Hence, with 0.524 mole of chlorine reacted per mole of benzene, most of the product is monochlorobenzene, with a little dichlorobenzene and a negligible quantity of trichlorobenzene.

To obtain the composition at a much higher value of x, choose $N_B = 0.001$. Then, proceeding in the same manner, most of the product is found to be mono- and dichlorobenzene with a little tri-substituted product. The results for a range of x up to 2.1 are summarized in Table 3-9.

TABLE 3-9. COMPOSITION OF CHLORINATED BENZENES

Compound	Mole fraction							
Benzene	1.0	0.50	0.10	0.01	0.001	10^{-4}	10^{-10}	10^{-20}
Monochlorobenzene	0	0.477	0.745	0.632	0.482	0.362	0.064	0.004
Dichlorobenzene	0	0.022	0.152	0.353	0.509	0.625	0.877	0.852
Trichlorobenzene	0	0.001	0.003	0.005	0.008	0.013	0.059	0.144
Total	1.000	1.000	1.000	1.000	1.000	1.000	1.000	1.000
(Moles of chlorine used)/(mole of original benzene), x	0	0.524	1.06	1.35	1.52	1.65	1.99	2.14

3-5. Interpretation of Kinetic Data in Flow Systems. The evaluation of a rate equation from data taken in a laboratory, or pilot-plant-scale, flow reactor is similar to the problem of designing a large-scale reactor from a known rate equation. In general the same procedures are necessary in the design problem as in the kinetic interpretation, except that they are carried out in the reverse order. However, it is frequently possible to operate the laboratory reactor under conditions of constant temperature or constant pressure when this is not possible in the commercial apparatus, and these simplifications lessen the difficulty of the kinetic interpretation problem. Because of their similarity the interpretation and design problems are considered together in Chap. 6. At this point only a single illustration (Example 3-5) of the general method will be given for the purpose of becoming familiar with the application of the flow equation [Eq. (3-6)].

Example 3-5. The catalytic hydrogenation of ethylene has been investigated, using the dynamic method (flow), by a number of investigators. The results obtained in a recent study[1] using a copper oxide–magnesia catalyst are as follows:

Mixtures of ethylene and hydrogen were passed through a tube, $\frac{1}{4}$ in. ID, packed with cubical catalyst pellets (mean size = 0.078 in.). The volume of the tube containing catalyst was small in order to operate at essentially constant temperature and with small conversions. The extent of the reaction was followed by analyzing the gas entering and leaving the catalyst bed for hydrogen. The temperature level, reactor volume, flow rate, and entering-gas composition were varied, as indicated by the results given in Table 3-10.

From this information determine whether or not the data fit a rate equation which is first-order with respect to hydrogen. Evaluate the specific reaction rate in the units of g moles $C_2H_6/(sec)(cc)(atm)$. The following nomenclature is suggested:

y Mole fraction
x' Conversion, moles C_2H_6 formed/mole total feed

[1] Raymond Wynkoop and R. H. Wilhelm, *Chem. Eng. Progr.*, **46**:300 (1950).

TABLE 3-10

Run	Feed rate, (g moles/sec) $\times 10^3$	Mole fraction hydrogen[†]		Temp, °C	Reactor vol., cc
		y_{a_o}	$y_{a_i} - y_{a_o}$		
1	1.41	0.38587	0.00302	77	0.664
2	1.41	0.38408	0.00320	77	0.664
3	1.41	0.38573	0.00165	63.5	0.664
4	1.41	0.38640	0.00079	53.3	0.664
5	1.41	0.38604	0.00074	53.3	0.664
6	1.72	0.54092	0.00233	77.6	0.664
7	1.72	0.53921	0.00229	77.6	0.664
8	1.72	0.53923	0.00121	77.6	0.664
9	1.72	0.53952	0.00069	52.9	0.664
10	1.72	0.53945	0.00067	52.9	0.664
11	2.11	0.63623	0.00174	77.6	0.664
12	2.11	0.63875	0.00103	62.7	0.664
13	2.11	0.64066	0.00050	53.7	0.664
14	2.11	0.64023	0.00049	53.7	0.664
15	1.885	0.84456	0.00140	79.5	0.664
16	1.885	0.84394	0.00142	79.5	0.664
17	0.93	0.39761	0.00224	64.0	0.664
18	0.93	0.39759	0.00234	64.0	0.664
19	0.538	0.43631	0.00212	54.5	0.664
20	0.481	0.38089	0.00364	39.2	5.10
21	0.469	0.42601	0.00424	38.3	5.10
22	0.358	0.54115	0.00917	49.4	5.10
23	0.266	0.40484	0.0148	40.2	5.10
24	0.266	0.40113	0.0151	40.2	5.10
25	0.362	0.61065	0.00945	40.2	5.10
26	0.362	0.61103	0.00952	40.2	5.10
27	0.698	0.77568	0.00349	39.7	5.10
28	0.564	0.9084	0.00240	40.2	5.10
29	0.766	0.93294	0.00134	40.2	5.10
30	0.766	0.93256	0.00136	40.2	5.10
		0.95126	0.00069	39.9	5.10
31	1.062	0.95113	0.00070	39.9	5.10
32	1.062				
33	0.360	0.60340	0.01034	39.8	5.10

[†] y_{a_i} = mole fraction H_2 entering reactor. y_{a_o} = mole fraction H_2 leaving reactor.

F Feed rate, moles/sec
V_R Reactor volume, cc
p Partial pressure, atm

Subscripts

a Hydrogen
b Ethylene
c Ethane
o Exit from reactor
i Inlet to reactor

NOTES. (1) The total pressure in the reactor is 1.0 atm. (2) At the temperatures involved the hydrogenation reaction is not reversible.

Solution

$$C_2H_4 + H_2 \rightarrow C_2H_6$$

Using the nomenclature suggested, the rate equation [Eq. (3-6)] in terms of the formation of ethane may be written

$$r = \frac{F\, dx_c'}{dV_R}$$

As noted in Example 3-3, the rate equation for gaseous reactions can be expressed in two ways,

$$r = kC_a$$

or

$$r = k_p p_a$$

Example 3-3 was solved using the first form. If the second is employed here,

$$r = \frac{F\, dx_c'}{dV_R} = k_p p_a \tag{A}$$

Under normal conditions the variation in rate as the gases pass through the reactor would be great enough to require expression of p_a in terms of x_c' before Eq. (A) is integrated. However, in this case the change in mole fraction between inlet to and exit from the reactor is so small that Eq. (A) may be integrated using an average value of r.[1]

$$r_{av} = \frac{F(x_{c_o}' - 0)}{(V_R - 0)} = k_p(p_a)_{av} \tag{B}$$

To determine the relationship between p_a, x_c', and the given composition data, the total moles per second passing any point in the reactor must be ascertained.

Moles C_2H_6/sec $= Fx_c'$
Moles H_2/sec $= Fy_{a_i} - Fx_c' = F(y_{a_i} - x_c')$
Moles C_2H_4/sec $= F(y_{b_i} - x_c')$
Total moles/sec $= F(y_{a_i} + y_{b_i} - x_c')$

Since $y_{a_i} + y_{b_i} = 1.0$,

$$\text{Total moles/sec} = F(1 - x_c')$$

[1] A comparison is given between the rigorous and approximate solutions later in the example.

Now, assuming the reaction mixture behaves as a perfect-gas mixture,

$$p_a = p_t y_a = y_a = \frac{y_{a_i} - x_c'}{1 - x_c'} \tag{C}$$

This is the desired relation between x_c' and y_a. At the exit of the reactor $x_c' = x_{c_o}$, and Eq. (C) becomes

$$y_{a_o} = \frac{y_{a_i} - x_{c_o}'}{1 - x_{c_o}'}$$

Solving this expression for x_{c_o}', the exit conversion, and substituting in Eq. (B) lead to the result

$$\frac{F}{V_R} \frac{y_{a_i} - y_{a_o}}{1 - y_{a_o}} = k_p(p_a)_{\mathrm{av}} \tag{D}$$

From Eq. (C) $p_a = y_a$ and the average of the values entering and leaving the reactor are as follows:

$$(p_a)_{\mathrm{av}} = (y_a)_{\mathrm{av}} = \tfrac{1}{2}(y_{a_i} + y_{a_o})$$

Substituting this into Eq. (D) and solving the result for k_p give

$$\frac{F}{V_R} \frac{y_{a_i} - y_{a_o}}{1 - y_{a_o}} = \frac{k_p}{2}(y_{a_i} + y_{a_o})$$

$$k_p = \frac{y_{a_i} - y_{a_o}}{1 - y_{a_o}} \frac{2}{y_{a_i} + y_{a_o}} \frac{F}{V_R} \tag{E}$$

This expression may be used to compute k_p from the known values of the hydrogen mole fraction entering and leaving the reactor and the ratio F/V_R. It may be noted that V_R/F has replaced θ, which occurs in batch equations for k (Examples 3-1 to 3-4). The reciprocal, F/V_R, is known as the space velocity (units, time^{-1}). This important quantity is discussed in detail in Chap. 4. The feed rate and reactor volume are the significant magnitude quantities in a flow reaction system, in comparison with time in the batch system.

If the integration of Eq. (A) is carried out rigorously, the procedure is as follows: Eq. (C) is solved for x_c' and then differentiated,

$$x_c' = \frac{y_{a_i} - y_a}{1 - y_a}$$

$$dx_c' = \frac{y_{a_i} - 1}{(1 - y_a)^2} dy_a \tag{F}$$

Substituting this equation, along with Eq. (C), into Eq. (A) yields

$$\frac{F}{dV_r} \frac{y_{a_i} - 1}{(1 - y_a)^2} dy_a = k_p y_a$$

or

$$\frac{k_p(V_R - 0)}{F} = (y_{a_i} - 1) \int_{y_{a_i}}^{y_{a_o}} \frac{dy_a}{(1 - y_a)^2 y_a} \tag{G}$$

TABLE 3-11

Run	$\dfrac{F}{V_R}$, [g moles/(sec)(cc)] $\times 10^3$	$1 - y_{a_o}$	k_p [Eq. (E)], [g moles/(sec)(cc)(atm)], $\times 10^5$	$\dfrac{1}{T} \times 10^3$, °K^{-1}
1	2.12	0.61413	2.70	2.86
2	2.12	0.61592	2.87	2.86
3	2.12	0.61427	1.48	2.97
4	2.12	0.61360	0.71	3.06
5	2.12	0.61396	0.66	3.06
6	2.59	0.45908	2.44	2.85
7	2.59	0.46079	2.40	2.85
8	2.59	0.46077	1.26	2.85
9	2.59	0.46048	0.72	3.07
10	2.59	0.46055	0.70	3.07
11	3.18	0.36377	2.40	2.85
12	3.18	0.36125	1.42	2.98
13	3.18	0.35934	0.69	3.06
14	3.18	0.35977	0.68	3.06
15	2.84	0.15544	3.03	2.83
16	2.84	0.15606	3.06	2.83
17	1.40	0.60239	1.31	2.97
18	1.40	0.60241	1.37	2.97
19	0.812	0.56369	0.70	3.05
20	0.0944	0.61911	0.146	3.20
21	0.0920	0.57399	0.159	3.21
22	0.0702	0.45885	0.260	3.10
23	0.0522	0.59516	0.322	3.19
24	0.0522	0.59887	0.323	3.19
25	0.0710	0.38935	0.283	3.19
26	0.0710	0.38897	0.284	3.19
27	0.137	0.22432	0.277	3.20
28	0.111	0.09196	0.318	3.19
29	0.150	0.06706	0.323	3.19
30	0.150	0.06744	0.326	3.19
31	0.208	0.04874	0.312	3.195
32	0.208	0.04887	0.314	3.195
33	0.0706	0.39660	0.307	3.195

This equation can be integrated directly, and has been, by Wynkoop and Wilhelm.[1] The result was presented in the form

$$k = \frac{F}{V_R} \frac{y_{a_i} - y_{a_o}}{y_{a_o}(1 - y_{a_o})} \tag{H}$$

Equations (E) and (H) are compared numerically for run 24, which has the highest conversion: From Eq. (E)

$$k_p = \frac{0.0151}{1 - 0.40113} \frac{2}{0.40113 + 0.41623} \frac{0.266 \times 10^{-3}}{5.10}$$
$$= 3.23 \times 10^{-6} \text{ g mole/(sec)(cc)(atm)}$$

From Eq. (H)

$$k_p = \frac{0.0151}{0.40113(1 - 0.40113)} \frac{0.266 \times 10^{-3}}{5.10} = 3.28 \times 10^{-6}$$

For the other runs the difference between the rigorous and approximate equations will be less. The values of k computed from Eq. (E) are given in Table 3-11. It is apparent that k is approximately the same at the same temperature, showing that the first-order rate equation fits the experimental data. However, all the data are based upon a total pressure of 1 atm. Information at widely different total pressures for this catalytic reaction might not fit the same mechanism. The importance of total pressure as a means of studying mechanism in catalytic reactions is considered in Chap. 9. The method of establishing the temperature dependency of the rate constants shown in the table is illustrated in Example 3-6.

THEORETICAL STUDIES OF REACTION RATE

3-6. Arrhenius Equation. The prudent starting point for developing a theory of reaction rates is the Arrhenius relationship showing the effect of temperature, for it has been thoroughly confirmed by experimental data.

The theory of the Arrhenius equation is based upon the variation of the equilibrium constant with temperature, i.e., the van't Hoff equation,

$$\frac{d \ln K}{dT} = \frac{\Delta H}{RT^2} \tag{3-18}$$

Since the equilibrium constant is equal to the ratio of k and k', the forward and reverse rate constants, Eq. (3-18) may be written

$$\frac{d \ln k}{dT} - \frac{d \ln k'}{dT} = \frac{\Delta H}{RT^2} \tag{3-19}$$

The right-hand side of Eq. (3-19) also could be divided into two parts provided the over-all heat of reaction is broken up into an energy change

[1] *Loc. cit.*

for each direction, as follows:

$$\Delta H = \Delta H - \Delta H' = E - E' \tag{3-20}[1]$$

Equation (3-19) then takes the form

$$\frac{d \ln k}{dT} - \frac{d \ln k'}{dT} = \frac{E}{RT^2} - \frac{E'}{RT^2} \tag{3-21}$$

The two separate expressions, one for the forward and one for the reverse reaction, having a difference in agreement with the equilibrium requirement (Eq. 3-21) are

$$\frac{d \ln k}{dT} = \frac{E}{RT^2} \tag{3-22}$$

$$\frac{d \ln k'}{dT} = \frac{E'}{RT^2} \tag{3-23}$$

Integration of Eq. (3-22) yields the Arrhenius equation,

$$k = Ae^{-E/RT}$$

or
$$\ln k = \ln A - \frac{E}{RT} \tag{3-24}$$

According to this equation a plot of $\ln k$ vs. $1/T$ should give a straight line with a slope of $-E/R$ and an intercept of $\ln A$.

The so-called activation energy E was interpreted by Arrhenius as the excess over the average energy that the reactants must possess in order for reaction to occur. The only limitation on E is that the difference $E - E'$ must be equal to the over-all heat of reaction, i.e., the average energy difference between the products and reactants. This idea suggests the existence of an intermediate state of activated reactants. The over-all reaction then could be looked upon as taking place by the following two-step process:

Reactants → activated reactants → products

The energy change for the formation of activated products is E and for the second part of the process, $-E'$. These energy changes are illustrated for both exothermic and endothermic examples in Fig. 3-4.

The Arrhenius theory can give no information about the numerical values of activation energies, although it is clear from Fig. 3-4 that E must be greater than ΔH for an endothermic reaction and E' greater than the absolute value of ΔH for an exothermic reaction.

[1] Although Arrhenius interpreted E as the energy of activation, it is now clear that this term should be the enthalpy change. This point is discussed more fully in relation to the free-energy change on activation in Sec. 3-10 (Appendix A). The symbol E and the term activation energy will be retained because of its widespread use.

Although Arrhenius developed his concept in 1889,[1] modern kinetic data agree with it remarkably well. In fact, when measured rates do not agree with the theory, i.e., when ln k vs. $1/T$ does not indicate a straight line, it has been found that unknown complexities, such as side reactions or catalytic effects, are affecting the measurements.

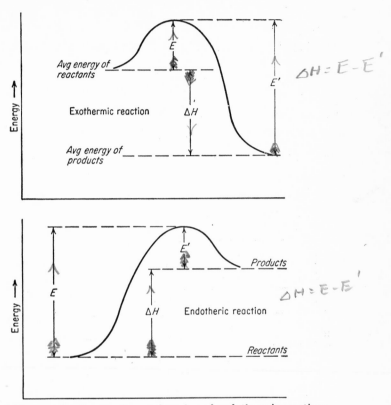

FIG. 3-4. Energy of activation for exothermic and endothermic reactions.

Equation (3-24) may be applied to the rate data interpreted in terms of either k_c or k_p. However, the values of ΔE will be different and may be designated E_c and E_p. Numerical calculations illustrating the difference in ΔE are given in connection with Example 3-8 (Appendix A).

Example 3-6. Using the results of Example 3-5, calculate the activation energy for the hydrogenation of ethylene, using a copper-magnesia catalyst.

Solution. In the last column of Table 3-11 the reciprocal of the absolute temperature is shown for each run. Figure 3-5 is a plot of log k_p vs. this temperature function. It is apparent that the data describe a straight line except for runs 8,

[1] S. Arrhenius, *Z. physik. Chem.*, **4**:226 (1889).

20, 21, and 22. Wynkoop and Wilhelm[1] suggest that there may have been water vapor present in the reactant gases in these cases, causing the low rates. Disregarding these four points, the slope of the line determined by the other runs can be obtained by subtracting the logarithm of k_p at two temperatures. If values of $1/T$ of 0.0028 and 0.0032 are chosen,

$$\text{Slope} = \frac{\ln 38.3 \times 10^{-6} - \ln 2.89 \times 10^{-6}}{0.0028 - 0.0032} = -5{,}075$$

According to Eq. (3-24), this slope is equal to $-E/R$. Hence

$$E_p = R \times 5{,}075$$
$$= 10{,}100 \text{ cal/g mole}$$

The activation energy determined in this manner is based upon a rate equation written in terms of partial pressures and is designated with the subscript p. The

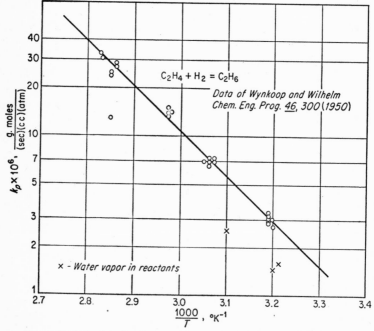

FIG. 3-5. Plot of Arrhenius equation for hydrogenation of ethylene.

value of E_c, based upon a rate equation in concentration units, would be slightly different.

3-7. The Collision Theory. The Arrhenius theory requires that, before reaction can occur, the molecules of reactants must have an energy

[1] *Loc. cit.*

of activation E above their normal, or average, energy. The possibility of some molecules possessing this excess exists because of the statistical distribution of energy over a wide range in the large number of molecules making up the system. Thus according to the classical kinetic theory some gaseous molecules will possess much larger amounts of translational energy than others, owing to variations in molecular velocities. It is logical to suppose that a collision between these molecules of reactants would provide a means of making available the activation energy necessary for the reaction to occur. By assuming that the molecules behave as hard spheres it is possible to develop simple expressions for the rate. This approach, originally advanced by Lewis[1] and Polanyi,[2] has become known as the collision theory.

The theory has a number of weaknesses and has been extended and supplemented by later developments. However, it offers a simple and clear picture of the mechanism of reactions and predicts reasonably good results for a number of gas- and liquid-phase reactions involving simple molecules.

According to the collision theory the number of molecules of product formed per unit time per unit volume, i.e., the rate, is equal to the number of collisions multiplied by a factor f. This factor takes into account the fact that only a fraction of the collisions involve molecules that possess the necessary excess energy (activation energy). For a simple gaseous reaction such as $A + B \rightarrow C + D$ this may be stated mathematically as follows:

$$r = zf \tag{3-25}$$

where z = number of collisions between molecules A and B in 1 cc of reaction mixture, per second.

From the kinetic theory, for ideal gases, the number of collisions is given by the expression

$$z = c_A c_B \sigma_{AB}^2 \left(8\pi RT \frac{M_A + M_B}{M_A M_B} \right)^{\frac{1}{2}} \tag{3-26}$$

where c = concentration, molecules/cc (not moles/cc)

σ_{AB} = effective diameter of A and B upon collision

M = molecular weight

R = gas constant = $k_B n$, the product of Boltzmann's constant and Avogadro's number, ergs/($°$K)(g mole)

Then the rate equation (3-25) may be written

$$r = f c_A c_B \sigma_{AB}^2 \left(8\pi RT \frac{M_A + M_B}{M_A M_B} \right)^{\frac{1}{2}} \tag{3-27}$$

[1] W. C. McC. Lewis, *J. Chem. Soc. (London)*, **113**:471 (1918).
[2] M. Polanyi, *Z. Elektrochem.*, **26**:48 (1920).

or it may be expressed in terms of the specific rate,

$$r = kc_A c_B \qquad (3\text{-}28)$$

Using the Arrhenius equation (3-24) for k, this last expression becomes

$$r = Ae^{-E/RT} c_A c_B \qquad (3\text{-}29)$$

Combining (3-27) and (3-29) gives the following result for A:

$$Ae^{-E/RT} = f\sigma_{AB}^2 \left(8\pi RT\, \frac{M_A + M_B}{M_A M_B}\right)^{\frac{1}{2}}$$

The fraction of the molecules that possess the required excess energy for reaction should not depend upon the number of collisions, but instead on the magnitude of the energy itself. Assuming a Maxwellian distribution, the fraction of the total molecules having an energy E can be shown to be $e^{-E/RT}$. Hence f may be taken as $e^{-E/RT}$, and then the frequency factor A is given by

$$A = \sigma_{AB}^2 \left(8\pi RT\, \frac{M_A + M_B}{M_A M_B}\right)^{\frac{1}{2}} \qquad (3\text{-}30)$$

Finally, substitution of this value of A in Eq. (3-24) gives the collision-theory expression for the specific reaction rate, i.e.,

$$k = \sigma_{AB}^2 \left(8\pi RT\, \frac{M_A + M_B}{M_A M_B}\right)^{\frac{1}{2}} e^{-E/RT} \qquad \text{cc/(molecule)(sec)} \qquad (3\text{-}31)$$

The first part of the equation represents the number of collisions per unit time per unit volume (when $c_A = c_B = 1$), and $e^{-E/RT}$ represents the fraction of the collisions that involve molecules with the necessary activation energy.

Example 3-7. The experimental data of Kistiakowsky were employed in Example 3-3 to determine the specific reaction rate for the decomposition of hydrogen iodide.

For comparison estimate the specific reaction rate at 321.4°C, using the collision theory. Assume that the collision diameter σ is 3.5A (i.e., 3.5×10^{-8} cm), and employ the activation energy of 44,000 cal/g mole determined experimentally by Bodenstein.[1]

Also, evaluate the frequency factor.

Solution. According to the collision theory the specific reaction rate is given by Eq. (3-31) in the units of cubic centimeters per molecule per second.

For the reaction $2HI \rightarrow H_2 + I_2$

$$M_A = M_B = M_{HI} = 128$$

[1] M. Bodenstein, *Z. physik. Chem.*, **100**:68 (1922).

The other numerical quantities required are

$$R = k_B n = (1.38 \times 10^{-16})(6.02 \times 10^{23})$$
$$= 8.30 \times 10^7 \text{ ergs}/(\text{°K})(\text{g mole}), \text{ or } 1.98 \text{ cal}/(\text{g mole})(\text{°K})$$
$$\sigma_{AB} = 3.5 \times 10^{-8} \text{ cm}$$
$$E = 44,000 \text{ cal/g mole}$$
$$T = 273.2 + 321.4$$
$$= 594.6\text{°K}$$

Substituting these values in Eq. (3-31),

$$k = (3.5 \times 10^{-8})^2[8\pi(8.30 \times 10^7)594.6 \times \tfrac{2}{128}]^{\frac{1}{2}}e^{-44,000/(1.98\times594.6)}$$
$$k = 1.70 \times 10^{-10}e^{-37.4} \quad \text{cc}/(\text{molecule})(\text{sec})$$

To convert this result to the usual units of liters per gram mole per second, it should be multiplied by Avogadro's number, 6.02×10^{23} molecules/mole, and divided by 1,000 cc/liter.

$$k = \frac{6.02 \times 10^{23}}{1,000} 1.70 \times 10^{-10}e^{-37.4}$$
$$k = 1.02 \times 10^{11}e^{-37.4} \tag{A}$$
$$= 5.7 \times 10^{-6} \text{ liter}/(\text{g mole})(\text{sec})$$

In Example 3-3 the rate constant was found from Kistiakowsky's data to be 2.0×10^{-6} liter/(g mole)(sec). The agreement between the collision theory and experimental results in this case is reasonably good. For reactions involving more complex molecules the experimental rates are frequently much less than the theory predicts.

By comparing the form of Eq. (A) and the Arrhenius expression

$$k = Ae^{-E/RT}$$

it is apparent that the frequency factor in this case is

$$A = 1.0 \times 10^{11} \text{ liters}/(\text{g mole})(\text{sec})$$

3-8. Theory of Absolute Reaction Rates (Activated-complex Theory). The collision theory has been found to give results in reasonably good agreement with experimental data for a number of bimolecular gas reactions. The decomposition of hydrogen iodide considered in Example 3-7 is an illustration. The theory has also been satisfactory for several reactions in solution involving simple ions. However, for many other reactions, in both the gas and the liquid phase, the predicted rates are much too large. Predicted frequency factors lie in the rather narrow range of 10^9 to 10^{11}, while measured values may be as low as 10^5. The deviation appears to increase with the complexity of the reactant molecules. As a means of recognizing this disagreement it has been customary to introduce a probability factor (having a value less than unity) in Eq. (3-31). To still retain the hard-sphere concept it is then necessary to explain why all the collisions supplying the necessary energy do not result in reaction.

This brief description[1] of the limitations of the collision approach suggests the need for developing a more flexible theory that will predict rates over a wide range of values. Beginning about 1930 the principles of quantum mechanics were applied by Eyring, Polanyi, and their coworkers to this problem, and there resulted what has become known as the absolute theory of reaction rates.[2] In this theory reaction is still presumed to occur as a result of collisions between reacting molecules, but what happens after collision is examined in more detail.   This examination is based upon the modern concept that molecules possess vibrational, rotational, and translational energy levels.

The essential feature of the theory is the postulation of an activated complex, an intermediate, unstable substance formed from the reactants and decomposing into the products.   A basic assumption that is made regarding this intermediate, activated complex is that it is in thermodynamic equilibrium with the reactants.   This means that the rate-controlling step in the over-all reaction is rate of decomposition of the activated complex into the products.   This concept of an equilibrium activation step followed by a slow decomposition is equivalent to assuming a time lag between activation and decomposition into the products of reaction.   It is the answer proposed by the absolute rate theory to the question of why all collisions are not effective in producing a reaction.

These ideas may be illustrated by a simple reaction between A and B to form a product C.   If the activated complex is designated by AB, the over-all process can be written as follows:

$$A + B \rightarrow AB \rightarrow C$$

The first step forming the complex AB is assumed to occur at equilibrium so that the concentrations of AB, A, and B are those determined by the conventional equilibrium constant.   Then the rate of the over-all reaction is equal to the product of the frequency of decomposition of the complex and its equilibrium concentration.   In equation form

$$\text{Rate of reaction} = r = v c_{AB} \qquad \text{molecules/(sec)(cc)} \qquad (3\text{-}32)$$

where v has the units per second and the concentration c_{AB} is in molecules per cubic centimeter.   If the equilibrium constant for the formation of AB is K, then

$$K = \frac{c_{AB}}{c_A c_B} \qquad (3\text{-}33)$$

---

[1] For a more detailed and complete description of the collision theory and its limitations see E. A. Moelwyn-Hughes, "Kinetics of Reactions in Solution," Oxford University Press, New York, 1946.

[2] The development of the theory is described in Samuel Glasstone, K. J. Laidler, and Henry Eyring, "The Theory of Rate Processes," McGraw-Hill Book Company, Inc., New York, 1941.

Equation (3-32) may be written

$$r = Kc_A c_B v \qquad (3\text{-}34)$$

The process by which the activated complex breaks down into the product C is supposed to take place as follows: AB is like a normal molecule except that one of the vibrational bonds is weak, making the complex unstable. This vibrational term in essence becomes a translational motion, and the decomposition occurs at a rate equal to the frequency of this weak vibrational degree of freedom. It is apparent that, if the structure of the activated complex is known, this unstable vibrational contribution can be ascertained and its frequency v assigned.

In order to evaluate properly this decomposition frequency it is necessary to express the equilibrium constant in terms of partition functions. This can be accomplished by using the concepts of statistical mechanics, and the method is clearly described by Glasstone.[1] The result is that for any reaction $A + B \rightarrow C + D$

$$K = \frac{Q_C Q_D}{Q_A Q_B} e^{-\Delta E_0/RT} \qquad (3\text{-}35)$$

where ΔE_0 represents the energy of the products minus that of the reactants at absolute-zero temperature. Q refers to the partition function defined by the expression

$$Q = \Sigma g_i e^{-\epsilon_i/k_B T} \qquad (3\text{-}36)$$

In Eq. (3-36), ϵ_i is the energy per molecule corresponding to one level; g_i is the number of slightly different energies in the same energy level; and the summation is over all the energy levels that the molecules may possess at equilibrium. If it is assumed that the translational, rotational, and vibrational energy levels do not have any effect upon each other, the partition function may be divided into separate parts, corresponding to the three contributions to the energy; i.e.,

$$Q = Q_{tr} Q_{rot} Q_{vib} \qquad (3\text{-}37)$$

If Eq. (3-35) is applied to the reaction for the formation of the activated complex AB,

$$K = \frac{c_{AB}}{c_A c_B} = \frac{Q_{AB}}{Q_A Q_B} e^{-\Delta E_0/RT} \qquad (3\text{-}38)$$

where ΔE_0 refers to the energy of the activated complex minus that of the reactants. This is the activation energy of the over-all reaction at

[1] Samuel Glasstone, "Theoretical Chemistry," chap. VIII, D. Van Nostrand Company, Inc., New York, 1944.

absolute zero.   Substituting this value of K into Eq. (3-34) gives

$$r = \frac{Q_{AB}}{Q_A Q_B} e^{-\Delta E_0/RT} c_A c_B v_i \qquad (3\text{-}39)$$

Since $r = k c_A c_B$, the specific-reaction velocity constant k is

$$k = \frac{Q_{AB}}{Q_A Q_B} e^{-\Delta E_0/RT} v_i \qquad (3\text{-}40)$$

Referring to the supposition that the decomposition of the complex occurs along a weak vibration bond, the total partition function Q_{AB} may be divided, according to Eq. (3-37), into two parts, that due to the weak vibrational frequency and all the rest; i.e.,

$$. \quad Q_{AB} = Q_{AB}^* Q_{v_i} \qquad (3\text{-}41)$$

where Q_{v_i} is the contribution to the partition function due to the vibration frequency by which decomposition occurs and Q_{AB}^* is the contribution from all the rest of the $3n - 1$ (n = number of atoms in the molecule) degrees of freedom in the complex.

Substituting Eq. (3-41) in Eq. (3-40),

$$k = \frac{Q_{AB}^*}{Q_A Q_B} e^{-\Delta E_0/RT} Q_{v_i} v_i \qquad (3\text{-}42)$$

The development for the rate constant k can be completed by relating the partition function Q_{v_i} to its frequency v_i.

Again from statistical mechanics it can be shown that the vibrational contribution to the partition function, described by Eq. (3-36), is

$$Q_{v_i} = \frac{1}{1 - e^{-\alpha_i}} \qquad (3\text{-}43)$$

$$\alpha_i = \frac{h v_i}{k_B T} \qquad (3\text{-}44)$$

The value of $Q_{v_i} v_i$ to substitute in the rate expression (3-42) will be that when the frequency v_i approaches zero.   This is so because, as the vibration transforms into a translational motion, there is no more oscillation or vibration, but simply motion in one direction.   Hence the limit of $Q_{v_i} v_i$ as v_i approaches zero is required, and it may be written

$$\lim_{v_i \to 0} \frac{v_i}{1 - e^{-\alpha_i}}$$

Treating this as an indeterminate form and differentiating the numerator and denominator separately with respect to v_i yields

$$\frac{1}{(h/k_BT)e^{-\alpha_i}}$$

or $$\lim_{v_i \to 0} Q_{v_iv_i} = \frac{1}{h/k_BT} = \frac{k_BT}{h} \qquad (3\text{-}45)$$

Substituting Eq. (3-45) in Eq. (3-42) gives the final equation for the rate constant k.

$$k = \frac{k_BT}{h} \frac{Q_{AB}^*}{Q_AQ_B} e^{-\Delta E_0/RT} \qquad (3\text{-}46)$$

where h = Planck's constant = 6.624×10^{-27} erg-sec
  k_B = Boltzmann's constant = 1.380×10^{-16} erg/°K
  In terms of the entropy and enthalpy of activation, Eq. (3-46) may be written

$$k = \frac{k_BT}{h} e^{\Delta S^*/R} e^{-\Delta H^*/RT} \qquad (3\text{-}63)$$

This thermodynamic form of the absolute rate theory is developed in Appendix A.

If the structure of the activated complex is known, or can be satisfactorily postulated, the partition functions and ΔE_0 in Eq. (3-46) can be predicted. Actually the computation of the zero-point activation energy is particularly difficult. The result is sensitive to small changes in the structure of the activated complex, and this structure is frequently uncertain. Therefore, it has not been possible to predict completely reaction-velocity constants from Eq. (3-46) for any reactions except those invo ving very simple molecules or atoms. However, if an experimental activation energy is available, the theory can be applied to complicated systems with somewhat more confidence. This application is illustrated in the example in Appendix A (Example 3-8).

The status of the problem of predicting a rate of reaction may be summarized in the following manner: The absolute reaction rate theory firmly relates the rate to chemical structure. It needs more development before accurate numerical values can be determined for most reactions. From an engineering viewpoint this means that experimental kinetic studies must still form the basis for the development of commercial reactors. Finally, the Arrhenius equation adequately predicts the effect of temperature on the rate when single-step chemical processes are involved.

3-9 to 3-12 (See Appendix A). Since experimental studies are necessary for designing reaction equipment, it is not worthwhile to devote additional attention here to the absolute rate concepts. However, applications of the theory, including the relationship between the enthalpy of activation and the different kinds of energy of activation, are considered in Appendix A.

3-13. Unimolecular Reactions and Kinetics. One of the limitations observed for the classical collision theory is that it fails to explain the occurrence of first-order unimolecular reactions, i.e., reactions in which only one molecule of reactant is involved. Examples are isomerizations such as that of n-butane and decomposition reactions such as that of acetaldehyde. The reason for the failure is that the number of collisions is proportional to the square of the concentration, giving rise to a second-order rate expression rather than a first-order one. The absolute rate theory can satisfactorily explain first-order unimolecular reactions and still utilize the collision concept as the mechanism of activation.[1] This is because the over-all reaction is assumed to take place in two stages, the formation of an activated complex and its subsequent decomposition.

The reactant A becomes activated by collision with another molecule of A, that is,

$$A + A \rightarrow A^* + A$$

As pointed out in the development of the absolute rate theory, this process is assumed to be relatively fast with respect to the second step, the decomposition to product B.

$$A^* \rightarrow B$$

The first step is a second-order one, and its rate is proportional to the square of the concentration of A. However, if it is fast with respect to the second step, the rate will be determined entirely by the decomposition reaction. This second step is first-order in agreement with observed results.

This procedure of breaking up the over-all reaction into two or more simple steps has been of great benefit in interpreting the mechanism and kinetics of reactions. Chemical kinetics is still a highly complex and confused field, but this one thing seems reasonably clear: over-all reactions, however complex they may be, take place by a series of simple processes involving unimolecular or bimolecular reactions.

3-14. Chain Reactions. It has been mentioned that the order of a rate equation may not correspond to the stoichiometry of the over-all reaction. In such cases it is helpful to follow the procedure just described, i.e., look for a sequence of simple, individual steps leading to rates in agreement with the experimentally determined results. Often reactions between free radicals or atoms can explain cases where the kinetics do not agree with the stoichiometry of the over-all reaction. An example is the formation HBr from hydrogen and bromine in the gas phase. The rate

[1] F. A. Lindemann, *Trans. Faraday Soc.*, **17**:598 (1922).

equation is not second-order according to the stoichiometric reaction

$$H_2 + Br_2 \rightarrow 2HBr$$

but instead the rate is given by the expression

$$\frac{dC_{HBr}}{d\theta} = \frac{kC_{H_2}C_{Br_2}^{\frac{1}{2}}}{1 + k'(C_{HBr}/C_{Br_2})} \tag{3-74}$$

This expression can be explained by assuming that the reaction occurs by the following series of steps:

1: $\qquad\qquad Br_2 \rightarrow 2Br$
2: $\qquad\qquad H_2 + Br \rightarrow HBr + H$
3: $\qquad\qquad H + Br_2 \rightarrow HBr + Br$
4: $\qquad\qquad H + HBr \rightarrow H_2 + Br$
5: $\qquad\qquad 2Br \rightarrow Br_2$

In reaction 1 are formed bromine atoms which may react in reaction 2 with H_2 to form the product HBr. Also formed in reaction 2 is a hydrogen atom. This may react with a bromine molecule to form another product molecule, and also regenerate a bromine atom so that reaction 2 can proceed again. It is apparent that reactions 2 and 3, occurring over and over again, provide a mechanism for the over-all reaction. It is also observed that only one molecule of bromine need be decomposed by reaction 1 before reactions 2 and 3 can begin to take place. Thus a large number of hydrogen and bromine molecules can react as a result of the formation of but one bromine atom. For this reason such reactions are called chain reactions. The hydrogen and bromine atoms are known as chain carriers. Experimental evidence of the possibility of producing a considerable amount of reaction from an insignificant number of chain carriers is available from the photochemical reaction between H_2 and Cl_2. At ordinary temperatures and under ordinary conditions a mixture of H_2 and Cl_2 gases does not react perceptibly for long periods of time. However, if a relatively small number of chlorine molecules are decomposed into atoms by illumination with light, the reaction between H_2 and Cl_2 may proceed with explosive rates.

Returning to the rate equation for the formation of HBr, the numerator can be explained qualitatively in a simple way by focusing attention on reactions 1 and 2. If both are assumed to control the rate, it is evident that the production of HBr should be proportional to the concentration of H_2 and Br from reaction 2. From reaction 1 it is seen that the Br concentration is proportional to the square root of the bromine concentration. Thus a combination of reactions 1 and 2 suggests that the rate should be proportional to the hydrogen concentration and square root of the bromine concentration, in agreement with the experimental result. Reactions 4 and 5 are chain-breaking steps in the process. Reaction 4 removes Br atoms and tends to prevent reaction 2. These two effects give rise to the denominator term in the rate equation. As the product concentration (HBr) builds up, reaction 4 becomes more important, and the over-all rate should be reduced. This is indicated by the denominator term in the rate equation. Similarly, high bromine concentrations tend to reduce reaction 5 and in so doing increase the rate of the over-all reaction. This explains the presence of the bromine concentration in the denominator of Eq. (3-74).[1]

The acceptance of the chain theory for explaining some complex reactions has been aided by (1) the establishment of the presence of free radicals and atoms by spectroscopic measurements and (2) the observation that known means of destroying free radicals result in a decreased rate of the over-all reaction.

Many combustion reactions are believed to occur by a chain mechanism involving free atoms. The available evidence strongly suggests that chain reactions forming and destroying free radicals are necessary to explain the thermal cracking of hydrocarbons. Lewis and von Elbe[2] have summarized recent experimental work and modern theoretical developments for chain reactions.

NOMENCLATURE

A	Frequency-factor constant in Arrhenius equation
A^*, B^*, C^*	Principal moments of inertia of activated complex (nonlinear molecule)
C	Concentration, moles/volume
c	Concentration, molecules/volume
E	Experimental energy of activation determined from Arrhenius equation (E_p is based upon rate data in pressure units; E_c is based upon rate data in concentration units)
ΔE_0	Energy of activation at absolute-zero temperature, i.e., energy of activated complex minus energy of reactants at absolute zero
ΔF^*	Free energy of activation ($\Delta F^* = \Delta H^* - T \, \Delta S^*$)
ΔH	Enthalpy of reaction
ΔH^*	Enthalpy of activation, i.e., enthalpy of formation of the activated complex from the reactants
I^*	Moment of inertia of activated, complex molecule (linear molecule)
h	Planck's constant, 6.624×10^{-27} erg-sec
k_B	Boltzmann's constant, 1.380×10^{-16} erg/°K
k	Specific-reaction rate (subscripts 1, 2, etc., are used to designate order of rate equation)

[1] For a quantitative and more rigorous deduction of Eq. (3-74) refer to K. J. Laidler, "Chemical Kinetics," p. 185, McGraw-Hill Book Company, Inc., New York, 1950.

[2] Bernard Lewis and Guenther von Elbe, "Combustion, Flames, and Explosions of Gases," Academic Press, Inc., New York, 1951.

k' Specific-reaction rate in reverse direction

k_c Specific-reaction rate expressed in concentration units

k_p Specific-reaction rate expressed in pressure units

K True-equilibrium constant (K_c and K_p are in terms of concentrations and partial pressures, respectively)

M Molecular weight

m Mass of a molecule

N Number of moles

N_0 Avogadro's number, 6.02×10^{23} molecules/mole

Δn Change in moles due to a reaction

p Partial pressure

Q Partition function, defined by Eq. (3-36)

(Q_t, Q_r, Q_v refer to translational, rotational, and vibrational contributions)

R Gas constant per mole $= N_0 k_B$

ΔS Entropy of reaction

ΔS^* Entropy of activation, i.e., entropy of formation of the activated complex from the reactants

T Absolute temperature

V Volume

v Fundamental vibration frequency

x Conversion

y Mole fraction of a component in a gas

α Dimensionless group, $\alpha_i = hv_i/k_B T$

ϵ_i Energy level i of a molecule

σ_{AB} Collision diameter of reactants A and B

θ Time

PROBLEMS

1. With HCl as a homogeneous catalyst, the rate of esterification of acetic acid and alcohol is increased. At 100°C the rates (in gram moles per liter per minute) of the forward and reverse reactions are as follows: for the forward reaction

$$r_2 = k_2 C_H C_{OH} \qquad k_2 = 4.76 \times 10^{-4} \text{ liters/(g mole)(min)}$$

and for the reverse reaction

$$r_2' = k_2' C_E C_W \qquad k_2' = 1.63 \times 10^{-4} \text{ liter/(g mole)(min)}$$

where C_H = concentration of acetic acid

C_{OH} = concentration of alcohol

C_E = concentration of ester

C_W = concentration of water

An initial mixture consists of equal masses of 90 per cent by weight aqueous solution of acid and 95 per cent by weight solution of ethanol. Supposing constant-volume conditions, calculate the conversion of acid to ester for various times of reaction. Assuming complete miscibility, estimate the equilibrium conversion.

2. Smith[1] has studied the gas-phase dissociation of sulfuryl chloride, SO_2Cl_2, into chlorine and sulfur dioxide at 279.2°C. The total-pressure method was employed to

[1] D. F. Smith, *J. Am. Chem. Soc.*, **47**:1862 (1925).

follow the course of the reaction. Under constant-volume conditions the results were:

Time, min...............	3.4	15.7	28.1	41.1	54.5	68.3	82.4	96.3
Total pressure, mm Hg...	325	335	345	355	365	375	385	395

What reaction order do these data suggest?

The conversion is 100 per cent at infinite time.

3. Two consecutive reversible chemical reactions (liquid-phase) may be represented by the equations

1:    $A \rightarrow B$
2:    $B \rightarrow C$

The rate constants and equilibrium data are as follows:

Forward rate constant for reaction 1: $k_1 = 1 \times 10^{-3}$ min^{-1}
Forward rate constant for reaction 2: $k_2 = 1 \times 10^{-2}$ min^{-1}
Equilibrium constant for reaction 1: $K_1 = 0.8$
Equilibrium constant for reaction 2: $K_2 = 0.6$

If the initial concentration of A is 1.0-molal, plot the concentration of A vs. time from 0 to 1,000 min.

Both reactions are first-order in the forward and reverse directions.

4. Using the collision theory, calculate the rate constant at 300°K for the decomposition of hydrogen iodide, assuming a collision diameter of 3.5 A and an activation energy of 44 kg cal (based upon a rate constant in concentration units, that is, k_c). To what entropy of activation does the result correspond?

5. The frequency factor for the gas-phase dissociation of the dimer of cyclopentadiene is 1.3×10^{13} sec^{-1}, and the activation energy is 35.0 kg cal (based upon k_c). Calculate (a) the entropy of activation, (b) the rate constant at 100°C, and (c) the rate at 100°C and 1 atm pressure.

6. The homogeneous dimerization of butadiene has been studied by a number of investigators[1-3] and found to have an experimental activation energy of 23,960 cal/g mole as indicated by the specific-reaction rate,

$$k_c = 9.2 \times 10^9 e^{-23,960/RT} \qquad cc/(g \text{ mole})(sec)$$

(based upon the disappearance of butadiene).

a. Using Eyring's theory of absolute reaction rates, predict a value of A at 600°K for comparison with the experimental result of 9.2×10^9. Assume the structure of the activated complex is

$$\overset{|}{C}H_2-CH=CH-CH_2-CH_2-\overset{|}{C}H-CH=CH_2$$

and use the group-contribution method (refer to Chap. 2) to estimate the thermodynamic properties required.

b. Also predict a value of A at 600°K, using the collision theory, and compare it with the experimental result. Assume the effective collision diameter is 5×10^{-8} cm.

[1] W. E. Vaughan, *J. Am. Chem. Soc.*, **54**:3863 (1932).
[2] G. B. Kistiakowsky and F. R. Lacher, *J. Am. Chem. Soc.*, **58**:123 (1936).
[3] J. B. Harkness, G. B. Kistiakowsky, and W. H. Mears, *J. Chem. Phys.*, **5**:682 (1937).

7. The thermal decomposition of dimethyl ether in the gas phase has been studied by Hinshelwood and Askey[1] by measuring the increase in pressure in a constant-volume reaction vessel.

At 504°C and an initial pressure of 312 mm Hg, the following data were obtained:

Time, sec	390	777	1,195	3,155	∞
Total pressure, mm	408	488	562	779	931

Assuming that only ether was present initially and that the reaction is

$$(CH_3)_2O \rightarrow CH_4 + H_2 + CO$$

determine a rate equation for the decomposition. What is the numerical value of the specific reaction rate at 504°C?

8.[*] The time required for one-half of a reactant to be converted in a batch reaction is called the half-life period. Suppose that a gaseous reaction between A and B is studied kinetically by making isothermal measurements of the half-life period for several initial compositions of reactants. The results for each of four different initial conditions are as follows:

Initial partial pressure of A, mm	500	125	250	250
Initial partial pressure of B, mm	10	15	10	20
Half-life period of B, min	80	213	160	80

If the rate is first order with respect to component A and second order with respect to B, what is the numerical value of the specific reaction rate?

9. The reaction mechanism for the decomposition of nitrogen pentoxide is complex, as described in Sec. 3-4. However, a satisfactory rate equation can be developed by considering the two reactions:

$$2N_2O_5 \rightarrow 2N_2O_4 + O_2$$
$$N_2O_4 \rightarrow 2NO_2$$

The second reaction is rapid with respect to the first, so that nitrogen dioxide and nitrogen tetroxide may be assumed to be in equilibrium. Hence, only the first reaction need be considered from a kinetic standpoint.

Calculate the specific reaction rate for the first reaction (which is essentially irreversible) from the following total pressure data[2] obtained at 25°C:

Time, min	Total Pressure, mm
0	268.7
20	293.0
40	302.2
60	311.0
80	318.9
100	325.9
120	332.3
140	338.8
160	344.4
∞	473.0

[1] C. N. Hinshelwood and P. J. Askey, *Proc. Roy. Soc.* (*London*), **A115**:215 (1927).
[2] F. Daniels and E. H. Johnston, *J. Am. Chem. Soc.*, **43**:53 (1921).
[*] Taken with permission of the authors from A. A. Frost and R. G. Pearson, "Kinetics and Mechanism," John Wiley & Sons, Inc., New York, 1953.

It may be assumed that only nitrogen pentoxide is present initially. The equilibrium constant K_p for the dissociation of nitrogen tetroxide into nitrogen dioxide at 25°C is 97.5 mm.

10.* The decomposition of nitrogen dioxide follows a second-order rate equation. Data at different temperatures are as follows:

T, °K	592	603	627	651.5	656
k_2, cc/(g mole)(sec)	522	755	1,700	4,020	5,030

Compute the energy of activation E_c from this information. If the reaction is

$$2NO_2 \rightarrow 2NO + O_2$$

also evaluate the activation energy E_p.

REFERENCES

Amis, E. S.: "Kinetics of Chemical Change in Solution," The Macmillan Company, New York, 1949.

Daniels, F., J. H. Mathews, J. W. Williams, and Staff: "Experimental Physical Chemistry," 4th ed., McGraw-Hill Book Company, Inc., New York, 1949.

Farkas, A., and H. W. Melville: "Experimental Methods in Gas Reactions," St. Martin's Press, Inc., New York, 1939.

Frost, A. A., and Ralph G. Pearson: "Kinetics and Mechanism," John Wiley & Sons, Inc., New York, 1953.

Hinshelwood, C. N.: "The Kinetics of Chemical Change," Oxford University Press, New York, 1941.

Kassel, L. S.: "Kinetics of Homogeneous Gas Reactions," Reinhold Publishing Corporation, New York, 1932.

Laidler, K. J.: "Chemical Kinetics," McGraw-Hill Book Company, Inc., New York, 1950.

Moelwyn-Hughes, E. A.: "Kinetics of Reactions in Solution," Oxford University Press, New York, 1946.

Noyes, W. A., and P. A. Leighton: "Photochemistry of Gas," Reinhold Publishing Corporation, New York, 1941.

Pease, R. N.: "Equilibrium and Kinetics of Gas Reactions," Princeton University Press, Princeton, N. J., 1942.

Steacie, E. W. R.: "Atomic and Free Radical Reactions," Reinhold Publishing Corporation, New York, 1946.

*Taken with permission of the authors from A. A. Frost and R. G. Pearson, "Kinetics and Mechanism," John Wiley & Sons, Inc., New York, 1953.

CHAPTER 4

INTRODUCTION TO REACTOR DESIGN

4-1. Nature of the Problem. To design a reactor is to determine the size of the vessel necessary to obtain the specified amount of product and to evaluate the temperature, pressure, and composition of reaction mixture that will exist in various parts of the equipment. To do this, it is necessary to know the initial or entrance conditions of temperature, pressure, and reactants composition and the method of operating the reactor, i.e., batch or flow, isothermal, adiabatic, etc. This information along with the required production of product constitutes the design conditions. They are the variables that can and must be chosen by the engineer before the design can be carried out. The size of reactor and operating conditions will be different for each set of design conditions. The optimum design is that which will be most economical, i.e., that which will require the lowest total cost per pound of product. Included in the total cost will be initial construction expenditures and all operating costs. The pattern for the ideal approach to design is apparent: first, the calculations should be carried out for a number of design conditions which are likely to result in low total costs; second, the optimum conditions are chosen from the results of these calculations. In practice there frequently is not time to carry out a complete economic balance to find the optimum operating conditions, and the final choice is made on the basis of but two or three sets of computations. In any event the problems encountered are essentially the same in each case so that nothing new, from an engineering viewpoint, is introduced by successive sets of calculations.

As the term is used in this book, design of reaction equipment refers to *process design* and not to mechanical or engineering design. For example, the process design of a continuous reactor where gases are passed over a solid catalyst would involve determining the length, diameter, and number of tubes, the size and shape of catalyst pellets, temperatures, pressures, and compositions of the reaction mixture at various locations in the reactor. Not included would be the mechanical problems of how the reactor tubes are to be supported, the design of the headers (tube sheets at the ends of the reactor tubes) to withstand the pressure of the system, etc.

The design calculations depend directly upon the available rate or kinetic data, and the design can be no more accurate than the rate information upon which it is based. A complete experimental investigation of the kinetics of a reaction preparatory to designing a commercial plant is usually unnecessary. For example, in the oxidation of sulfur dioxide, the reactants must contain relatively large amounts of air with respect to sulfur dioxide in order to prevent high temperatures and the accompanying reduction of conversion.[1] Hence, in obtaining rate data for designing a reactor for a sulfuric acid plant it is not necessary to investigate the full range of reactants composition but only those compositions where a considerable excess of air is used.

The required rate information can be obtained in two ways: (1) by a kinetic study in a small-size reactor[2] or (2) indirectly by interpreting the conversion information determined in a pilot plant in terms of an assumed rate equation. To illustrate these two methods of arriving at the data necessary for design calculations, consider again the oxidation of sulfur dioxide. In a direct kinetic investigation on a flow basis the reactants would be passed over a very small amount of catalyst and the rate of production of sulfur trioxide determined by measuring the rates of flow and composition of the inlet and exit streams. This production rate divided by the mass of catalyst would represent the rate of reaction, for example, in grams of sulfur trioxide per hour per gram of catalyst. It would approach a point rate rather than an average value, because the amount of catalyst is small enough so that the temperature, pressure, and composition changes in passing over the catalyst are likewise small.[3] In the second approach the amount of catalyst in the pilot-plant reactor is sufficient to cause a considerable conversion, and the temperature, pressure, and composition will change appreciably as the mixture passes through the reactor. Since the rate of reaction is a function of these variables, it varies from location to location and the measured production of sulfur trioxide represents an integrated average of all the point rates. To reduce these data (called integral-conversion, or integral-reactor, data) to rate information requires a procedure that is in essence the reverse of the design calculations. A promising rate equation is

---

[1] Due to reduction of equilibrium yield, not reduction of the rate.

[2] In flow systems such small-scale reactors are commonly called differential reactors, since the changes in temperature, pressure, and composition with position in the reactor are small.

[3] Note that the change in composition between the inlet and exit streams must be sufficiently large for accurate measurement, for otherwise the rate of conversion in the reactor cannot be accurately established. This restriction imposes a limitation on the usefulness of the method. If precise analytical methods of determining small composition changes are not available for the particular reaction, a close approach to a point value of the rate cannot be ascertained.

assumed, and then the design calculations are carried out to see whether or not the predicted conversions agree with the experimental results. By repetition of this procedure an equation for the rate can be found. Because of the indirect approach it is generally not possible by this method to determine the mechanism of the reaction, and the rate equation is perhaps best looked upon as simply an empirical expression which fits the pilot-plant data.

Both methods have advantages, and it is desirable to carry out investigations by both before building the commercial-scale reactor. The direct evaluation of rates yields more knowledge about the kinetics of the reaction; i.e., it tells the engineer more accurately just what variables affect the rate and how they influence the course of the reaction. This information is particularly valuable if it is ever necessary to predict how the commercial-scale plant will be affected by a change of operating conditions not specifically considered in the pilot-plant work.

On the other hand, the kinetic study does not provide answers to many of the engineering problems that may arise in connection with the subsequent design calculations for the commercial-scale equipment. Pilot-plant studies, duplicating the commercial reactor in every way but size, can provide such information. If design procedures for reactors were as well established as those for heat exchangers, pilot-plant investigations would not be necessary. However, at present the results in the pilot plant serve to guide the design calculations so that serious errors are unlikely in the final plant design. A simple illustration of this is the case where the kinetic studies are carried out in a batch apparatus and the commercial plant is to be continuous. In this situation the kinetic data may not be directly applicable for design calculations because of diffusion effects. For example, if the products and reactants are all gases but a solid catalyst is involved, the rate of diffusion of reactants and products to and from the catalyst surface may affect the rate of conversion. Since the diffusion rates will not be the same under batch and flow conditions, because of the differences in gas velocity near the catalyst, the over-all rates of reaction will also be different. While the importance of such effects can be estimated, as explained in Chap. 9, the assumptions involved are sometimes severe, so that the experimental verification obtainable from pilot-plant data is required. Even in the case where the kinetic studies are carried out in a flow system similar to that to be employed in the large plant, pilot-plant investigations are invaluable in giving information on such important problems as temperature distribution in the reactor and the effect of specialized designs in improving the process. In this latter classification are included such schemes as fluidized-bed and moving-bed reactors.

In summary, the pilot-plant results are useful in two ways: (1) to determine an empirical, but frequently satisfactory, rate equation; (2) to serve as a guide for the large-scale design calculations. A kinetic study gives a more complete analysis of the rate of the reaction and factors which affect it.

In the chapters that follow the methods of carrying out design calculations and obtaining rate equations from pilot-plant data are discussed for different kinds of reactor systems. In the remainder of this chapter the classifications of reactors and the fundamental design equations for several types will be presented.

4-2. Classification of Reactors According to Operating Characteristics and Geometry. Reaction equipment can be conveniently classified according to method of operation. If there is not a continuous withdrawal of products and addition of reactants, but instead a batch of reactants are added to the equipment at one time and the entire contents withdrawn at a subsequent time, the reaction system is termed *batch*, or *nonflow*. The *flow*, or continuous, reactor is one in which products are removed continuously and reactants added continuously. A steady-state flow reactor operates at steady-state conditions. This means that there is no change in any of the properties of the reaction system with respect to time. In fact the most significant difference between batch and flow reactors is that temperature, pressure, and composition may all vary with time in the batch-operated system. Mathematically speaking, time is an independent variable in batch reactors. The corresponding variable in tubular flow reactors is position, measured in the direction of flow in the reactor. For example, in the commercial process for the manufacture of butadiene by dehydrogenation of butylenes, butylene is passed through a cylindrical tube, packed with a catalyst, in a continuous, steady-state process. In the direction of flow, measured as catalyst bed depth, there is a change in temperature, pressure, and composition of the reaction gases. However, there is no change in any of these quantities with time, at a fixed position in the reactor. Conversely, in batch reactors if the contents of the reaction vessel are well agitated, there is no significant variation in temperature, pressure, or composition with position in the reactor—but all these quantities do vary with the time that the material has been in the vessel.

Classification of reactors according to shape is also important. Batch reactors are usually constructed in the form of a tank or similar shape where all three dimensions are about the same magnitude (Fig. 4-4 is an illustration). This shape is desired in order that good mixing, and hence uniform temperature, composition, and pressure, can be obtained throughout the vessel. Flow reactors are commonly of two types: the tank form, or a tubular shape in which the length-to-diameter ratio is several-fold. Subdivision into tank and tubular types is helpful because the design methods are not the same in the two cases. The difference arises because of differences in extent of mixing in the two shapes, a point which is discussed in detail in Chap. 6.

These three kinds of reactors are illustrated in Fig. 4-1A and B. In A the usual batch system is shown as a tank equipped with a stirrer to indicate good mixing. In B the steady-state flow category is divided into the tubular and tank classifications.

In some cases the operation may be neither flow nor batch but a combination of the two. As a specific example, benzene may be chlorinated in a tank reactor by first adding the charge of liquid benzene and catalyst and then continuously adding chlorine gas until the required ratio of chlorine to benzene has been obtained. Operation of this type is certainly batch from the point of view that the composition of the reaction

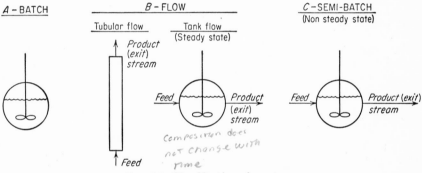

FIG. 4-1. Classification of reactors.

mixture changes with time. However, from a process standpoint the chlorine is added continuously. Such a case might be classified as a non-steady-state flow reactor, but the term semibatch will be used in this text. An advantage of semibatch operation is the possibility of maintaining a small concentration of one reactant (the chlorine in this example) at all times. This may be important when it is desired to obtain a predominate amount of one product out of several possibilities. Thus a large concentration of chlorine would favor the formation of di- and trichlorobenzenes, while the monochlorination of the benzene ring is favored when a small amount of chlorine is present.

Semibatch operation is also advantageous when a high heat of reaction would cause excessive temperature changes in normal batch operation. For example, hexamethylene tetramine is manufactured by reacting ammonia and formaldehyde. If the reaction is carried out in the liquid phase by using ammonium hydroxide and formalin solutions, ordinary batch operation, consisting of mixing the two reactants, may result in a large increase in temperature because of the highly exothermic heat of reaction. The temperature rise may be reduced and controlled by adding the ammonium hydroxide continuously, at a controlled rate, to the reactor containing formalin. In this example the actual rate of reaction is extremely rapid, the ammonia reacting just as soon as it is mixed with the formalin. Hence the rate of conversion is controlled by the rate of addition of the ammonia rather than the rate of the chemical reaction.

The semibatch reactor may be considered as the fourth type in a classification of reactors. The two examples just cited are special cases in which there was no exit stream and no change in flow rate of the feed stream. In its general form this type includes variations in both the rate and state of the inlet and exit streams with respect to time. In certain types of jet-propulsion equipment (liquid rockets) the combustion zone is an example of such a case, for as the fuel and oxidant are consumed, their state (temperature, pressure, and composition) and flow rates from the fuel tanks may change. In Fig. 4-1C the stirred tank with variable inlet and effluent streams is used to designate the semibatch classification.

The design equations for batch, tubular flow, and tank flow reactors are very briefly considered in the following sections. Chapters 5 and 6 are devoted to the detailed consideration of these three types. Included in Chap. 7 is the design of semibatch reactors for special cases. In all instances the design is based upon the general material balance expression

$$
\begin{pmatrix} (1) \\ \text{Reactant} \\ \text{added in} \\ \text{feed stream} \end{pmatrix} - \begin{pmatrix} (2) \\ \text{reactant} \\ \text{lost in exit} \\ \text{stream} \end{pmatrix} - \begin{pmatrix} (3) \\ \text{reactant} \\ \text{converted} \\ \text{in reactor} \end{pmatrix} = \begin{pmatrix} (4) \\ \text{rate of change} \\ \text{of reactant} \\ \text{in reactor} \end{pmatrix} \quad (4\text{-}1)
$$

The first two terms represent rates of flow of the particular reactant that is used to follow the course of the reaction. The third term depends upon the rate of reaction, written for the same reactant, and the volume of the reactor. The fourth expresses the rate of change, with respect to time, of the amount of this reactant in the system.

4-3. Design Equations for Batch Reactors. In the batch case (Fig. 4-1A) the first and second terms of Eq. (4-1) do not exist. The equality of the third and fourth terms may be expressed in terms of the conversion x' in the following manner,

$$
- r V_B = - m_t \frac{dx'}{d\theta} \quad (4\text{-}2)[1]
$$

---

[1] This form of the batch equation, and that for the flow equation which follows, was originally proposed by O. A. Hougen and K. M. Watson (for example, in "Chemical Process Principles," pt. III, John Wiley & Sons, Inc., New York, 1947). As these authors pointed out, the use of separate equations for batch- and flow-reactor design (rather than trying to use modifications of a single equation) emphasizes the important distinction that time is not a variable in the flow reactor.

where m_t = total mass of material charged to reactor

x' = conversion at any time θ, measured as mass[1] of a particular reactant converted, divided by *total* mass of charge, m_t

r = rate of reaction, as defined in Chap. 3, and measured as mass of same reactant converted per unit volume of reaction system per unit time

V_B = effective volume of batch reaction system, i.e., volume occupied by reaction mixture

θ = time measured from beginning of reaction

Ideally any product or reactant can be chosen as a medium for measuring the conversion x', as long as the rate r is also for the same component. In fact, a product may be used with no change in the form of Eq. (4-2) if the conversion is looked upon as the mass formed per unit mass of charge and the rate as the mass of the product formed per unit volume per unit time. Practical considerations usually limit the choice. For example, in the nitration of benzene the amount of the benzene converted, or nitrobenzene produced, is the more important quantity economically, rather than how much acid is consumed. Hence it is logical to base the rate equations on either the rate of disappearance of benzene or the rate of formation of nitrobenzene.

The mass m_t and the volume V_B of the reaction mixture are not independent quantities but are related to the density of the mixture according to the relation $V_B \rho = m_t$. Hence, Eq. (4-2) can be rearranged, and the integration process indicated as follows:

$$\theta = m_t \int_0^{x_1'} \frac{dx'}{V_B r} = \int_0^{x_1'} \rho \frac{dx'}{r} \qquad (4\text{-}3)$$

The importance of arranging the expression in this way is that the independent design variable, time, is separated from the dependent variables characteristic of the chemical reaction. If the conditions which determine r and the density of the reaction mixture are known, the value of the integral for any desired conversion can be evaluated without reference to reaction equipment. Then the various combinations of time and mass of charge that will give the required production rate of product can be examined separately. To obtain a clearer picture of the significance of this point, Eq. (4-3) can be considered as relating the time, θ, to an integral dependent upon the series of intensive states experienced by the reaction mixture. However, it should be pointed out that the rate of reaction does frequently depend upon physical aspects of the reactor other than size. For example, the degree of agitation may influence the

[1] The conversion and rate may be based upon the moles of reactant rather than mass, if desired.

rate significantly, as may also the area per unit mass of the catalyst used in a catalytic reaction.

Frequently it is more convenient to express the conversion as the ratio of the mass of reactant converted to the mass of the same reactant available. This latter term will be given the symbol x, without the prime. The two definitions of conversion are related through the mass of reactant originally present, m, and the total, m_t, in the following way,

$$x' = x \frac{m}{m_t} \tag{4-4}$$

or in differential form[1]

$$dx' = \frac{m}{m_t} dx$$

In terms of the conversion x, Eq. (4-3) becomes

$$\theta = \frac{m}{m_t} \int_0^{x_1} \rho \, \frac{dx}{r} = m \int_0^{x_1} \frac{dx}{V_B r} \tag{4-5}$$

Equations (4-2), (4-3), and (4-5) are entirely general. They may be simplified when assumptions can be made regarding the behavior of the reaction system. For example, if the volume is constant, a reasonable assumption for many liquid-phase reactions, the density and volume V_B are constant and Eq. (4-5) may be written

$$\theta = \frac{m\rho}{m_t} \int_0^{x_1} \frac{dx}{r} = C_0 \int_0^{x_1} \frac{dx}{r} \tag{4-6}$$

where $C_0 = m/V_B$ is the original concentration of the reactant upon which x and r are based.

Since the integral $\displaystyle\int_0^{x_1'} \rho \, \frac{dx'}{r}$ does not depend basically on the size of the reactor, it can be evaluated in small pilot-plant-size equipment and then employed through Eq. (4-3) to design commercial-scale equipment. This method of projecting pilot-plant results requires that all the factors that determine r will be the same in the pilot-plant and large-size reactor. Thus the heat-transfer conditions must be such that the same temperatures are obtained, the degree of agitation must be the same, catalyst conditions the same, etc.

4-4. Design Equations for Flow Reactors. *Tubular Type.* In the application of Eq. (4-1) to tubular flow reactors it is necessary to recall that the properties of the reaction mixture may change with respect to length along the tube. Hence a differential element dV_R should be used for the material balance. The mass of reactant entering the element

---

[1] Note that both m and m_t are constant during the course of the reaction.

will be $Fz_0 - Fx'$, where z_0 is the weight fraction of the reactant in the feed and x' is the conversion. If the conversion in the element is dx', the mass of reactant leaving will be $Fz_0 - F(x' + dx')$. Applying Eq. (4-1) to this steady-state flow reactor,

$$F(z_0 - x') - F(z_0 - x' - dx') - r\,dV_R = 0$$

or
$$F\,dx' = r\,dV_R \qquad (4\text{-}7)[1]$$

where F = mass feed rate, mass per unit time
x' = conversion, measured as mass of a particular reactant converted per total mass of feed
r = rate of reaction [identical to rate of reaction used in Eq. (4-2)]
V_R = volume of tubular flow reactor corresponding to a conversion x'

In this equation F is a constant so that the integrated form is

$$\frac{V_R}{F} = \int_0^{x_1'} \frac{dx'}{r} \qquad (4\text{-}8)$$

This method of writing the design equation, like (4-3) for batch reactors, groups the variables V_R/F and relates them to a quantity dependent upon the intensive states that the reaction mixture passes through. In flow systems the rate of reaction not only depends upon the temperature, pressure, and composition but may be affected by the degree of turbulence or mixing in the reactor, just as agitation may influence the rate in batch systems.

It is observed that the right-hand members of Eqs. (4-3) and (4-8) are identical except for the physical property ρ, which is not dependent upon reaction kinetics. Therefore it should be possible to measure the rate of reaction r in a small-scale batch reactor and use such information to design a large-scale tubular reactor. However, the requirement that *all* the factors affecting the rate must be identical in the two reactors should not be overlooked. Frequently it is difficult to duplicate some of these conditions, such as temperatures and degree of turbulence, making the projection of batch-scale pilot-plant results to large-scale tubular reactors a doubtful procedure. A much less hazardous approach is to carry out the pilot-plant experiments in a flow system.

It is worthwhile to note the similarity between Eq. (4-8) and the more familiar design equation for heat-transfer equipment, which may be written

$$\frac{A}{F_h} = \int_{t_1}^{t_2} \frac{c_p\,dt}{U\,\Delta t} \qquad (4\text{-}9)$$

[1] In this expression as in the batch-design equation F, x', and r can also all be expressed in molal instead of mass units.

where A = required heat-transfer area, analogous to reactor volume V_R in Eq. (4-8)

F_h = mass flow rate of one fluid through exchanger, analogous to feed rate F

It is seen that the rate of reaction r plays the same role in reactor design as the product of the over-all heat-transfer coefficient U and the temperature difference Δt plays in sizing heat-transfer equipment. Thus the numerical value of the integrals in Eqs. (4-3), (4-8), and (4-9) represents the degree of difficulty of the job to be done—whether it be chemical conversion or heat transfer. Similarly the design equation for the absorption of a gas in a packed column through which an absorbent is passed can be written

$$\frac{V}{L} = \int_{C_1}^{C_2} \frac{dC}{K_L a (C_e - C)} \tag{4-10}$$

where V = volume required for absorption tower

L = volumetric rate of flow of liquid absorbent

$K_L a$ = rate of absorption per unit concentration difference $(C_e - C)$

The similarity to Eq. (4-8) is apparent here as well. Again the integral measures the difficulty of the job.[1]

It is clear that the design equations for tubular flow reactors involve no new concepts but simply substitute a rate of reaction for a heat-transfer rate or mass-transfer-rate function. The increased complexity of reactor design in comparison with the design of equipment for the purely physical processes arises in the difficulty in evaluating the rate of reaction r. The rate of reaction is dependent upon more, and less clearly defined, variables than a heat- or mass-transfer coefficient. Accordingly it has been more difficult to develop correlations of experimental rates and theoretical means of predicting rates of reaction.

When the chemical reaction takes place at the surface of a catalyst, it is better to base the rate of reaction upon a unit mass of catalyst rather than a unit volume of reactor, as it was defined in Eqs. (4-3) and (4-8). This procedure eliminates the effect of variations in the mass of catalyst that may be packed in the reactor volume. However, basing the rate upon the mass of catalyst does not eliminate the difficulty due to variations in rate of reaction with the magnitude of catalyst surface. Thus the same mass of $\frac{1}{8}$- and $\frac{1}{4}$-in. silica gel particles would not show the same rate of reaction between methane and sulfur vapor to give carbon disul-

---

[1] In this comparison between heat-transfer, mass-transfer, and reaction rates it is worthwhile to mention one difference. Heat- and mass-transfer rates are flow quantities, and their magnitude depends upon an area perpendicular to the direction of flow. In contrast, the reaction rate depends upon the volume of the system. Mathematically, heat- and mass-transfer rates are vectors, while reaction rate is a scalar.

fide. The $\frac{1}{8}$-in. material would give the larger rate of reaction per unit mass because of the increased surface of the smaller particles. Similarly, the rate per unit mass of porous catalyst particles would be higher than that for nonporous catalysts because of the increased surface for reaction provided by the internal pores. From this point of view it would be most desirable to base the rate of reaction upon a unit surface of catalyst. However, the magnitude of effective catalyst surface is difficult to measure, so that it is necessary to refer the rate to the mass of the catalyst, remembering that this rate may vary with any of the factors which affect the amount and character of the surface.

With this in mind, the design expression for catalytic reactors may be written

$$\frac{W}{F} = \int_0^{x_1'} \frac{dx'}{r_c} \tag{4-11}$$

where W = mass of catalyst

r_c = rate, defined as mass of product produced per unit mass of catalyst per unit time

Tank Flow Reactor. In the tank flow reactor, illustrated in Fig. 4-1B, the characteristic of steady-state operation means that the mass rate of flow of the feed and exit streams will be the same. Hence the first and second terms of Eq. (4-1) are $F(z_0 - x_F')$ and $F(z_0 - x_E')$, where x_F' and x_E' correspond to the conversion in the feed and exit streams, respectively. Since the fourth term is zero for steady-state conditions, the design equation becomes

$$F(z_0 - x_F') - F(z_0 - x_E') - rV_B = 0$$

or
$$\frac{V_B}{F} = \frac{x_E' - x_F'}{r} \tag{4-12}$$

This result may be compared with Eq. (4-8) for the tubular flow case.

It will be observed that, in the three types of reactors considered so far, one or more terms in the general material balance did not exist. In the general treatment of the fourth case, semibatch reactors, all four terms may be important. This complicates the design equation considerably. Simplified cases are solved in Chap. 7 for special types of semibatch reactors.

4-5. Space Velocity and Residence Time in Tubular Flow Reactors. It is clear from the foregoing discussion that the term V_R/F is an important characteristic of a flow reactor. The larger its numerical value, the greater must be the size of the reactor necessary to process a given feed rate F. The inconsistency of comparing volume with mass in the ratio V_R/F can be overcome by converting the feed rate to a volumetric basis. Thus, if v_F is the volume per mole of the feed, Fv_F represents the feed rate as volume per unit time. Then the ratio of size of reactor to feed rate in volumetric units is equal to V_R/Fv_F and is called the reciprocal of the space velocity (SV).

$$\frac{1}{SV} = \frac{V_R}{Fv_F}$$

or
$$SV = \frac{Fv_F}{V_R} \tag{4-13}$$

By considering V_R equal to unity the space velocity may be defined as the permissible feed rate per unit volume of reactor. It is the permissible feed rate because larger values would not result in the required conversion x_1'; that is, larger values of space velocity would correspond to smaller values of V_R/F, and hence smaller values of the integral in Eq. (4-8). Therefore the space velocity is a measure of the ease of the reaction job. A high space velocity means that the reaction can be accomplished with a small-sized reactor, or that a given conversion can be obtained with a high feed rate.

The reciprocal of the space velocity has the units of time and permits writing Eq. (4-8) for flow reactors in a manner similar to that for batch reactors [Eq. (4-3)]. If θ_F' is defined as a hypothetical residence or contact time by the expression

$$\theta_F' = \frac{V_R}{Fv_F} = \frac{1}{SV} \tag{4-14}$$

the design equation (4-8) may be written

$$\theta_F' = \frac{1}{v_F} \int_0^{x_1'} \frac{dx'}{r} \tag{4-15}$$

Equation (4-14) usually has little physical significance for gaseous reactions because θ_F' is not the actual time that a slug of gas is in the reactor, but simply a hypothetical quantity related to V_R/F. Thus variations in the temperature, pressure, and moles of reaction mixture can all cause the true volume per mole to change during the reactor and be unequal to v_F.

The actual time required for an element of gas to pass through a volume of reactor dV_R is

$$d\theta_F = \frac{\text{distance}}{\text{velocity}} = \frac{(\text{cross-sectional area})(\text{distance})}{(\text{cross-sectional area})(\text{velocity})} = \frac{dV_R}{N_t v} \tag{4-16}[1]$$

where N_t = molal flow rate in reactor at point in question in reactor
  v = volume of reaction mixture per mole at point in question

[1] This equation assumes that there is a constant velocity across the tube diameter and that longitudinal diffusion is negligible.

If there is no change in temperature, pressure, and moles of reaction mixture from one point to another in the reactor, N_t is constant and equal to F. Likewise v is constant and equal to v_F. Then Eq. (4-16) is identical with Eq. (4-14), and θ'_F equals the actual residence time θ_F. When this is not true, the actual time must be obtained by integration. Since N_t and v are more easily related to the conversion x' than to V_R, it is convenient to substitute for dV_R the value from Eq. (4-7). This yields

$$d\theta_F = \frac{F\,dx'}{N_t vr}$$

Integrating this formally,

$$\theta_F = F \int_0^{x'} \frac{dx'}{N_t vr} \tag{4-17}$$

Example 4-1. Acetaldehyde vapor is being decomposed in a tubular reactor according to the following reaction:

$$CH_3CHO \rightarrow CH_4 + CO$$

The reaction tube is 3.3 cm ID, 80 cm long, and is maintained at a constant temperature of 518°C.

The acetaldehyde vapor is measured at room temperature and slightly above atmospheric pressure. For consistency the measured flow rate is corrected to standard conditions (0°C and 1 atm) before reporting the space velocity.

In one run, at a reported space velocity of 8.0 hr^{-1}, 35 per cent of the acetaldehyde is decomposed in the reactor.

The second-order specific-rate constant is 0.33 liter/(sec)(g mole) at 518°C, and the reaction is irreversible. The pressure in the reactor is essentially atmospheric.

Calculate the actual residence time, and compare it with the hypothetical value determined from Eq. (4-14).

Solution. The rate equation may be written

$$r = kC_A^2 = \text{g moles/(liter)(sec)}$$

At a point in the reactor where the conversion is x, the molal flow rate of

$$CH_3CHO = F(1-x)$$
$$CH_4 = Fx$$
$$\underline{CO = Fx}$$
$$\text{Total flow rate } N_t = F(1+x)$$

Since the feed is entirely acetaldehyde, x and x' are equivalent and also F is equal to the entering flow rate of acetaldehyde.

The molal concentration of CH_3CHO is the ratio of $F(1-x)$ to the total volumetric flow rate V_t. Hence

$$C_A = \frac{F(1-x)}{V_t} = \frac{F(1-x)p_t}{N_t RT} = \frac{1-x}{1+x}\frac{p_t}{RT}$$

The rate in terms of x is

$$r = k \left(\frac{1-x}{1+x}\right)^2 \left(\frac{p_t}{RT}\right)^2$$

The volume per mole of reaction mixture, under perfect-gas conditions, will be

$$v = \frac{(1)RT}{p_t}$$

and

$$N_t = F(1 + x)$$

Substituting these values for r, v, and N_t in Eq. (4-17),

$$\theta_F = F \int_0^{x_1} \frac{p_t(1 + x)^2 \, dx}{F(1 + x)(RT)k(1 - x)^2(p_t/RT)^2}$$

$$= \frac{RT}{p_t k} \int_0^{x_1} \frac{(1 + x) \, dx}{(1 - x)^2} = \frac{RT}{p_t k} \left[\frac{2}{1 - x} + \ln (1 - x)\right]_0^{x_1}$$

Substituting the exit conversion $x_1 = 0.35$,

$$\theta_F = \frac{0.082(518 + 273)}{1 \times 0.33} \left[\frac{2}{1 - 0.35} + \ln (1 - 0.35) - 2\right]$$

$$= 127 \text{ sec}$$

The hypothetical residence time, based upon the space velocity, is

$$\theta'_F = \frac{1}{SV} = \frac{1}{8.0}$$

$$= 0.125 \text{ hr, or } 450 \text{ sec}$$

The major difference between θ_F and θ'_F arises because the space velocity was based upon a flow rate at standard temperature 273°C.

If the volume per mole of feed, v_F in Eq. (4-14), were based upon the actual reaction temperature of 518°C (791°K), the residence time would be much lower. Thus if the space velocity were corrected to the reactor temperature by Eq. (4-13), it would become

$$SV \text{ at } 791°K = 8.0 \frac{v_F \text{ at } 791°K}{v_F \text{ at } 273°K}$$

$$= 8.0 \times \tfrac{791}{273}$$

$$= 23.2 \text{ hr}^{-1}$$

and

$$\theta'_F = \frac{1}{23.2} \times 3,600$$

$$= 155 \text{ sec}$$

The difference between this value and the actual θ_F is due to the increase in the number of moles occurring as a result of reaction. This increase lowers the actual residence time from 155 to 127 sec.

4-6. Homogeneous and Heterogeneous Reactors. When a chemical reaction takes place in a single phase and the components are well mixed, there are no diffusion resistances to retard the rate of the reaction. For example, in a reaction between gases A and B the molecules of A and B are present in the same proportion (composition) throughout the mixture, provided good mixing is obtained. Similarly the temperature and pressure are the same. As a result the rate of reaction is the same at all points in the system, and no concentration differences build up during the reaction. However, if the reaction is between gas A and solid B to produce gas C, the reaction occurring at the solid-gas interface will deplete the gas adjacent to the interface in molecules of gas A and increase the concentration of the product C. As a result the rate of reaction will decrease. However, the concentration gradient between the main body of the gas and the region of the interface will cause a mass transfer of gas A toward the interface, and a transfer of product C away from the interface out into the main body of the gas. At steady-state conditions an equilibrium will be established so that the rate of transfer of reactant A from the main body of the gas to the interface will be balanced by the rate of removal of A at the interface by chemical reaction. It is apparent that this over-all steady-state rate will be determined by the relative resistances of the transfer process bringing A to the interface and the chemical reaction process removing A. This means that both the physical process of mass transfer and the chemical process of reaction must be taken into account in determining the over-all rate of conversion of A to C.

Because of this basic difference between single-phase and multiphase reactions it is useful to classify reactors as homogeneous or heterogeneous. The gaseous reaction requiring a solid-phase catalyst is of the heterogeneous type, even though all the reactants and products are gases. Thus in the oxidation of sulfur dioxide with a platinum catalyst there is a mass transfer of sulfur dioxide and oxygen from the main body of the gas phase to the catalyst surface and a diffusion of sulfur trioxide from the interface out into the bulk gas mixture.

In many instances the resistance to mass transfer is small in comparison with the resistance to conversion at the interface. In such cases the concentration gradient is negligible, so that, from a reactor-design viewpoint, there is essentially no difference between homogeneous and heterogeneous reactions.

If the conditions for good mixing do not exist, there may be concentration gradients affecting the rate of reaction even in homogeneous systems. The most obvious case is where the reactants entering the reactor are not properly mixed. Another possibility is the result of nonuniform temperatures in the reactor. As an illustration, consider a reactor consisting of a tube which must be heated externally to maintain a suitable temperature within the homogeneous liquid reaction mixture. If the rate of flow through the tube is low, the temperature profile across the diameter of the reactor at any section may be far from uniform, the temperature being higher near the wall than at the center. The corresponding higher reaction rate near the wall will use up the reactants more rapidly there. As a consequence there will be a higher concentration of reactants near the center than near the wall. As a result of the concentration difference there will be a transfer of reactants by diffusion toward the wall, and of products in the reverse direction. The importance of the effect will be dependent upon the degree of mixing of the liquid as it moves through the reactor. This in turn depends upon the size of the pipe, the average velocity of flow, and physical properties of the system. At very low velocities, where the flow is streamline in character, the variation in concentration radially would be large. In contrast, at high Reynolds numbers, the mixing would be excellent, so that significant concentration gradients would not be likely to exist. As in the heterogeneous case, the importance of these diffusional resistances is also directly dependent upon the rate of the chemical-reaction step. If this rate is much lower than that of the physical transfer process, the rate of chemical reaction will control the over-all process.

4-7. **Classification According to Temperature Conditions.** In a few commercially important reactions the heat of reaction is so small and the heat transfer to the surroundings such that the change in temperature is negligible. The problem of design for such isothermal reactors is greatly simplified because the variation in rate of reaction with temperature need not be considered. The isomerization of n-butane (ΔH at 25°C = -1600 cal/g mole) is an example of this class of reactions. Even when the heat of reaction is moderate, it may be possible to approach isothermal operation by addition or removal of heat from the reactor. In the sulfuric acid alkylation process for producing isooctane from isobutane and butenes the heat of reaction is about $-17,000$ cal/g mole at 25°C. However, by cooling the liquid mixture in the reactor by external cooling jackets it is possible to reduce the temperature variation to 20 to 40°F.

When the heat of reaction is large, sizable temperature variations will be present even though heat transfer between the reactor and surroundings is facilitated. In such cases it is necessary to consider the effect of temperature on the rate of reaction. Reactors operating in this fashion are frequently termed pseudo-isothermal, or nonadiabatic (since at least an attempt is made to achieve isothermal operation).

Reactors (both flow and batch) may also be insulated from the surroundings so that their operation approaches adiabatic conditions. If the heat of reaction is significant, there will be a change in temperature with time (batch reactor) or position (flow reactor). However, in the flow reactor this variation in temperature will be limited to the direction of flow; i.e., there will be no variation in temperature in the radial direction in a tubular flow reactor. This will be found in Chap. 11 to simplify considerably reactor-design procedures over those necessary for nonadiabatic cases.

Other schemes are used, in addition to external transfer of heat, to try to approach isothermal operating conditions. For example, in the dehydrogenation of butylenes to butadiene the temperature must be maintained at a rather high level (1200 to 1400°F) in order to have a favorable equilibrium conversion. However, the endothermic nature of the reaction means that the reaction mixture will cool off as it flows through the reactor bed. It is both difficult and expensive to transfer heat to the reaction mixture at this high temperature level by external heating. Instead, high-temperature steam is added directly to the butenes entering the reactor. The large quantity of steam serves as a source of heat to maintain the reaction mixture at a high temperature level.[1] Another device frequently employed is internal cooling or heating by placing coils within the reactor proper. A modification of the same principle is illustrated by the Downs[2] reactor for the oxidation of naphthalene to phthalic anhydride. The flow reactor is divided into a large number of small tubes rather than a single large-diameter tube. Each small tube is surrounded with cooling fluid which absorbs the heat of reaction. In this particular case boiling mercury is employed as the cooling medium. Under actual operating conditions some naphthalene is oxidized completely to carbon dioxide and water vapor so that the heat of reaction per gram mole of naphthalene is as high as $-570,000$ cal.

This discussion may be summarized by noting that the operation of commercial reactors falls into three categories, isothermal, adiabatic, and the broad division of nonadiabatic, where attempts are made to approach isothermal conditions, but the magnitude of the heat of reaction or the temperature level prevents attaining this objective.

4-8. Mechanical Features. *Batch Reactors.* The batch reactor is, in essence, a kettle or tank. It should have a number of accessories in order to be operated satisfactorily. First of all it generally must be closed, except for a vent, in order to prevent loss of material and danger to the operating personnel. For reactions carried out under pressure the vent is replaced by a safety valve.

High-pressure conditions frequently introduce complications in the design and greatly increase the initial cost. For example, the top closure

---

[1] Steam has other advantages. Particularly, it reduces polymerization.

[2] C. R. Downs, *Ind. Eng. Chem.*, **32**:1294 (1940); U.S. Patent 1,604,739 (1926).

must be able to withstand the same maximum pressure as the rest of the autoclave. At medium pressures a satisfactory closure can be assembled by using bolts or studs and suitable flanges and gaskets. The seal is obtained by tightening the six or more bolts holding the flange to the head. Care must be taken to tighten the bolts evenly in order that the gasket will be deformed uniformly. Such a closure is illustrated in the batch reactor shown in Fig. 4-2. For higher pressures (above approximately 5,000 psia) this type of construction is not desirable because of the very high stresses that the bolts must withstand. The preferred design is one in which the pressure itself seals the vessel, and increases in pressure do not cause a corresponding increase in stress in the bolts. An

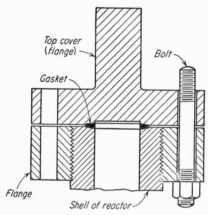

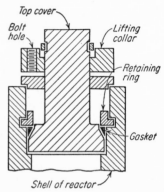

FIG. 4-2. Conventional flange and bolt closure for batch reactor.

FIG. 4-3. Closure for high-pressure batch reactor.

example of this self-sealing closure is shown in Fig. 4-3. The pressure acting on the head is transmitted to the gasket, which is confined by the reactor wall, the head, and a retaining ring. The internal pressure pushes the head against the gasket, thus augmenting the force exerted by the bolts through the lifting collar. Gooch,[1] Storch,[2] and Moss[3] have discussed in some detail the problems encountered in designing batch reactors for medium- and high-pressure operation.

It is usually necessary to agitate the reaction mixture in batch systems. This can be done mechanically with stirrers operated by a shaft extending through the reactor wall. In high-pressure reactors rather complicated packing glands around the shaft are necessary to prevent leakage.

[1] D. B. Gooch, *Ind. Eng. Chem.*, **35**:927 (1943).

[2] E. L. Clark, P. L. Golber, A. M. Whitehouse, and H. H. Storch, *Ind. Eng. Chem.*, **39**:1955 (1947).

[3] F. D. Moss, *Ind. Eng. Chem.*, **45**:2135 (1945).

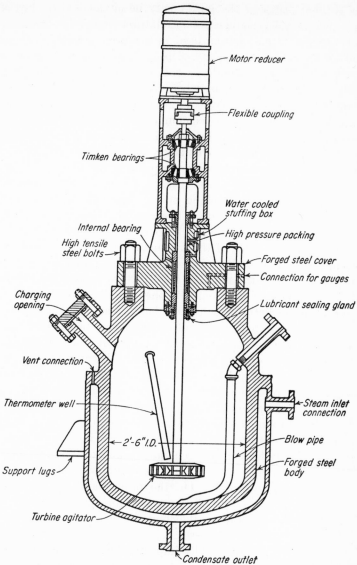

Fig. 4-4. Jacketed batch reactor. [*Reproduced by permission from Ind. Eng. Chem.,* **35**:927 (1943).]

A typical design is illustrated in Fig. 4-4, where the mechanical details of a reactor, which is also jacketed, are shown.

Provision for heating or cooling the reaction contents is often required. This may be accomplished by circulating a fluid through a jacket surrounding the reactor. Where heat effects are large enough to require the most rapid heat transfer, the jacket may be augmented by heating or cooling coils immersed in the reaction mixture.

The materials of construction used in batch reactors vary from ordinary steel to glass-lined equipment, depending upon the properties of the reaction mixture. In pilot-plant operations either stainless-steel or glass-lined reactors are ordinarily used because of their corrosion resistance, and hence general applicability to a variety of systems. In commercial-scale equipment it may be more economical to use ordinary steel because of its low cost, even though corrosion is significant. In the food and pharmaceutical industries it is frequently necessary to use glass-lined or stainless-steel equipment to protect the purity of product.[1]

Flow Reactors. Flow reactors may be constructed in a number of ways. The conventional thermal-cracking units in the petroleum industry are examples of a noncatalytic type. The gas oil or other petroleum fraction is passed through a number of lengths of alloy-steel tubes placed in series on the walls and roof of the furnace. Heat is transferred by convection and radiation to the tube surface in order to raise the temperature of the gas oil to the reaction level (600 to 1000°F) and to supply the endothermic heat of reaction. On the other hand, flow reactors may consist of a tank or kettle, much like a batch reactor, with provision for continuously adding reactants and withdrawing product. This tank type is not suitable for reactions such as thermal cracking, where large quantities of thermal energy must be supplied, because of the low-heat-transfer surface per unit volume of reactor. Tank-type flow reactors are advantageous for reactions where a large reaction time is required to achieve the desired conversion, and where high heat-transfer rates are not necessary. From a design viewpoint the essential difference between tubular and tank reactors lies in the degree of mixing obtained. In the tubular type, where the length is generally large with respect to the tube diameter, the forced velocity in the direction of flow is sufficient to retard mixing in the axial direction. On the other hand, in tank reactors it is possible to obtain essentially complete mixing by mechanical agitation. Under these conditions the composition, temperature, and pressure are uniform through the vessel.

A large number of commercially important reactions are of the fluid-solid catalytic class. Examples are the catalytic cracking of petroleum, oxidation of sulfur dioxide, dehydrogenation of butenes to butadiene, and oxidation of naphthalene to phthalic anhydride. In this group of reactions the solid catalyst may be held in a fixed position while the fluid moves through it (fixed-bed reactors), or much smaller catalyst particles may be suspended in the fluid phase by the motion of the fluid (fluidized-

---

[1] See J. H. Perry, "Chemical Engineers' Handbook," McGraw-Hill Book Company, Inc., New York, 1950.

bed reactor), or the solid particles may be in point-to-point contact and fall slowly by gravity through the fluid (moving-bed reactor).

Fixed-bed reactors are more economical to build in the form of a single large-diameter tube than in multitubular design. However, the latter arrangement may be required when it is necessary to transfer large quantities of heat to the surroundings, as in the case of a highly exothermic reaction. The smaller the tube diameter, the larger the ratio of heat-transfer surface to mass of reaction mixture in the tube, and the easier it is to limit temperature changes between inlet and exit. Of course, the low capacity of small tubes means that a larger total number of tubes must be built into the reactor in parallel in order to obtain a given production rate of product. As mentioned in Sec. 4-7, other means of preventing large temperature variations in fixed-bed reactors may be used. In addition to the devices suggested earlier the catalyst bed may be divided into sections, with heating or cooling coils placed in between each section, in order to reduce the temperature change in the catalyst bed.

It may be noted that all these devices to reduce temperature gradients in the fixed-bed reactor are corrective rather than preventative. In solid catalytic reactors the potentially large temperature variations in the direction of flow are due to the fact that the solid catalyst is unable to mix and reach a more uniform temperature. Near the entrance to the bed the rate of reaction is high, and large quantities of heat are evolved (for an exothermic reaction), while near the exit, where the rate is low, there is a relatively small evolution of heat. Because the heat transfer rate from pellet to adjacent pellet and between pellet and gas is small, each layer of catalyst in the bed is, in effect, partially insulated from adjacent layers. This effectively prevents the flow of heat from the entrance to the exit of the catalyst bed. This in turn results in significant temperature gradients. The fluidized-bed reactor eliminates this problem by getting at the source of the difficulty, the stationary condition of the bed. The rapid movement of the small catalyst particles goes a long way toward eliminating temperature variations within the solid phase. Any one particle may be near the entrance of the reactor one instant and near the exit at the next. This rapid mixing serves to equalize both fluid- and solid-phase temperatures so that the entire reactor system maintains a nearly uniform temperature. The small size (generally 5 to 100 microns) of the fluidized particles provides a large heat-transfer area per unit mass and in this way increases the heat-transfer rates between solid and gas phases. It has been established that the general motion of the solid particles is upward near the center of the bed and downward against the gas flow near the wall. However, there are large deviations in the motion of different particles, and each single particle follows a tortuous path in the bed. Although the resultant motion of the gas is upward through the reactor, there is some tendency for the gas surrounding a solid particle to follow the downward motion near the wall.[1]

Another advantage of the fluidized-bed in comparison with the fixed-bed type is the possibility of regeneration of catalyst without disturbing the operation of the reactor. Thus in the fluidized catalytic cracking units a portion of the solid particles are continuously removed from the reactor and regenerated in a separate unit. The regeneration is accomplished by burning off the carbon with air, and the reactivated catalyst is continuously returned to the reactor proper. In the fixed-bed reactor the closest approach to continuous operation obtainable with a catalyst of limited life is to construct two or more identical reactors and switch streams from one to the other when the catalyst needs to be regenerated.

A disadvantage of fluidized reactors is the large-size equipment required. In order not to blow the solid particles out the top of the reactor, the gas velocity must be low. This in turn necessitates large-diameter vessels and increases the first cost. There are also losses of catalyst fines from the reactor so that expensive dust-collection equipment must be used in the exit gases.

Moving-bed systems do not permit the uniformity of temperature achieved in fluidized reactors, but they do allow a continuous handling of the solid phase. This is advantageous in some operations, such as catalyst or adsorbent regeneration. For example, the regeneration of the charcoal adsorbent for the hypersorption process[2] of separating hydrocarbons has been accomplished in a moving-bed reactor. The deactivated charcoal is added to the top of the regenerator, and steam passed upward through the slowly moving bed of solid to strip out and react with the adsorbed hydrocarbons. Moving-bed systems have been employed more for heat-transfer (pebble-type heat exchangers) and adsorption operations than as a type of chemical reactor, although modifications of the general classification, such as vertical and horizontal limekilns, are in widespread use.

NOMENCLATURE

c_p Specific heat at constant pressure
C Concentration, moles/unit volume
C_0 Reactant concentration initially in a batch reactor, or entering a flow reactor
F Feed rate to a reactor, mass or moles/unit time
$K_{L}a$ Over-all absorption-rate coefficient, per unit volume of absorption tower, i.e., moles absorbed/(unit volume)(unit driving force)(unit time)
L Volumetric flow rate

[1] H. S. Mickley and C. A. Trilling, *Ind. Eng. Chem.*, **41**:1135 (1949).
[2] Clyde Berg, *Trans. AIChE*, **42**:685 (1946).

m_t Total mass of reaction mixture

m Mass of reactant

N_t Total molal flow rate in a reactor

r Rate of reaction, mass or moles converted/(unit time)(unit volume)

r_c Rate of a solid catalytic reaction, mass or moles reacted/(unit time)(unit mass of catalyst)

SV Space velocity $(\text{time})^{-1}$

Δt Temperature driving force in a heat exchanger

U Over-all heat-transfer coefficient in a heat exchanger

v Volume/mole of reaction mixture

v_F Volume/mole of feed

x Conversion, amount of reactant converted/total amount of same reactant available

x' Conversion, amount of reactant converted/total amount of feed or charge to the reactor

x'_E Conversion in the exit stream from a tank-type flow reactor

x'_F Conversion in the feed stream to a tank flow reactor

x'_1 Exit conversion in a tubular flow reactor

z Weight fraction of reactant in mixture

z_0 Weight fraction of reactant at zero conversion

ρ Density of reaction mixture, mass or moles/unit volume

θ Time in a tank-type reactor

θ_F True, or actual, residence time in a tubular flow reactor

θ'_F Hypothetical residence time in a tubular reactor $= 1/\text{SV}$

PROBLEMS

1. In studying the kinetics of the homogeneous gas-phase reaction between sulfur vapor and methane, R. A. Fisher[1] reported conversions for various space velocities. These space velocities were defined as the volumetric flow rate in milliliters per hour divided by the total volume of empty reactor in cubic centimeters. The flow rate is based upon all the sulfur being considered as S_2 and is referred to 0°C and 1 atm pressure.

From the fact that the operating pressure was 1.0 atm and the temperature 600°C, compute the values of V_R/F corresponding to the space velocities given in the reference for runs 55, 58, 57, 78, and 79. V_R/F is the ratio of the volume of reactor to the molal feed rate in gram moles per hour.

Also determine the true contact time for a slug of reaction mixture for each of the runs, i.e., the time it takes for a slug of gas to pass through the reactor.[2]

2. The production of toluene from benzene and xylenes was studied by Johanson and Watson[3] in a standard 1-in. pipe reactor using a silica-alumina catalyst. At the reactor temperature of 932°F the reaction mixture is in the vapor phase. However, the benzene and xylenes were measured and pumped separately into the system as liquids, using a proportioning pump. Hence the space velocity was reported on a liquid-hourly basis; that is, as the ratio of the feed rate in cubic centimeters of liquid per hour to the total volume of the reactor in cubic centimeters.

[1] R. A. Fisher, *Ind. Eng. Chem.*, **42**:704 (1950).

[2] See the reference for the conversion values for the runs.

[3] L. N. Johanson and K. M. Watson, *Natl. Petroleum News*, Aug. 7, 1946.

The feed consisted of an equimolal mixture of benzene and xylenes and the liquid rates were corrected to 60°F before reporting the following information:

Liquid-hourly space velocity, hr^{-1}	Reactor pressure, psia
0.5	20
0.25	20
1.0	65
2.0	65
2.0	115
4.0	115

The reactor contained 85 g of catalyst packed in a volume of 135 cc, and the densities of benzene and xylenes at 60°F may be taken as 0.879 and 0.870 g/cc, respectively.

From the data determine corresponding values of W/F in the units of g of catalyst/(g mole)/(hr).

3. Convert the liquid-hourly space velocities in Prob. 2 to a gas basis; that is, to space velocities defined as the ratio of the gas-flow rate at reaction conditions to the total reactor volume. Then calculate the actual contact time for each run. The gases may be assumed to obey the perfect gas law.

The reaction does not result in a change in number of total moles:

$$C_6H_6 + C_6H_4(CH_3)_2 = 2C_6H_5CH_3$$

CHAPTER 5

HOMOGENEOUS BATCH REACTORS

After considering the problem of reactor design in a general way in Chap. 4 the next objective is the more specific design of equipment for homogeneous reactions. The present chapter is concerned with batch reactors and the following one with flow systems. To carry out the design calculations requires a prior knowledge of the reaction rate. The methods of measuring rates of reaction and interpreting the resulting data in the form of kinetic rate equations for batch reactions were discussed in Chap. 3. Hence we may proceed directly to the design problem.

There are homogeneous reactions of commercial importance of both the noncatalytic and the catalytic type. For example, one process for the production of ethylene dichloride consists of the reaction between ethylene and chlorine in the presence of bromine, all three materials being in the vapor phase. The bromine reacts with chlorine to form the unstable bromine chloride, which behaves as a catalyst in accordance with the following reactions:

$$C_2H_4 + BrCl \rightarrow C_2H_4BrCl$$
$$C_2H_4BrCl + Cl_2 \rightarrow C_2H_4Cl_2 + BrCl$$

Illustrations of noncatalytic homogeneous reactions are numerous. The thermal cracking of hydrocarbons, the combustion of gaseous fuels such as natural gas, and various inorganic reactions in aqueous solutions are types included in this classification.

Batch[1] reactors are seldom employed on a commercial scale for gas-phase reactions because the quantity of product that can be produced in a reasonably sized reactor is small. The chief use of batch systems for gaseous reactions is for kinetic studies. On the other hand, batch reactors are frequently used for liquid-phase reactions, particularly when the required production is small. Batch reactors are generally more expensive to operate than continuous ones for the same production rate. However, the initial cost of a continuous system may be higher because of the instrumentation required. Therefore, for relatively high-priced

[1] This is the first type of reactor discussed in Chap. 4 and illustrated in Fig. 4-1A.

products (such as pharmaceuticals) where operating expense is not a predominant factor in the total cost, batch reactors are commonly used.

The basic design equation as presented in Chap. 4 is

$$\theta = \int_0^{x_1'} \frac{\rho \, dx'}{r} = m_t \int_0^{x_1'} \frac{dx'}{V_B r} \qquad (5\text{-}1)$$

where the conversion x' refers to the mass of a specific reactant converted per total mass of charge m_t. In terms of the fractional conversion x of a specific reactant the design equation for batch reactors is [Eq. (4-5)]

$$\theta = \frac{m}{m_t} \int_0^{x_1} \frac{\rho \, dx}{r} = m \int_0^{x_1} \frac{dx}{V_B r} \qquad (5\text{-}2)$$

or if the volume is constant,

$$\theta = C_0 \int_0^{x_1} \frac{dx}{r} \qquad (5\text{-}3)$$

The difficulty in integrating these expressions depends upon the number of variables influencing the rate of reaction r. For example, if the rate of formation of the desired product depends upon only one irreversible reaction, the expression for r will be simpler than if reversible or multiple reactions are involved. The integration of Eq. (5-1) for various simple reaction mechanisms under constant-temperature conditions was considered in Chap. 3. At that point the objective was the determination of the rate constant k. In reactor design the situation is reversed: k and r are known, and the time θ necessary to obtain a given conversion x is required.

Since r is a function of temperature, the application of Eq. (5-1) is simplest for isothermal conditions. Generally graphical procedures are necessary when the reactor is to be operated adiabatically or in another nonisothermal manner.

5-1. Isothermal Reactor Design (Batch). The laboratory-scale data of Leyes and Othmer[1] on the rate of esterification of butanol and acetic acid in the liquid phase can be used to illustrate the design problem of predicting the time-conversion relationship for a batch reactor.

Example 5-1. Butyl acetate is to be produced in a batch-operated reactor at 100°C, using sulfuric acid as a catalyst. The original feed contains 4.97 moles of butanol per mole of acetic acid, and the catalyst concentration is 0.032 per cent by weight H_2SO_4.

1. Calculate the time required to obtain a conversion of 50 per cent.

2. Determine the size of reactor and the original mass of reactants that must be charged to the reactor in order to produce ester at the average rate of 100 lb/hr.

[1] C. E. Leyes and D. F. Othmer, *Ind. Eng. Chem.*, **36**:968 (1945).

Only one reactor will be used, and this unit will be shut down 30 min between batches for removal of product, cleaning, and starting up.

DATA. The following rate equation was found by Leyes and Othmer to correlate the data when an excess of butanol was used in the esterification:

$$r = kC_A^2$$

where C_A = acetic acid concentration, g moles/ml
r = rate of reaction, g moles acid disappearing/(ml)(min)

For a ratio of butanol to acid of 4.97 and a sulfuric acid concentration of 0.032 per cent by weight the reaction-velocity constant was

$$k = 17.4 \text{ ml/(g mole)(min)}$$

Densities of mixtures of acetic acid, butanol, and butyl acetate are not known. Leyes and Othmer reported values for each of the three compounds at 100°C.

$$\rho \text{ (acetic acid)} = 0.958 \text{ g/ml}$$
$$\rho \text{ (butanol)} = 0.742$$
$$\rho \text{ (butyl acetate)} = 0.796$$

While the density of the reaction mixture will vary with conversion, the excess of butanol will reduce the magnitude of the change. Therefore as an approximation the density of the mixture will be assumed constant and equal to 0.75 g/ml.

Solution. The molecular weights are as follows:

$$\text{Ester} = 116$$
$$\text{Butanol} = 74$$
$$\text{Acetic acid} = 60$$

1. The concentration of acetic acid C_A is related to the conversion in the following way:

$$C_A = C_{A_0}(1 - x)$$

where C_{A_0} = initial acid concentration.

Substituting this expression in the rate equation gives

$$r = kC_{A_0}^2(1 - x)^2$$

The design expression [Eq. (5-3)], applicable at constant volume or density, can be written in terms of the variables θ and x.

$$\theta = C_{A_0} \int_0^{x_1} \frac{dx}{kC_{A_0}^2(1 - x)^2} = \frac{1}{kC_{A_0}} \int_0^{x_1} \frac{dx}{(1 - x)^2} \tag{A}$$

Integrating and substituting a final value of $x_1 = 0.50$ lead to the result

$$\theta = \frac{1}{kC_{A_0}} \left(\frac{1}{1 - x_1} - \frac{1}{1 - 0} \right) = \frac{1}{kC_{A_0}} (2 - 1)$$

$$= \frac{1}{kC_{A_0}} \tag{B}$$

The initial concentration of acetic acid, assuming a density for the mixture of 0.75, is

$$C_{A_0} = \frac{1 \times 0.75}{4.97 \times 74 + 1 \times 60}$$
$$= 0.0018 \text{ g mole/ml}†$$

Note that this concentration must be expressed in metric units since it is to be used in Eq. (B), where k is known in metric units.

From Eq. (B) the time required for a conversion of 50 per cent is

$$\theta = \frac{1}{17.4 \times 0.0018}$$
$$= 32 \text{ min, or } 0.53 \text{ hr}$$

2. The production rate (pounds per hour of ester) of the reactor in terms of the pounds of acid charged, m_A, will be

$$100 = \frac{(m_A/60)(116 \times 0.5)}{0.53 + 0.50}$$

This expression allows 30 min for shutdown time per charge and takes into account that the conversion is 50 per cent.

$$m_A = 106 \text{ lb acetic acid/charge}$$
$$\text{Total charge} = 106 + 4.97 \times \tfrac{74}{60} \times 106$$
$$= 756 \text{ lb}$$

The volume occupied by the charge will be

$$V_B = \frac{756}{0.75 \times 62.4 \times 0.1337}$$
$$= 121 \text{ gal}$$

The reactor must be large enough to handle 121 gal of reaction mixture. The charge would consist of 106 lb of acid and 650 lb of butanol.

When the rate of the reverse reaction is significant (i.e., when equilibrium is approached in the reactor) or when more than one reaction is involved, the mechanics of solving the design equation may become more complex but the principles involved are the same. Equation (5-1) is applicable, but the more complicated nature of the rate function may make the mathematical integration difficult. However, in multiple-reaction cases, the true mechanism may be so poorly understood that quantitative kinetic equations in terms of the actual mechanism cannot be written. In such cases it is necessary, in order to approach the

† Note that in this example r and x and C are expressed in molar units rather than in mass units. In general the design equations can be used with either molar or mass units as long as r and x are consistent.

reactor-design problem from a quantitative viewpoint, to find an empirical rate equation which agrees well with available rate data. This was the situation in the example just considered. The actual series of reactions by which the ester is formed is not definitely known, but, on the basis of Goldschmidt's[1] and Smith's[2] studies and their own results, Leyes and Othmer postulated the following series of steps as probable:

$$H_2SO_4 + C_4H_9OH \rightarrow C_4H_9SO_4H + H_2O$$
$$C_4H_9SO_4H + H_2O \rightarrow C_4H_9SO_4 + H_3O^+$$
$$C_4H_9OH + H_3O^+ \rightarrow C_4H_9OH_2 + H_2O$$
$$C_4H_9OH_2 + (CH_3COOH)_2 \rightarrow C_4H_9OOCCH_3 + HOOCCH_3 + H_3O^+$$

Assuming that the actual mechanism of ester formation is by these reactions, a rigorous reactor design would require knowing a rate equation for each separate step. Since the experimental data available consisted only of concentrations of ester, acetic acid, butanol, and catalyst, evaluation of the rates of the intermediate steps was impossible. Hence the only quantitative approach available was an empirical one for the over-all reaction, which led to the expression that the rate of ester formation was proportional to the square of the acid concentration (when an excess of butanol was employed).

The calculations involved for a reversible reaction are illustrated in Example 5-2, concerned with the esterification of ethyl alcohol.

Example 5-2. In the presence of water and hydrochloric acid (as a catalyst) the rate of esterification (gram moles per liter per minute) of acetic acid and ethyl alcohol at 100°C is given by the equations

$$r = kC_HC_{OH} \qquad k = 4.76 \times 10^{-4} \text{ (liter)/(min)g mole}$$

The rate of the reverse reaction, the hydrolysis of the ester in the same concentration of catalyst, is

$$r_2 = k'C_EC_W \qquad k' = 1.63 \times 10^{-4} \text{ (liter)/(min)g mole}$$
$$CH_3COOH + C_2H_5OH \underset{k'}{\overset{k}{\rightleftharpoons}} CH_3COOC_2H_5 + H_2O$$

1. A reactor is charged with 100 gal of an aqueous solution containing 200 lb of acetic acid, 400 lb of ethyl alcohol, and the same concentration of HCl as used to obtain the reaction-velocity constants. What will be the conversion of acetic acid to ester after 120 min reaction time? The density may be assumed constant and equal to 8.7 lb/gal. Neglect the water vaporized in the reactor.
2. What is the equilibrium conversion?

[1] H. Goldschmidt, Z. physik. Chem., **60**:728 (1907), **81**:30 (1912), **143**:139, 278 (1929).
[2] H. A. Smith, J. Am. Chem. Soc., **61**:254 (1939).

Solution. 1. The net rate of formation of acid is obtained by combining the rate expressions for the forward and reverse reactions.

$$r = kC_H C_{OH} - k'C_E C_W$$

Before this equation can be used directly in Eq. (5-3), the concentrations must be expressed in terms of the conversion x by suitable material balances. The initial concentration of acid C_H, alcohol C_{OH}, and water C_W are as follows:

$$C_{H_0} = \frac{200}{100 \times 60} \frac{454 \times 1,000}{0.1337 \times 30.5^3}$$

$$= 4.00 \text{ g moles/liter}$$

$$C_{OH_0} = \frac{400}{100 \times 46} \frac{454 \times 1,000}{0.1337 \times 30.5^3}$$

$$= 10.8 \text{ g moles/liter}$$

$$C_{W_0} = \frac{8.7 \times 100 - (200 + 400)}{100 \times 18} \frac{454 \times 1,000}{0.1337 \times 30.5^3}$$

$$= 18.0 \text{ g moles/liter}$$

Basing the conversion on the acid, as required by the statement of the problem, the concentrations at any time are

$$C_H = 4.0(1 - x) \qquad x = \frac{moles\ reacted}{moles\ available}$$
$$C_{OH} = 10.8 - 4x$$
$$C_E = 4.0x$$
$$C_{H_2O} = 18 + 4x$$

These relationships between concentrations and conversion rest upon the assumption of a constant density during the reaction. However, the problem could still be solved without this assumption, provided data on the variation in density with conversion were available.

Substituting the expressions for concentration in the rate equation,

$$r = k \times 4(1 - x)(10.8 - 4x) - k' \times 4x(18 + 4x)$$

Using the numerical values for k and k', the following equation for r in gram moles per liter per minute is obtained:

$$r = (0.257 - 0.499x + 0.062x^2)(8 \times 10^{-2})$$

Substituting this in the design equation for constant volume [Eq. (5-3)] yields

$$\theta = \frac{C_{H_0}}{8 \times 10^{-2}} \int_0^{x_1} \frac{dx}{0.257 - 0.499x + 0.062x^2}$$

$$\theta = 50 \int_0^{x_1} \frac{dx}{0.257 - 0.499x + 0.062x^2}$$

This expression can be integrated analytically or numerically. Using the former approach,

$$\theta = \frac{50}{0.430} \left[\ln \frac{0.125x - 0.499 - 0.430}{0.125x - 0.499 + 0.430} \right]_0^{x_1}$$

$$\theta = \frac{50}{0.430} \ln \frac{(0.125x_1 - 0.929) \times 0.069}{(0.125x_1 - 0.069) \times 0.929}$$

The conversion is desired for a time of 120 min.   Hence

$$\frac{120 \times 0.430}{50} = 1.03 = \ln \frac{0.125x_1 - 0.929}{0.125x_1 - 0.069} \frac{0.069}{0.929}$$

or
$$\frac{0.125x_1 - 0.929}{0.125x_1 - 0.069} \frac{0.069}{0.929} = e^{1.03} = 2.80$$

Solving for the conversion, $x_1 = 0.365$, or 36.5 per cent of the acid is converted to ester.

It is interesting to compare this result with that based upon neglecting the reverse reaction.   Under this condition the rate equation is

$$r = kC_H C_{OH} = kC_{H_0}(1 - x)(C_{OH_0} - C_{H_0}x)$$

The design equation becomes

$$\theta = C_{H_0} \int_0^{x_1} \frac{dx}{kC_{H_0}(1 - x)(C_{OH_0} - C_{H_0}x)}$$

$$= \frac{1}{k(C_{OH_0} - C_{H_0})} \int_0^{x_1} \left(\frac{1}{1 - x} - \frac{C_{H_0}}{C_{OH_0} - C_{H_0}x} \right) dx$$

$$\theta = \frac{1}{k(C_{OH_0} - C_{H_0})} \left[- \ln (1 - x_1) + \ln \frac{C_{OH_0} - C_{H_0}x_1}{C_{OH_0}} \right]$$

Simplifying,

$$\theta = \frac{1}{k(C_{OH_0} - C_{H_0})} \ln \frac{C_{OH_0} - C_{H_0}x_1}{C_{OH_0}(1 - x_1)}$$

or

$$\frac{C_{OH_0} - C_{H_0}x_1}{C_{OH_0}(1 - x_1)} = e^{\theta k(C_{OH_0} - C_{H_0})} = e^{120(4.76 \times 10^{-4})(10.8 - 4.0)} = 1.474$$

Solving for x_1,

$$x_1 = \frac{0.474 C_{OH_0}}{1.474 C_{OH_0} - C_{H_0}} = \frac{0.474 \times 10.8}{1.474 \times 10.8 - 4.0} = 0.43$$

By neglecting the reverse reaction the conversion is in error by $(43 - 36.5)/36.5 \times 100$, or 18 per cent.   This deviation would increase as equilibrium is approached.

2. The conventional method of evaluating the equilibrium conversion is first to calculate the equilibrium constant from the forward- and reverse-reaction rates (that is, $K = k/k'$), and then use this value of K for the equilibrium ratio of the

concentrations. However, it is easier in this example to utilize the already available expression for the net rate of reaction.

$$r = (0.257 - 0.499x - 0.0626x^2)(8 \times 10^{-2})$$

At equilibrium the net rate must be zero. Hence the equilibrium conversion is determined by the expression

$$0.257 - 0.499x_e + 0.0626x_e^2 = 0$$

Solving,

$$x_e = 0.55, \text{ or } 55\%$$

5-2. Nonisothermal Reactor Design (Batch). The design of reactors for nonisothermal operation is more complicated than the isothermal case because the rate is affected by temperature as well as composition changes. The importance of the resultant effect on the conversion vs. time relationship depends upon the magnitude of the heat of reaction and on the magnitude of the rate change with temperature (i.e., the activation energy). If quantitative information on the variation of the rate with temperature is available, the integration of the design equations can be carried out by combination with an energy balance.

In adiabatic operation the heat effect accompanying the reaction will be completely absorbed by the system and will be solely responsible for temperature changes in the reactor. In an exothermic reaction the temperature will increase, which in turn will increase the rate of reaction, so that the net result will be a greater conversion in a given time than would be obtained under isothermal conditions.[1] When the reaction is endothermic, the decrease in temperature of the system results in a lower conversion than that associated with the isothermal case. If the endothermic heat of reaction is large, the reaction may essentially stop because of the decrease in temperature.

It may be desirable to provide for the transfer of thermal energy between the reaction mixture and the surroundings. This can be accomplished by constructing the reactor with a jacket through which a hot or cold fluid is circulated, or by heat exchange coils built into the reactor and immersed in the reaction mixture. In such cases the effect of the heat of reaction can be diminished or even reversed.

The energy balance for a batch reactor may be written in the following way:

$$(-\Delta H)V_B r \, d\theta - Q'_s \, d\theta = m_t c_v \, dt \tag{5-4}$$

The first term represents the energy evolved due to the amount of reaction occurring in the time $d\theta$. For constant-volume reactions the heat of reaction is ΔE rather than ΔH as shown in the equation. However,

---

[1] This presupposes that side reactions do not become important as the temperature increases.

for liquid reaction systems the difference between ΔH and ΔE is usually insignificant, and even for gaseous systems the difference is small. Therefore the more readily available ΔH is used. The second term represents the heat transfer, in time $d\theta$, to the surroundings. If the surroundings temperature is t_s, the over-all heat-transfer coefficient between reaction mixture and heating or cooling medium is U, and the heat-transfer area is A, Eq. (5-4) may be written

$$(-\Delta H)V_B r \, d\theta - UA(t - t_s) \, d\theta = m_t c_v \, dt \tag{5-5}$$

The third term is the net energy added to the reaction mixture in time $d\theta$ and is written in terms of the heat capacity $m_t c_v$ and temperature of the mixture. Since batch processes usually occur at constant volume, the correct specific heat is c_v. For liquid systems c_p and c_v are nearly the same (except near the critical point) so that either value may be used.

Equation (5-5) provides a relationship between the temperature, rate, and time of reaction. In conjunction with the design equation (5-1) or (5-2) and an expression for the rate in terms of temperature and conversion, the conversion may be evaluated as a function of reaction time. Generally the solution must be carried out by stepwise integration of Eqs. (5-2) and (5-5) because the functions are too complex for analytical treatment.

The energy balance can be expressed in terms of the conversion x rather than the rate by combining Eqs. (5-1) and (5-5) to eliminate r,

$$(-\Delta H)m_t \, dx' - UA(t - t_s) \, d\theta = m_t c_v \, dt \tag{5-6}$$

This form has an advantage for adiabatic operation $[UA(t - t_s) \, d\theta = 0]$ because θ is not involved, and direct integration leads to a relationship between temperature and conversion. Then the necessity for simultaneous solution of the design and energy-balance equations is eliminated.

The calculations for nonisothermal batch reactors are illustrated in the following example:

Example 5-3. The production of drying oils by the decomposition of acetylated castor oil has been studied by Grummitt and Fleming.[1] They were able to correlate their decomposition data on the basis of a first-order reaction equation written as follows:

$$\text{Acetylated castor oil } (l) \rightarrow CH_3COOH(g) + \text{drying oil } (l)$$
$$r = kC$$

where r = rate of decomposition, g acetic acid produced/(min)(ml)

C = g/ml acetic acid equivalent to acetylated castor oil present at any time

Data obtained over the temperature range 295 to 340°C indicated an activation energy of 44,500 cal/g mole in accordance with the following expression for

[1] *Ind. Eng. Chem.*, **37**:485 (1945).

the specific-reaction-rate constant k:

$$\ln k = \frac{-44{,}500}{RT} + 35.2 \qquad T = {}^{\circ}K$$

If a batch reactor initially contains 500 lb of acetylated castor oil at 340°C (density = 0.90) and the operation is adiabatic, plot curves of conversion (fraction of the acetylated oil that is decomposed) and temperature vs. time.

It is estimated that the endothermic heat effect for this reaction is 15,000 cal/g mole of acetic acid vapor produced during the decomposition. The acetylated oil charged to the reactor contains 0.156 g of equivalent acetic acid per gram of oil; i.e., complete decomposition of 1 g of the oil would yield 0.156 g of acetic acid. Assume that the specific heat of the liquid reaction mixture is constant and equal to 0.6 Btu/(lb)(°F). Suppose also that the acetic acid vapor produced as a result of the reaction leaves the reactor at the temperature of the reaction mixture.

Solution. The design equation for this case, assuming no change in volume during the course of the reaction, is

$$\theta_1 = C_0 \int_0^{x_1} \frac{dx}{r}$$

where C_0 and r are measured in terms of equivalent acetic acid. Replacing r with the rate equation, this expression becomes

$$\theta_1 = \int_0^{x_1} \frac{C_0 \, dx}{C e^{35.2 - 44{,}500/RT}} \tag{A}$$

The relationship between the concentration and the conversion is

$$C = C_0(1 - x)$$

In terms of x Eq. (A) may be written

$$\theta_1 = \int_0^{x_1} \frac{dx}{e^{35.2 - 44{,}500/RT}(1 - x)} \tag{B}$$

Since the reactor operates adiabatically, the preferred form to use for the energy balance is Eq. (5-6), with $UA(t - t_s) \, d\theta = 0$.

$$(-\Delta H)m_t \, dx' = (-\Delta H)m_A \, dx = m_t c_v \, dt$$

Using numerical values,

$$[(500 \times 0.156) \, dx] \frac{-15{,}000}{60} \times 1.8 = 500 \times 0.6 \times 1.8 \, dT \tag{C}$$

where dT is in degrees absolute (°K), consistent with Eq. (B).

Note that the total mass of the system occurs in both terms and may be canceled, showing that for adiabatic operation the energy balance may be written for unit mass of reaction system. Simplifying the expression,

$$\int_{613^\circ K}^{T} dT = \frac{(0.156 \times 15{,}000)\, dx}{0.6 \times 60} = \int_{0}^{x} -65\, dx$$

Integrating,

$$T - (340 + 273) = -65(x - 0) = -65x$$
$$T = 613 - 65x \tag{D}$$

There are two methods available to obtain a curve of θ vs. x from Eqs. (B) and (D). Direct integration of (B) by substitution of (D) is not practical because of the complexity of the expression so obtained. However, Eq. (B) can be written in difference form for a small change in conversion, Δx, and solved by stepwise numerical integration. This procedure will be illustrated by following through three incremental calculations. Equation (B) is written

$$\Delta\theta = \left[\frac{1}{(1 - x)e^{35.2 - 44{,}500/RT}}\right]_{av} \Delta x = \left(\frac{1}{R}\right)_{av} \Delta x \tag{B'}$$

It is noted that it is the total value of the multiplier of Δx that must be averaged. This means that the reciprocal of the rate is averaged over the increment, not the rate itself. Entering the reactor,

$$T_0 = 613^\circ K$$
$$x_0 = 0$$
$$\frac{1}{R_0} = \frac{1}{(1 - C)e^{35.2 - 44{,}500/(1.98 \times 613)}} = 4.15$$

For the first increment choose $\Delta x = 0.1$. Then at x from Eq. (D)

$$T_1 = 613 - 65 \times 0.10 = 606.5^\circ K$$
$$\frac{1}{R_1} = \frac{1}{(1 - 0.1)e^{35.2 - 44{,}500/(1.98 \times 606.5)}} = 6.15$$

For the first increment of Δx the average value of $1/R$ will be

$$\left[\frac{1}{R}\right]_{av} = \frac{4.15 + 6.15}{2} = 5.15$$

Substituting this result in Eq. (B') gives the time θ, at the end of the first increment,

$$\Delta\theta_1 = \theta_1 - 0 = 5.2 \times 0.1$$
$$= 0.52 \text{ min}$$

The procedure for the second increment would be similar. A value of $1/R_2$ would be calculated at $x_2 = 0.2$ and $T_2 = 606.5 - 6.5 = 600^\circ K$. This would be averaged with $1/R_1$ and Eq. (B') used to compute $\Delta\theta_2$ and θ_2. The results for three increments are shown in Table 5-1.

TABLE 5-1

Conversion	Temp, °K	Time, min
0	613	0
0.10	606.5	0.52
0.20	600.0	1.40
0.30	593.6	3.00

The smaller the size of the increment of conversion, the more appropriate would be the use of an arithmetic average value of $1/R$ and the more accurate the final results.

An alternate approach, instead of stepwise numerical integration, is to plot temperature vs. conversion from Eq. (D), and then from this information plot $1/r$ vs. conversion. Graphical integration under this second curve up to any conversion x would correspond to the value of the integral of dx/r. This multiplied by C_0 would equal the time required for that conversion. The calculations for this procedure are as follows:

Figure 5-1 represents the temperature vs. conversion relationship corresponding to Eq. (D). At any conversion the temperature and $1/r$ can be evaluated. For

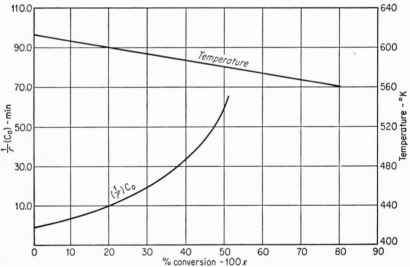

FIG. 5-1. Decomposition of acetylated castor oil (Example 5-3): Temperature vs. conversion.

example, at $x = 0.2$, $T = 600°K$ from Fig. 5-1, and

$$r = C_0(1 - x)e^{35.2 - 44,500/RT}$$
$$= 0.8e^{-2.2}C_0 = 0.0886C_0$$
$$\frac{1}{r} = \frac{11.3}{C_0}$$

Also shown on Fig. 5-1 is the resultant plot of the C_0/r values obtained in this manner. Graphical integration under this curve yields the time θ for any x, as shown by Eq. (A). The results are summarized in Table 5-2. The con-

TABLE 5-2

Conversion	θ, min
0	
0.10	0.54
0.20	1.43
0.30	2.93
0.40	5.53

version vs. time values obtained by the numerical-integration process are approximately equivalent to those listed in Table 5-1.   The differences are primarily due to the use of an arithmetic average temperature and conversion in the numerical solution of Eq. (B).

The final curves of temperature and conversion vs. time (Fig. 5-2) show the necessity of supplying energy (as heat) to a highly endothermic reaction if large

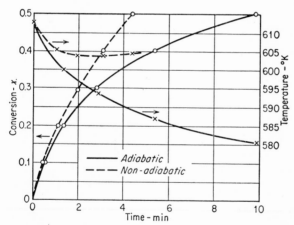

FIG. 5-2. Temperature and conversion vs. time (Example 5-3).

conversions are desired.   In the present case where no energy was supplied, the temperature decreased so rapidly that the reaction essentially stopped after a conversion of 50 per cent had been reached.   If, instead of operating adiabatically, a constant rate of energy Q'_s Btu/min had been removed from the reactor, the energy balance according to Eq. (5-4) is

$$-Q'_s \, d\theta + 500 \times 0.156 \, dx \, \frac{-15{,}000 \times 1.8}{60} = 500 \times 0.6 \times 1.8 \, dT$$

Integrating gives the desired relation between T and x_1, but in this case the time is also involved.

$$\Delta T = -0.00185 Q'_s \, \Delta\theta - 65 \, \Delta x \qquad\qquad (D')$$

Equation (D′) is analogous to Eq. (D) for the adiabatic case. The graphical solution cannot be employed in this case because curves of T and $1/r$ vs. conversion cannot be determined, independent of the time. However, the numerical-solution approach is satisfactory. The equations involved would be (D′) and the design expression (B′).

$$\Delta\theta = \left[\frac{1}{(1 - x)e^{35.2-44,500/RT}} \right]_{av} \Delta x \tag{B′}$$

These twin expressions can be solved by choosing an increment of conversion, assuming a corresponding time interval $\Delta\theta$, and evaluating T_1 at $x_1 = 0 + \Delta x$ from Eq. (D′). Then check the assumed values of $\Delta\theta$ from Eq. (B′). For example, let $Q'_s = -3000$ Btu/min, and choose Δx equal to 0.10. As a first trial assume $\Delta\theta$ is equal to 0.50 min, somewhat less than the adiabatic case. Then from Eq. (D′)

$$T_1 = 613 + \Delta T_1 = 613 - 65 \times 0.1 - 0.00185 \times -3,000 \times 0.50$$
$$= 613 - 6.5 + 2.8$$
$$= 609.3°K$$

Now $\Delta\theta$ can be obtained from Eq. (B′). First the average value of $(1/R)$ over the increment must be determined. At $x = 0.0$

$$R_0 = (1 - 0)e^{35.2-44,500/(R \times 613)} = e^{-1.4}$$
$$\frac{1}{R_0} = 4.15$$

At $x_1 = 0.1$

$$R_1 = (1 - 0.1)e^{35.2-44,500/(R \times 609.3)} = 0.9e^{-1.6}$$
$$\frac{1}{R_1} = 5.50$$
$$\left[\frac{1}{R} \right]_{av} = \frac{4.15 + 5.50}{2} = 4.83$$

From Eq. (B′)

$$\Delta\theta = 4.83 \times 0.10$$
$$= 0.48 \text{ min}$$

TABLE 5-3

Conversion	Nonadiabatic		Adiabatic	
	Temp, °K	Time, min	Temp, °K	Time, min
0	613	0	613	0
0.10	608.7	0.48	605.5	0.54
0.20	605.5	1.08	600.0	1.43
0.30	604.0	1.97	593.5	2.96
0.40	603.9	3.10	587.0	5.53
0.50	604.3	4.39	580.5	9.85

This is close enough to the assumed value of $\Delta\theta = 0.50$ to be satisfactory. Values of $\Delta\theta$ for successive increments can be obtained by repeating the previous calculations. The results are summarized in Table 5-3. For comparison the adiabatic operating conditions are also shown.

These results show that 30 per cent conversion is obtained in 30 per cent less time when 3000 Btu/min, or $3,000/500 = 6$ Btu/lb of charge, is added to the reactor. Temperature and conversion curves for this nonadiabatic case are also indicated on Fig. 5-2.

NOMENCLATURE

A Heat-transfer area
C Concentration
c_p Specific heat at constant pressure
c_v Specific heat at constant volume
ΔH Heat absorbed/mole as a result of a chemical reaction
k Specific-reaction rate
m_A Mass of component A
m_t Total mass charged to a batch reactor
Q'_s Rate of heat transfer to the surroundings
r Rate of reaction
t Temperature of reaction mixture, °C or °F
t_s Surroundings temperature, °C or °F
T Absolute temperature
U Over-all heat-transfer coefficient, Btu/(hr)(°F)(sq ft)
V_B Effective volume of batch reactor
x' Conversion based upon total charge to reactor (x = conversion based upon charge of one component to reactor)
θ Time
ρ Density of reaction mixture

PROBLEMS

1. The liquid-phase hydrolysis of dilute aqueous acetic anhydride solutions is second-order (and irreversible) as indicated by the reaction

$$(CH_3CO)_2O + H_2O \rightarrow 2CH_3COOH$$

A batch reactor for carrying out the hydrolysis is charged with 200 liters of anhydride solution at 15°C. The initial concentration of the anhydride is 2.16×10^{-4} g moles/cc. The specific heat and density of the reaction mixture are essentially constant and equal to 0.9 cal/(g)(°C) and 1.05 g/cc. The heat of reaction may be assumed constant and equal to $-50,000$ cal/g mole. The rate of reaction has been investigated over a range of temperatures, of which the following results are typical:

t, °C	Rate, g moles/(cc)(min)
10	$0.0567C$†
15	$0.0806C$
25	$0.1580C$
40	$0.380C$

† C = acetic anhydride concentration, gram moles per cubic centimeter.

a. Explain why the rate expression can be written as shown in the table, even though the reaction is second-order.

b. If the reactor is cooled so that operation is isothermal at 15°C, what time would be required to obtain a conversion of 70 per cent of the anhydride?

c. Determine an analytical expression for the rate of reaction in terms of temperature and concentration.

d. What time is required for a conversion of 70 per cent if the reactor is operated adiabatically?

2. Nitrous oxide decomposes approximately according to a second-order rate equation. The specific-reaction rate in the forward direction

$$2N_2O \rightarrow 2N_2 + O_2$$

is $k = 977$ cc/(g mole)(sec) at 895°C.

Calculate the fraction decomposed at 1.0 and 10 sec. and at 10 min. The rate of the reverse reaction is negligible, and the initial pressure is one atmosphere.

3. An aqueous solution of ethyl acetate is to be saponified with sodium hydroxide. The initial concentration of ethyl acetate is 5.0 g/liter and that of caustic soda 0.10 normal. Values of the specific-reaction rate are:

k, liters/(g mole)(min)	Temp, °C
23.5	0
92.4	20

The reaction is essentially irreversible. Estimate the time required to saponify 95 per cent of the ester at 40°C.

4. It has been mentioned that gaseous reactions are more suitably carried out on a commercial scale in flow equipment than batch reactors. To illustrate this point, consider the following example:

K. M. Watson[1] has studied in a flow reactor the thermal (noncatalytic) cracking of butenes at 1 atm pressure. The rate equation determined from their experimental data is

$$\log k_1 = -\frac{60,000}{4.575T} + 15.27 \qquad T = °K$$

$$k_1 = \text{g moles butenes cracked/(hr)(liter)(atm)}$$

While the feed consists of a number of different butenes and the products vary from coke to butadiene, the irreversible reaction may be considered as a first-order one, as follows:

$$C_4H_8 \rightarrow C_4H_6 + H_2$$

It is desired to crack butenes in a batch-type reactor which will operate at 1200°F and which will be equipped for efficient agitation.

The initial charge to the reactor will consist of 1 lb mole of butenes and 10 lb moles of steam. Under these conditions the change in number of moles during the course of the reaction can be neglected.

a. Determine the time required for a conversion of 30 per cent of the butenes.

b. Determine the reactor volume required.

c. Suppose that the feed consists of 10 moles of steam per mole of hydrocarbon as before, but that this time the hydrocarbon fraction contains 60 mole per cent butenes and 40 per cent butadiene. The butadiene may undergo two reactions: (1) cracking;

[1] *Chem. Eng. Prog.*, **44**:229 (1948).

(2) polymerization to the dimer. Assuming that the rates of these reactions are known, outline a method of solution to determine the conversion of butenes and of butadiene for a given time of reaction.

5. Refer to Example 5-3. A reactor for the production of drying oils by the decomposition of acetylated castor oil is to be designed for a conversion of 70 per cent. The initial charge will be 500 lb and the initial temperature 340°C as in Example 5-3. In fact, all the conditions of Example 5-3 will be followed except, instead of operating adiabatically, heat will be supplied electrically with a cal-rod unit in the form of a coil 1 in. OD immersed in the reaction mixture. The power input and the stirring in the reactor will be such that the surface temperature of the heater will be maintained constant at 700°K. The heat-transfer coefficient may be taken equal to 60 Btu/(hr)(sq ft)(°F).

What length of heater will be required if the conversion of 70 per cent is to be obtained in 20 min?

6.[1] A stage in the production of propionic acid, C_2H_5COOH, is the acidification of a water solution of the sodium salt, according to the reaction

$$C_2H_5COONa + HCl \rightarrow C_2H_5COOH + NaCl$$

The reaction rate may be represented by a second-order reversible equation.

Laboratory data on the rate of the reaction are obtained by taking 10-ml samples of the reaction solution at varying times and neutralizing the unreacted HCl with 0.515-normal NaOH. The original amount of acid is determined from a sample taken at zero time. The temperature is 50°C, and the initial moles of HCl and C_2H_5COONa are the same. The data are as follows:

Time, min	Ml NaOH required
0	52.5
10	32.1
20	23.5
30	18.9
50	14.4
∞	10.5

It is desired to determine the size of an agitated batch reactor to produce propionic acid at an average rate of 1,000 lb/hr. Twenty minutes is required for charging the reactor and heating to 50°C, and 10 min is necessary for cooling and removing the products. The final conversion is to be 75 per cent of the sodium propionate.

The initial charge to the reactor will contain 256 lb of C_2H_5COONa and 97.5 lb of HCl per 100 gal.

Assume that the density of the reaction mixture is 9.9 lb/gal and remains constant.

[1] This problem was taken from W. F. Stevens, "An Undergraduate Course in Homogeneous Reaction Kinetics," presented at Fourth Summer School for Chemical Engineering Teachers, Pennsylvania State University, June 27, 1955.

CHAPTER 6

HOMOGENEOUS FLOW REACTORS

TUBULAR FLOW REACTORS[1]

For the design for a tubular flow reactor it is advantageous to have the laboratory data also on a flow basis. In other words, the most desirable approach is to determine the rate equation for the process in a small-scale flow reactor operated at as close to constant-temperature and -pressure conditions as possible. Then this information along with some pilot-plant data may be applied with reasonable confidence to the design of the commercial reactor. From the engineer's standpoint the project is a two-step problem: (1) interpretation of the laboratory and pilot-plant data in terms of a rate equation; (2) the application of the rate equation to the design of the large-scale reactor. Since one step is the reverse of the other, the calculational methods are, in general, the same. The chief difference arises because it is desirable, although not always possible, to obtain the laboratory data in a reactor operated at constant pressure and temperature in order that the interpretation of the results is not complicated by many variables. In the commercial-scale reactor it may not be feasible to operate with a uniform temperature and pressure throughout the reactor so that the design methods must be flexible enough to take these complications into account. For example, the evaluation of the temperature variation with position in the commercial reactor requires the application of heat-transfer calculations along with the basic reactor-design equations presented in Chap. 4. It is logical to expect, then, that the second step, the design of the commercial reactor, will be likely to involve rather tedious calculations, frequently of a trial-and-error nature. Only brief consideration was given in Sec. 3-5 to the analysis of kinetic data obtained on a flow basis. Therefore this first step will be treated again here before proceeding to the design problem.

6-1. Determination of Rate Equations from Laboratory Data. The difficulty in interpreting laboratory kinetic data depends upon the number of variables involved. Operation at constant temperature and pres-

[1] This is the second type in the classification of reactors discussed in Chap. 4 and illustrated in Fig. 4-1B.

130

sure is of considerable advantage.   This advantage is augmented if in addition the measurements are made in a reactor small enough in size so that the change in composition is also small.   Under these restrictions the rate is essentially constant throughout the reactor.   The calculation of the rate where such *differential* reactor conditions exist is illustrated in the following example:

Example 6-1.   The homogeneous reaction between sulfur vapor and methane has been studied in a small silica tube reactor of 35.2 ml volume.[1]   In a particular run at 600°C and 1 atm of pressure the measured quantity of carbon disulfide produced in a 10-min run was 0.10 g.   Assume all the sulfur present is the molecular species S_2.   The sulfur-vapor (considered as S_2) flow rate was 0.238 g moles/hr.

1. What was the rate of reaction expressed as gram moles of carbon disulfide produced per hour per milliliter of reactor volume?

2. The rate at 600°C may be expressed by the following second-order equation:

$$r = k p_{CH_4} p_{S_2}$$

where p = partial pressure, atm

Using the rate determined in (1) and this form of the rate equation, calculate the specific reaction rate in units of g mole/(ml)(atm²)(hr).   The methane flow rate was 0.119 g moles/hr and the H_2S and CS_2 concentrations in the reactants were zero.

3. Also compute the value of k without making the assumption that the rate is constant and that average values of the partial pressures may be used.   That is, consider the equipment to operate as an integral, rather than a differential, reactor.   By comparing the results, comment on the suitability of the apparatus as a differential reactor.

Solution

$$CH_4 + 2S_2 \rightarrow CS_2 + 2H_2S$$

1. The carbon disulfide formation in gram moles per hour is

$$\frac{0.10}{76} \frac{60}{10} = 0.0079$$

Then the rate of reaction per milliliter of reactor volume will be

$$r = 0.0079 \frac{1}{35.2}$$
$$= 2.2 \times 10^{-4} \text{ g mole/(hr)(ml)}$$

This rate is not a point value at a constant composition but represents an integrated value over the range of compositions between the entrance and exit of the reactor.   However, the composition changes are small and the average values in the reactor may be used to approximate the specific reaction rate.

[1] R. A. Fisher and J. M. Smith, *Ind. Eng. Chem.*, **42**:704 (1950).

2. Assuming that at 600°C and 1 atm pressure the components behave as perfect gases, the partial pressure is related to the mole fraction by the expression

$$p_{CH_4} = p_t y_{CH_4} = (1) \, y_{CH_4}$$

where y_{CH_4} represents the mole fraction methane in the reaction mixture. The average composition in the reactor will be that corresponding to a carbon disulfide rate of $(0 + 0.0079)/2 = 0.0040$ g mole/hr.

At this point the molal rates of the other components will be

$$CS_2 = 0.0040 \text{ g mole/hr}$$
$$S_2 = 0.238 - 2 \times 0.0040 = 0.230$$
$$CH_4 = 0.119 - 0.0040 = 0.1150$$
$$H_2S = 2 \times 0.0040 = 0.0079$$
$$\text{Total} = 0.357 \text{ g mole/hr}$$

The partial pressures will be

$$p_{CH_4} = \frac{0.1150}{0.357} = 0.322 \text{ atm}$$

$$p_{S_2} = \frac{0.230}{0.357} = 0.645 \text{ atm}$$

From the rate equation, using the value of r obtained in (1),

$$k = \frac{r}{p_{CH_4} \, p_{S_2}} = \frac{2.2 \times 10^{-4}}{0.322 \times 0.645}$$
$$= 1.08 \times 10^{-3} \text{ g mole/(ml)(atm}^2)(\text{hr})$$

3. If the variations in rate through the reactor are taken into account, the integral design expression from Eq. (4-8) should be used.

$$\frac{V_R}{F} = \int_0^{x_1'} \frac{dx'}{r}$$

If the conversion is based upon methane instead of the total feed, this equation may be written

$$\frac{V_R}{F_A} = \int_0^{x_1} \frac{dx}{r} \tag{A}$$

where F_A is the methane feed rate.

At a point in the reactor where the conversion of methane is x, the molal flow rate of each component will be

$$CS_2 = 0.119x$$
$$S_2 = 0.238(1 - x)$$
$$CH_4 = 0.119(1 - x)$$
$$H_2S = 0.238x$$
$$\text{Total} = 0.357 \text{ g mole/hr}$$

Using this information, the rate equation may be written in terms of x:

$$r = ky_{CH_4}y_{S_2} = k\,\frac{0.119 \times 0.238(1 - x)^2}{0.357^2} \tag{B}$$

Equation (A) may be integrated from the entrance to the exit of the reactor using Eq. (B).

$$\frac{V_R}{F_A} = \frac{4.5}{k} \int_0^{x_1} \frac{dx}{(1 - x)^2} = \frac{4.5}{k}\,\frac{x_1}{1 - x_1}$$

Solving for k,

$$k = \frac{4.5}{V_R/F}\,\frac{x_1}{1 - x_1}$$

The conversion of methane at the exit of the reactor is

$$x_1 = \frac{0.0079}{0.119} = 0.0664$$

Hence the specific reaction rate is

$$k = \frac{4.5}{35.2/0.119}\,\frac{0.0664}{1 - 0.0664} = 1.08 \times 10^{-3}\ \text{g mole/(ml)(atm}^2)(\text{hr})$$

It is apparent in this instance that the change in composition in the reactor is sufficiently small that a rate corresponding to the average composition may be used to evaluate the specific reaction rate. In other words, the concept of a differential reactor used in (1) and (2) to evaluate k is satisfactory. If the conversion had been considerably larger than $x = 0.066$, this would not have been true.

While the differential-reactor system just described was satisfactory, in many cases difficulties arise in connection with this method of approach. If the small differences in concentrations between entering and exit streams cannot be determined accurately, the method is not satisfactory. Also, because of a high heat of reaction, or particularly high rate, or a combination of both, it may not be possible to operate even a small reactor at conditions approaching constant temperature and concentration.

When the conditions of approximately constant rate cannot be met, the measured conversion data will represent the integrated value of the rates existing in all parts of the reactor. A reactor operated in this way is commonly termed an *integral* reactor. The problem of obtaining a rate equation is essentially one of differentiating the measured over-all conversion to give point values of the rate. To give this differentiation process a reasonable chance of success, it is clear that as many variables as possible should remain constant. The ideal situation is one in which the only variable is composition, i.e., in which the temperature and pressure are the same in all parts of the reactor. In essence this type of integral operation is but one step removed from a differential reactor. If the temperature as well as composition changes significantly in the integral reactor, the process of differentiating the experimental data to obtain a rate equation becomes of doubtful accuracy and, indeed, is seldom successful. These conclusions concerning the ease of interpretation of laboratory data in terms of a rate equation are summarized in Table 6-1.

TABLE 6-1. EXPERIMENTAL METHODS OF OBTAINING RATE DATA FOR TUBULAR FLOW SYSTEMS

Type of reactor	Characteristics	Interpretation of data
Differential........	Constant temperature, composition, and pressure (i.e., constant rate)	Rata data obtained directly. Interpretation simple
Integral (A).......	Constant temperature and pressure (rate depends upon composition only)	Interpretation of integral data usually satisfactory by graphical differentiation or fitting of integral-conversion curves
Integral (B).......	Constant pressure only	Interpretation complicated by temperature variation. If effect of temperature on rate is known from independent measurements, interpretation is theoretically possible

A complete set of integral-reactor data consists of measurements of the conversion for different flow rates through the reactor, each run being made at constant reactants ratio, pressure, and temperature (if possible). Then an additional set of conversion vs. flow runs is made at a different reactants ratio but at the same pressure and temperature. This procedure is continued until data are obtained over the entire reactants-ratio, temperature, and pressure ranges that may be used in the commercial reactor. A useful means of summarizing the results is to prepare graphs of V_R/F (analogous to the reciprocal of the space velocity) vs. conversion x' at constant values of reactants ratio, T, and p. Such graphs for representing the experimental data are suggested by the form of the basic design equation for flow reactors [Eq. (4-8)],

$$\frac{V_R}{F} = \int_0^{x_1'} \frac{dx'}{r} \tag{6-1}$$

The shape of these curves is determined by the nature of the rate equation and hence they are useful in a qualitative way for telling something about the reaction mechanism.

Two procedures for treating such integral-reactor data are the integration and differential methods first described in Chap. 3 and illustrated there for batch systems (Examples 3-1 and 3-2). In the integration approach a rate equation is assumed, and then the design expression [Eq. (6-1)] integrated. This integration gives a relationship between V_R/F and x', which may then be compared with the experimental data. The final step is the choice of the rate equation which gives the best agreement with the experimental V_R/F vs. x' curves under all conditions of reactants ratio, temperature, and pressure.

The differential method involves differentiating graphically the V_R/F vs. x' curves and thus obtaining the rate of reaction as a function of composition. Various assumed rate equations can then be tested for agreement with the rate-composition data.

It may not be immediately evident under what conditions the slope of a V_R/F vs. x' plot is equal to the rate r. In applying Eq. (6-1) the integration is to be carried out at constant feed rate and variable reactor volume. Hence if experimental data are obtained by measuring conversions at various volumes for constant F, Eq. (6-1) may be directly differentiated, giving

$$r = \frac{dx'}{dV_R/F} = \frac{dx'}{d(V_R/F)} = \text{slope of } V_R/F \text{ vs. } x' \text{ graph} \qquad (6\text{-}2)$$

However, it is much easier experimentally to determine the data by varying the feed rate and using one reactor volume. Now, to obtain the rate, Eq. (6-1) must be differentiated at constant volume but variable feed rate. The left-hand side may still be written as $d(V_R/F)$, but, to obtain dx'/r for the right side, the rate must not depend upon the feed rate, since this is a variable. The rate will be a function of F when diffusion resistances are an important contribution to the over-all reaction process. This may be the case in fixed-bed catalytic reactors or in homogeneous reactions where the rate is very high (e.g., some combustion reactions). Under these conditions the slope of a V_R/F vs. x' plot is not equal to the rate. For most homogeneous reactions the reactor design is such that the rate is not a function of the feed rate and Eq. (6-2) is valid. The role of diffusion in fixed-bed catalytic reactions is considered in detail in Chap. 9.

Perhaps the clearest way of explaining these methods of interpreting laboratory data is to carry out specific examples in some detail, pointing out the features of the method which are general and applicable to any reaction. In Example 6-2 the integration and differential methods are applied to a simple system. Example 6-3, which is concerned with the homogeneous reaction of sulfur vapor and methane to produce carbon disulfide, is a more complex illustration. It is complicated by the fact that the sulfur vapor is present as three different species, S_8, S_6, and S_2. The temperature is constant in both examples so that they are illustrations of an integral reactor, case A, described in Table 6-1.

Example 6-2. A kinetic study is made of the decomposition of acetaldehyde at 518°C and 1 atm pressure in a flow apparatus. The reaction is

$$CH_3CHO \rightarrow CH_4 + CO$$

Acetaldehyde is boiled in a flask and passed through a reaction tube maintained by a surrounding furnace at 518°C. The reaction tube is 3.3 cm ID and 80 cm long. The flow rate through the tube is varied by changing the boiling rate. Analysis of the products from the end of the tube gives the results in Table 6-2.

TABLE 6-2

Rate of flow, g/hr	Fraction of acetaldehyde decomposed
130	0.05
50	0.13
21	0.24
10.8	0.35

What is a satisfactory rate equation for these data?

Solution. A second-order rate equation, $r = k_2 C_A^2$, will be tested by both the integral and the differential method. To utilize either, it is necessary to express the rate in terms of the conversion of acetaldehyde, x (which is equal to x' in this case). This may be accomplished by applying material balances and the perfect-gas law.

The molal flow rate of acetaldehyde entering the reaction tube is F. At a point where the conversion is x it will be

$$N_A = F - Fx$$

The molal rates of the other components will be

$$N_{CH_4} = xF$$
$$N_{CO} = xF$$

Total flow rate $N_t = F(1 + x)$

From the perfect-gas law

$$C_A = \frac{N_A}{V} = \frac{N_A}{N_t RT/p_t} = \frac{N_A}{N_t} \frac{p_t}{RT}$$

$$C_A = \frac{1 - x}{1 + x} \frac{p_t}{RT}$$

The second-order rate expression in terms of conversion is

$$r = k_2 C_A^2 = k_2 \left(\frac{p_t}{RT}\right)^2 \left(\frac{1 - x}{1 + x}\right)^2 \tag{A}$$

INTEGRATION METHOD. Equation (A) may be substituted in the design expression, Eq. (6-1), to evaluate the second-order assumption.

$$\frac{V_R}{F} = \frac{1}{k_2 \left(\dfrac{p_t}{RT}\right)^2} \int_0^{x_1} \frac{dx}{\left(\dfrac{1-x}{1+x}\right)^2}$$

Integrating yields

$$k_2 \left(\frac{p_t}{RT}\right)^2 \frac{V_R}{F} = \frac{4}{1-x} + 4 \ln (1-x) + x - 4 \qquad \text{(B)}$$

Equation (B) provides the required relationship between V_R/F and x which should now be tested with the experimental data. Noting that

$$V_R = \pi \left(\frac{3.3^2}{4}\right) \times 80 = 684 \text{ cc}$$

the experimental data may be expressed in terms of V_R/F as shown in Table 6-3.

TABLE 6-3

Conver-sion x	Feed rate		V_R/F, (liters)(sec)/g mole	k_2, liters/(g mole)(sec)
	G/hr	G moles/sec		
0.05	130	0.000825	828	0.32
0.13	50	0.000316	2,160	0.33
0.24	21	0.000131	5,210	0.32
0.35	10.8	0.0000680	10,000	0.33

Equation (B) may be used to compute a value of k for each of the sets of x and V_R/F values given in the table. For example, at $x = 0.13$, substituting in Eq. (B),

$$k_2 \left[\frac{1}{0.082(518 + 273)}\right]^2 \times 2{,}160 = \frac{4}{1 - 0.13} + 4 \ln (1 - 0.13) + 0.13 - 4$$

$$k_2 = 0.33 \text{ liter/(g mole)(sec)}$$

Values of k_2 for the other three sets, shown in the last column of Table 6-3, are in good agreement with each other.

DIFFERENTIAL METHOD. The experimental V_R/F data are plotted vs. conversion in Fig. (6-1). According to Eq. (6-2) the slope of this curve at any conversion gives the rate of reaction at that point. The slopes of the curve at the experimental conversions are given in the second column of Table 6-4.

These slopes or experimental rates may be compared with the assumed rate equation by (1) plotting $\ln r$ vs. $\ln \dfrac{1-x}{1+x}$, according to Eq. (A), and noting whether or not a straight line of slope $= 2$ is obtained; or (2) by computing values of k_2 directly from Eq. (A). Following this second procedure, at $x = 0.13$,

$$r = 4.9 \times 10^{-5} = k_2 \left(\frac{1}{0.082 \times 791}\right)^2 \left(\frac{1 - 0.13}{1 + 0.13}\right)^2$$

$$k_2 = 0.35 \text{ liter/(sec)(g mole)}$$

The results at other conversions are shown in the third column of Table 6-4. While there is some variation from point to point, a significant trend does not

TABLE 6-4

Conversion, x	Slope from Fig. (6-1), g moles/(liter)(sec)	k_2, liters/(sec)(g mole)	k_1, sec^{-1}
0.05	6.2×10^{-5}	0.32	0.0045
0.13	4.9×10^{-5}	0.35	0.0041
0.24	2.8×10^{-5}	0.33	0.0030
0.35	2.0×10^{-5}	0.35	0.0027

exist. Hence the differential method also confirms the validity of a second-order rate equation. The variation is due to errors associated with the measurement of slopes of the curve in Fig. 6-1.

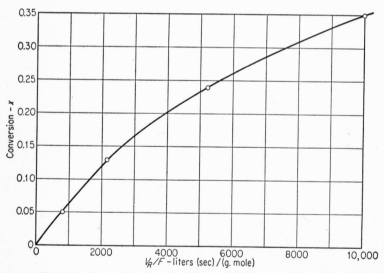

FIG. 6-1. Conversion data for decomposition of acetaldehyde.

FIRST-ORDER RATE EQUATION. For comparison the differential method will be applied to a first-order mechanism. The rate expression, replacing Eq. (A), will be

$$r = k_1 C_A = k_1 \frac{p_t}{RT} \frac{1 - x}{1 + x} \tag{C}$$

This mechanism may be tested by computing k_1 values from the experimental rates of reaction, using Eq. (C). For example, at $x = 0.13$,

$$r = \text{slope} = 4.9 \times 10^{-5} = k_1 \frac{1}{0.082 \times 791} \frac{1 - 0.13}{1 + 0.13}$$

$$k_1 = 0.0041 \text{ sec}^{-1}$$

The k_1 values for other conversions (fourth column of Table 6-4) show a distinct trend toward lower values at higher conversions. This indicates that the first-order rate is not a likely one.

Example 6-3. A flow reactor consisting of a 1-in. stainless-steel pipe 6 in. long and packed with inert rock salt is used to study the noncatalytic homogeneous reaction

$$\frac{4}{b} S_b + CH_4 \rightarrow 2H_2S + CS_2$$

The measurements are carried out at atmospheric pressure in the vapor phase at 600°C. From available data on the rate of dissociation of the sulfur species it is reasonable to assume that the reactions

$$S_8 \rightarrow 4S_2$$
$$S_6 \rightarrow 3S_2$$

are very fast with respect to the combination of sulfur vapor with methane. Accordingly, assume that equilibrium exists between S_8, S_6, and S_2. The void volume, measured by benzene displacement, was 35.2 ml. The conversion of methane to carbon disulfide (x) was measured for various flow rates and initial reactants ratios, and the results are as shown in Table 6-5.

The symbol (S_2) refers to the total amount of sulfur vapor present, expressed as S_2; i.e.,

$$(S_2) = N_{S_2} + 3N_{S_6} + 4N_{S_8}$$

where the N values refer to the number of moles of each sulfur species.

TABLE 6-5

Run	Flow rates, g moles/hr			Reactants ratio, moles (S_2)/moles (CH_4)	Conversion
	CH_4	(S_2)	CS_2		
55	0.02975	0.0595	0.0079	2	0.268
58	0.0595	0.119	0.0086	2	0.144
57	0.119	0.238	0.0078	2	0.066
59	0.119	0.238	0.0072	2	0.060
56	0.238	0.476	0.0059	2	0.025
75	0.0595	0.119	0.0079	2	0.133
76	0.02975	0.0595	0.0080	2	0.269
77	0.119	0.238	0.0069	2	0.058
78	0.0893	0.0893	0.0087	1	0.0975
79	0.119	0.0595	0.0096	0.5	0.0807

1. Assuming first that the only species of sulfur which exists is S_2 (this is equivalent to choosing $b = 2$ in the chemical reaction), test the assumptions of first- and second-order rate equations with the experimental data.

2. Repeat part 1, assuming that equilibrium exists between S_2, S_6, and S_8, but that only S_2 reacts with CH_4.

3. Using a second-order rate expression, determine which assumption regarding the reactive sulfur species best fits the experimental data.

Solution. The tabulated experimental data should be converted to a table of V_R/F and x'. For run 55

$$F = \text{molal feed rate} = 0.02975 + 0.0595$$
$$= 0.0892 \text{ g moles/hr}$$

$$\frac{V_R}{F} = \frac{35.2}{0.0892} = 395$$

The conversion x is the fraction of the methane that is actually converted to CS_2. The moles of CS_2 per mole of feed, x', is

$$x' = \frac{0.0079}{0.0892} = 0.0890$$

Table 6-6 shows the corresponding values of x' and V_R/F. These results are

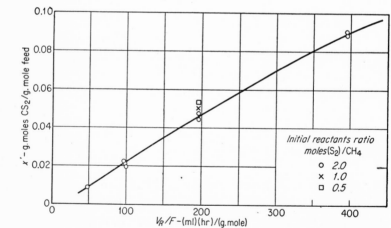

FIG. 6-2. Experimental conversion data for the sulfurization of methane.

also plotted in Fig. 6-2. Note that

$$x' = \frac{\text{moles product}}{\text{moles total feed}} = x\,\frac{\text{moles }CH_4\text{ in feed}}{\text{moles total feed}} = x\,\frac{1}{1 + a}$$

or

$$x = (a + 1)x'$$

where the moles of sulfur in the feed, per mole of methane, is a.

1. Two first-order mechanisms may be assumed, one with respect to methane and one with respect to sulfur vapor (S_2).   Starting with the former and applying Eq. (6-1),

$$\frac{V_R}{F} = \int_0^{x_1'} \frac{dx'}{r} = \int_0^{x_1'} \frac{dx'}{k_1 p_{CH_4}} = \int_0^{x_1'} \frac{dx'}{k_1 y_{CH_4}} \tag{A}$$

Assuming perfect-gas behavior at 600°C and 1 atm total pressure,

$$p_{CH_4} = y_{CH_4} p_t = y_{CH_4}$$

The mole fraction methane y_{CH_4} varies with the conversion.   Hence, to relate y_{CH_4} to x' requires a knowledge of the number of moles of each component present as a function of conversion.   Since it is to be assumed in part (1) that all the

TABLE 6-6

Run	Conversion		$\frac{V_R}{F}$, (ml)(hr)/g mole	$-\log [1 - (a + 1)x_1']$ or $-\log (1 - x_1)$	$k_1 \times 10^4$	$k_{1,s} \times 10^4$
	x_1	x_1'				
55	0.268	0.0890	395	0.135	7.87	3.93
58	0.144	0.0480	197	0.0675	7.90	3.95
57	0.066	0.022	98.6	0.0297	6.93	3.46
59	0.060	0.020	98.6	0.0269	6.29	3.15
56	0.025	0.00833	49.3	0.0110	5.14	2.57
75	0.133	0.0443	197	0.0620	7.25	3.62
76	0.269	0.0895	395	0.136	7.95	3.97
77	0.058	0.0193	98.6	0.0269	6.05	3.02
78	0.0975	0.0487	197	0.045	5.30	5.45
79	0.0807	0.0538	197	0.0368	4.31	9.90

sulfur present is S_2, the number of moles of S_2 and CH_4 are simple to ascertain. Thus entering the reactor, for a mole ratio of S_2 to CH_4 of 2,

$$y_{CH_4} = \frac{1}{2 + 1} = 0.333$$

If a basis of 1 mole of CH_4 and 2 moles of S_2 is chosen, at a point in the reactor where the conversion is x', the number of moles of each component will be

$$CS_2 = x = 3x'$$
$$H_2S = 2x = 6x'$$
$$CH_4 = 1 - x = 1 - 3x'$$
$$S_2 = 2 - 6x'$$
$$\overline{\text{Total} = 3}$$

$$y_{CH_4} = \frac{1 - 3x'}{3} = 0.333 - x' \qquad y_{S_2} = \frac{2 - 6x'}{3} = 0.667 - 2x'$$

More generally, if the initial mole ratio of sulfur to CH_4 is a,

$$y_{CH_4} = \frac{1 - (1 + a)x'}{1 + a} = \frac{1}{1 + a} - x'$$

$$y_{S_2} = \frac{a - 2(1 + a)x'}{1 + a} = \frac{a}{1 + a} - 2x' \tag{B}$$

Using the integral method, Eq. (A) can now be integrated with Eq. (B),

$$\frac{V_R}{F} = \frac{1}{k_1} \int_0^{x_1'} \frac{dx'}{1/(1 + a) - x'} = \frac{1}{k_1} \ln \frac{1/(1 + a) - x_1'}{1/(1 + a)} = -\frac{1}{k_1} \ln [1 - (a + 1)x_1']$$

$$= -\frac{1}{k_1} \ln (1 - x_1) \tag{C}$$

where x_1' is the conversion leaving the reactor. The V_R/F vs. x' data shown in Table 6-6 can now be used to test Eq. (C), and hence the assumption of a first-order reaction. Rather than plot curves obtained from Eq. (C) with different k values for comparison with the experimental curve (Fig. 6-2), it is more effective to use one of two other approaches:

    a. Plot the experimental V_R/F vs. x data given in Table 6-6 as V_R/F vs. log $(1 - x_1)$.

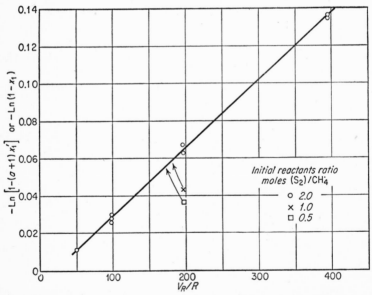

FIG. 6-3. Test of first-order mechanism with respect to CH_4.

    This method of plotting should result in a straight line if the assumed rate expression is correct. Figure 6-3 shows that this is not true if the rate is first-order with respect to methane. At a constant reactants ratio of $a = 2.0$ the points fall on a straight line, but the data for other ratios deviate widely from the line.

  b. From the data in Table 6-6 compute values of k_1 required by Eq. (C) for each of the runs.   If these values are essentially constant, the assumed mechanism fits the data.   For this case the resulting k_1 values are given in column 6 of Table 6-6.   Again the runs for different reactants ratios show that the assumed rate equation does not fit the data.

  As will be seen later in this example, the nature of the assumed rate equation may be complex enough to prevent analytical integration of the design equation (6-1) or Eq. (A).   However, in such cases it is still possible to evaluate the integral $\int dx'/r$ graphically and then apply either method a or method b to determine the suitability of the rate assumption.   Hence either method a or method b is general and as such is applicable to any reaction.

  The design equation for an assumed mechanism which is first-order with respect to sulfur vapor, S_2, will be similar to Eq. (C), i.e.,

$$\frac{V_R}{F} = \int_0^{x_1'} \frac{dx'}{k_{1,S} y_{S_2}} = \frac{1}{k_{1,S}} \int_0^{x_1'} \frac{dx'}{a/(1+a) - 2x'} = -\frac{1}{2k_{1,S}} \ln \frac{a - 2(a+1)x_1'}{a}$$

$$= -\frac{1}{2k_{1,S}} \ln \left(1 - \frac{2x_1}{a}\right) \quad \text{(D)}$$

For $a = 2$ Eq. (D) becomes the same as Eq. (C) if $k_{1S} = \frac{1}{2}k_1$.   Hence the test of this mechanism is whether or not the two runs for $a = 1.0$ and $a = 0.5$ (1) are brought in line with the other data on a plot similar to Fig. 6-3 or (2) give the same value of $k_{1,S}$.   The values of $k_{1,S}$ are given in the last column of Table 6-6. It is clear that the results for the runs with $a = 1.0$ and 0.5 are far removed from the rest of the data.   Hence neither first-order mechanism is satisfactory.

  If a second-order mechanism is tried, again assuming all the sulfur vapor is present as S_2, the design equation is

$$\frac{V_R}{F} = \int \frac{dx'}{k_2 p_{CH_4} p_{S_2}} = \frac{1}{k_2} \int \frac{dx'}{y_{CH_4} y_{S_2}} = \frac{1}{k_2} \int \frac{dx'}{\left(\dfrac{1}{1+a} - x'\right)\left(\dfrac{a}{1+a} - 2x'\right)}$$

  This expression can be simplified and integrated to become

$$\frac{V_R}{F} = \frac{a+1}{k_2} \int_0^{x_1} \frac{dx}{(1-x)(a-2x)} = \frac{a+1}{a-2} \frac{1}{k_2} \left[\ln \left(1 - \frac{2}{a}x_1\right) - \ln (1 - x_1) \right] \quad \text{(E)}$$

or

$$= \frac{3}{2k_2} \frac{x_1}{1 - x_1} \quad \text{for } a = 2\dagger$$

  Now it is possible to use this equation and the experimental data to determine the suitability of a second-order rate equation, just as Eqs. (C) and (D) were employed, to test first-order assumptions.

  † Equation (E) becomes indeterminate when $a = 2$.   Hence it is necessary to substitute $a = 2$ prior to integration and obtain the particular solution given.

Figure 6-4 shows a plot of V_R/F vs. $\dfrac{a+1}{a-2}\left[\ln\left(1-\dfrac{2}{a}x_1\right)-\ln\left(1-x_1\right)\right]$,

or $\dfrac{3}{2}\dfrac{x_1}{1-x_1}$ for $a=2$, for the experimental data. It is apparent that this correlation is an improvement over the previous ones, since the point for $a=1.0$ is close to the straight line. However, the data point for $a=0.5$ is still not satisfactorily correlated.

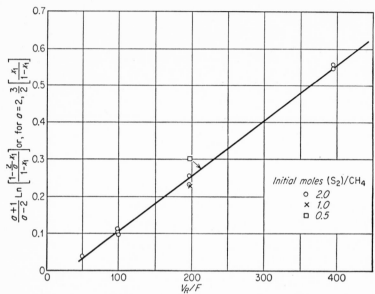

Fig. 6-4. Test of second-order reaction mechanism.

From this preliminary investigation, neglecting the S_6 and S_8 species, it is concluded that a second-order rate is more appropriate than a first-order one. The next step is to refine the analysis by considering the distribution of sulfur vapor between S_2, and S_6 and S_8.

2. To take into account the presence of the S_6 and S_8 species, equilibrium will be assumed between S_2, S_6, and S_8, utilizing the following equilibrium constants at 600°C:

$$\tfrac{1}{4}S_8 \rightarrow S_2 \qquad K_p = 0.930 \text{ (atm)}^{\frac{3}{4}}$$
$$\tfrac{1}{3}S_6 \rightarrow S_2 \qquad K_p = 0.669 \text{ (atm)}^{\frac{2}{3}}$$

This information along with the stoichiometry of the reaction can be used to develop expressions analogous to Eqs. (B) for the relation between y_{S_2} and y_{CH_4} and the conversion x. As in part 1, suppose that entering the reactor there are a moles of sulfur vapor per mole of CH_4. However, let a refer to the total moles of sulfur considered as S_2, not to the sum of the moles of S_2, S_6, and S_8. If α_0, β_0, and γ_0 represent the moles of S_2, S_6, and S_8 entering the reactor, the total moles of sulfur, considered as S_2, will be

$$a = \alpha_0 + 3\beta_0 + 4\gamma_0$$

At a point in the reactor where the conversion is x, the moles of each component will be

$$CS_2 = x$$
$$H_2S = 2x$$
$$CH_4 = 1 - x$$
$$S_2 = \alpha$$
$$S_6 = \beta$$
$$S_8 = \gamma$$
$$\text{Total} = n = \alpha + \beta + \gamma + 2x + 1$$

The conversion x has been defined in terms of the methane reacted. It can be written also in terms of the sulfur used, thus providing a relationship between x, α, β, and γ. If (S_2) represents the total moles of sulfur (considered as S_2) present at any point in the reactor,

$$x = \tfrac{1}{2}[a - (S_2)]$$

but
$$S_2 = \alpha + 3\beta + 4\gamma$$

so that

1:
$$x = \frac{a - \alpha - 3\beta - 4\gamma}{2}$$

Two additional relationships between x, α, β, and γ must exist because of the dissociation equilibria. These are as follows:

2:
$$0.930 = \frac{p_{S_2}}{(p_{S_8})^{\frac{1}{4}}} = \frac{y_{S_2}}{(y_{S_8})^{\frac{1}{4}}} = \frac{\alpha}{(\gamma)^{\frac{1}{4}}(\alpha + \beta + \gamma + 2x + 1)^{\frac{3}{4}}}$$

and

3:
$$0.669 = \frac{p_{S_2}}{(p_{S_6})^{\frac{1}{3}}} = \frac{y_{S_2}}{(y_{S_6})^{\frac{1}{3}}} = \frac{\alpha}{(\beta)^{\frac{1}{3}}(\alpha + \beta + \gamma + 2x + 1)^{\frac{2}{3}}}$$

Equations (1), (2), and (3) permit the evaluation of α, β, and γ at any conversion and reactants ratio a. Then the mole fractions are immediately obtainable from the expressions

$$y_{S_2} = \frac{\alpha}{\alpha + \beta + \gamma + 2x + 1}$$
$$y_{CH_4} = \frac{1 - x}{\alpha + \beta + \gamma + 2x + 1}$$

To illustrate the method of calculation, take $a = 2$, the stoichiometric ratio. Entering the reactor, $x = 0.0$, and Eqs. 1, 2, and 3 become

$$2 = \alpha + 3\beta + 4\gamma$$
$$(\gamma)^{\frac{1}{4}}(\alpha + \beta + \gamma + 1)^{\frac{3}{4}} = \frac{\alpha}{0.93}$$
$$(\beta)^{\frac{1}{3}}(\alpha + \beta + \gamma + 1)^{\frac{2}{3}} = \frac{\alpha}{0.669}$$

Solving these by trial gives

$$\alpha = 0.782 \qquad y_{S_2} = \frac{0.782}{2.171} = 0.360$$

$$\beta = 0.340 \qquad y_{S_6} = \frac{0.340}{2.171} = 0.156$$

$$\gamma = 0.049 \qquad y_{S_8} = \frac{0.049}{2.171} = 0.023$$

$$\underline{CH_4 = 1.000} \qquad y_{CH_4} = \frac{1.000}{2.171} = 0.461$$

$$\text{Total} = 2.171 \qquad \Sigma y = 1.000$$

In a similar manner the mole fractions corresponding to any conversion can be evaluated. The results of such calculations are shown in Fig. 6-5, where com-

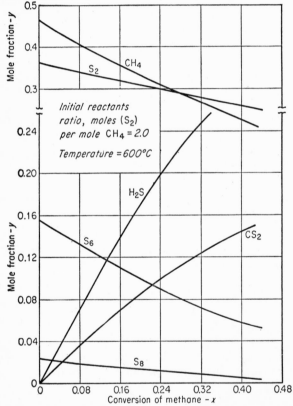

FIG. 6-5. Composition of reaction mixture vs. conversion for the sulfurization of methane.

position of the reaction mixture is plotted vs. the conversion x. Similar information for other values of a are obtained in an analogous fashion.

The necessary data are now at hand for testing the second-order rate expression. However, the calculational procedure used in part 1 is not applicable in this case because the design equation

$$\frac{V}{F} = \frac{1}{k_2'} \int_0^{x_1'} \frac{dx'}{y_{CH_4}y_{S_2}}$$ (F)

cannot be integrated analytically. Two alternatives are possible. The integral method involves graphical evaluation of the integral in Eq. (F) for each experimental point, using the measured value of the conversion as the upper limit in each case. This procedure leads to values of $\int_0^{x_1'} dx'/y_{CH_4}y_{S_2}$ for each value of V_R/F shown in Table 6-6. The results are given in the fourth column of Table 6-7 and plotted in Fig. 6-6, where V_R/F is the abscissa and $\int_0^{x_1'} dx'/y_{CH_4}y_{S_2}$ the ordinate. If the assumed mechanism is a satisfactory interpretation of the data,

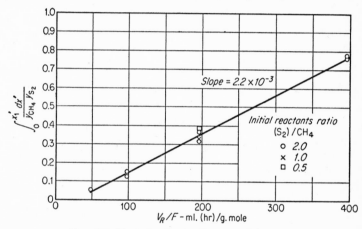

Fig. 6-6. Test of rate equation $r = k_2' p_{CH_4} p_{S_2}$.

Fig. 6-6 should be a straight line with a slope equal to k_2'. This is apparent if Eq. (F) is rearranged as follows:

$$\int_0^{x_1'} \frac{dx'}{y_{CH_4}y_{S_2}} = k_2' \frac{V_R}{F}$$

It is evident from the plot that this condition is essentially satisfied.

The other approach, the differential method, involves graphical differentiation of the data for comparison with the differential form of Eq. (F). If the data are plotted as x' vs. V_R/F, as in Fig. 6-2, the slope of the curve is equal to the rate of reaction. Thus from Eq. (F)

$$d\left(\frac{V_R}{F}\right) = \frac{dx'}{k_2' y_{CH_4}y_{S_2}}$$

or

$$\frac{dx'}{d(V_R/F)} = \text{slope} = k_2' y_{CH_4}y_{S_2}$$

If the slope is taken at various values of the conversion from Fig. 6-2, and the corresponding values of y_{CH_4} and y_{S_2} read from Fig. 6-5, and this is done for each reactants ratio, complete information on the effect of composition on the rate is available. The equation $r = k_2' y_{CH_4} y_{S_2}$ then can be tested by observing the constancy in computed values of k_2'.

3. The results of part 2 indicated that the assumption of S_2 as the active sulfur-vapor species in the second-order mechanism gave a satisfactory interpretation of the conversion data. However, it is important to know whether equally good

TABLE 6-7. TEST OF REACTION MECHANISMS: SULFURIZATION OF METHANE

Run	Reactants ratio, a	$\dfrac{V_R}{F}$	$\displaystyle\int_0^{x_1'} \dfrac{dx'}{y_{CH_4} y_{S_b}}$		
			$b = 2$	$b = 6$	$b = 8$
55	2	395	0.762	2.11	17.0
58	2	197	0.347	0.890	6.64
57	2	98.6	0.144	0.350	2.48
59	2	98.6	0.130	0.315	2.23
56	2	49.3	0.052	0.123	0.885
75	2	197	0.316	0.800	5.88
76	2	395	0.765	2.17	17.1
77	2	98.6	0.126	0.303	2.15
78	1	197	0.315	1.27	12.1
79	0.5	197	0.388	2.97	36.8

correlations would be obtained by assuming that S_6 or S_8 is the reactive form. To do this, the design equations, corresponding to (F), for the other species may be written as follows:

$$\frac{V_R}{F} = \frac{1}{k_6'} \int_0^{x_1'} \frac{dx'}{y_{CH_4} y_{S_6}} \tag{G}$$

$$\frac{V_R}{F} = \frac{1}{k_8'} \int_0^{x_1'} \frac{dx'}{y_{CH_4} y_{S_8}} \tag{H}$$

Figures 6-7 and 6-8, which show V_R/F plotted vs. the integrals in (G) and (H), were prepared by graphical integration, using Fig. 6-5 for the relations between x' and y_{S_6} and y_{S_8}. The values of the integrals are given in the last two columns of Table 6-7. In contrast to Fig. 6-6 based upon S_2 it is seen that the data do not fall on a straight line as required by Eqs. (G) and (H). Also, the points for various reactants ratios are not in agreement. It is concluded that a second-order mechanism based upon either S_6 or S_8 as the reactive sulfur species does not agree with the experimental data. Note that the alternate method of differentiating curves of V_R/F vs. x' to obtain the rate of reaction could also have been used in this part of the problem, as in part 2.

The preferred equation for the rate of reaction is

$$r = k_2' p_{CH_4} p_{S_2}$$

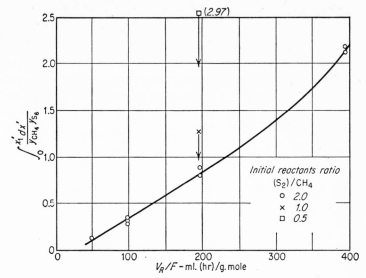

FIG. 6-7. Test of rate equation $r = k_6'p_{CH_4}p_{S_6}$.

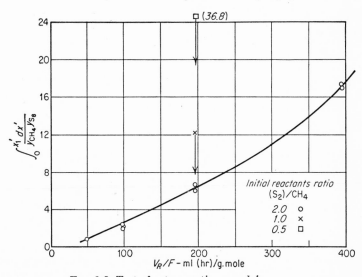

FIG. 6-8. Test of rate equation $r = k_8'p_{CH_4}p_{S_8}$.

From Fig. 6-6 the slope of the straight line is 2.2×10^{-3} g mole/(hr)(ml)(atm)^2. Since this number is equal to k_2', the final expression for the rate of reaction at 500°C[1] is

$$r = 2.2 \times 10^{-3}p_{CH_4}p_{S_2}$$

[1] By evaluating the specific-reaction rate k_2 at other temperatures an activation energy can be determined. For this aspect of the problem see Fisher and Smith, loc. cit.

It should be emphasized that it is not advisable to make a firm statement regarding the mechanism of a reaction from a limited amount of data such as was available in Example 6-3. It is perhaps best to consider that the above rate equation is a satisfactory interpretation of the kinetic data. More knowledge concerning the actual mechanism of the reaction could be obtained if the pressure had been one of the variables studied as well as reactants ratio and conversion.

The problem of interpreting laboratory kinetic data in terms of a rate equation will be considered again in Chap. 9, for catalytic reactions.

6-2. Isothermal Design (Tubular Flow). Once a satisfactory expression is known for the rate of reaction, the problem of determining the size of a flow reactor as a function of operating variables is one of combining and solving the rate and design equations. Since a number of variables such as temperature, pressure, and mass velocity can be changed it is necessary to solve the equations for a number of sets of operating conditions and then choose the conditions which will result in the most practical and economical reactor. While this optimizing of the design is of great importance in practice, the repetition of the calculations is unnecessary for an understanding of the principles of reactor design and no attempt will be made to illustrate economic-balance processes. Instead, design calculations will be carried out for single sets of operating conditions for several different types of flow reactors.

As pointed out earlier, the design procedures are the simplest when temperature and pressure changes within the reactor can be neglected. They become more complex for adiabatic and pseudo-isothermal reactors where significant temperature differences exist.

The isothermal design calculations are essentially the reverse of the procedures illustrated in Example 6-3 for establishing the rate equation from integral-reactor data. They are illustrated in Example 6-4.

Example 6-4. Hougen and Watson[1] in an analysis of Kassell's data for the vapor-phase dehydrogenation of benzene in a flow reactor (homogeneous) reported the following rate equations:

1:
$$2C_6H_6(g) \rightarrow C_{12}H_{10}(g) + H_2(g)$$

$$r_1 = 14.96 \times 10^6 e^{-15,200/T} \left(p_B^2 - \frac{p_D p_H}{K_1} \right)$$

r_1 = lb moles benzene reacted/(hr)(cu ft)

?:
$$C_6H_6(g) + C_{12}H_{10}(g) \rightarrow C_{18}H_{14}(g) + H_2$$

$$r_2 = 8.67 \times 10^6 e^{-15,200/T} \left(p_B p_D - \frac{p_T p_H}{K_2} \right)$$

r_2 = lb moles triphenyl produced (or diphenyl reacted)/(hr)(cu ft)

[1] O. A. Hougen and K. M. Watson, "Chemical Process Principles," vol. 3, p. 846, John Wiley & Sons, Inc., New York, 1947.

where p_B = partial pressure of benzene, atm

$\quad p_D$ = partial pressure of diphenyl, atm

$\quad p_T$ = partial pressure of triphenyl, atm

$\quad p_H$ = partial pressure of hydrogen, atm

$\quad T$ = °K

K_1, K_2 = equilibrium constants for the two reactions in terms of partial pressures

The data upon which the rate equations are based were obtained at a total pressure of 1 atm and at temperatures of 1265 and 1400°F in a 0.5-in. tube, 3 ft long.

It is now proposed to design a tubular reactor which will operate at 1 atm pressure and 1400°F. Determine the total conversion of benzene to di- and triphenyl as a function of space velocity. Also, determine the reactor volume required to process 10,000 lb/hr of benzene as a function of the total conversion. In order to obtain a relatively simple picture of the method of approach, first carry out the solution, assuming that only reaction 1 occurs, and then proceed to the complete solution, considering both reactions.

Assume that the reactor will be operated isothermally and that no other reactions are significant.

Solution. Since the reactor is isothermal, the equilibrium constants K_1 and K_2 will have fixed values. They may be estimated at 1400°F from equations developed by Hougen and Watson,[1] using methods analogous to those described in Chap. 2. The results are

$$K_1 = 0.312$$
$$K_2 = 0.480$$

As these values are not large, the reverse reactions may well be important. Hence the negative terms in the two rate equations cannot be neglected. At 1400°F (1033°K) in terms of the rate of disappearance of benzene the two rates are

$$r_1 = (14.96 \times 10^6)e^{-14.7}\left(p_B^2 - \frac{p_D p_H}{0.312}\right) = 6.23\left(p_B^2 - \frac{p_D p_H}{0.312}\right) \tag{A}$$

$$r_2 = (8.67 \times 10^6)e^{-14.7}\left(p_B p_D - \frac{p_T p_H}{0.480}\right) = 3.61\left(p_B p_D - \frac{p_T p_H}{0.480}\right) \tag{B}$$

The design expression for the reactor can be written

$$\frac{V_R}{F} = \int \frac{dx'}{r}$$

where x' represents the moles of benzene reacted per mole of feed.

Since reactions 1 and 2 occur simultaneously in the same reactor, an equation of the preceding type must hold for each reaction individually. These expressions are

$$\frac{V_R}{F} = \int \frac{dx_1'}{r_1} \tag{C}$$

[1] *Loc. cit.*

$$\frac{V_R}{F} = \int \frac{dx_2'}{r_2} \tag{D}$$

where x_1' = lb moles benzene disappearing by reaction 1 per lb mole feed
  x_2' = lb moles benzene disappearing by reaction 2 per lb mole feed

An expression could also be written for the total rate of disappearance of benzene by reactions 1 and 2, and it would be

$$\frac{V_R}{F} = \int \frac{dx_1' + dx_2'}{r_1 + r_2} = \int \frac{dx_{tot}'}{r_1 + r_2} \tag{E}$$

However, this equation by itself cannot be used to obtain the conversion as a function of space velocity, because it does not take into account that each reaction is occurring separately in the reactor and, therefore, that the design equation must be satisfied for both reactions. Equations (C) and (D) do express this restriction and can be used for the required solution, once the rates r_1 and r_2 are expressed in terms of the conversions x_1' and x_2'. These latter relationships depend only upon the stoichiometry of the reactions and may be developed in the following way:

Take as a basis 1.0 mole of entering benzene. When the conversion by the first reaction is x_1' and by the second is x_2', the moles of each component will be

Moles hydrogen $= \frac{1}{2}x_1' + x_2'$
Moles $C_{12}H_{10} = \frac{1}{2}x_1' - x_2'$
Moles $C_6H_6 = 1 - x_1' - x_2'$
Moles $C_{18}H_{14} = x_2'$
Total moles $= 1.0$

Since the total moles are equal to 1.0 regardless of x_1' and x_2', the mole fractions of each component are also given by the above quantities. If the components are assumed to behave as perfect gases, the partial pressures will be

$p_H = 1.0(\frac{1}{2}x_1' + x_2') = \frac{1}{2}x_1' + x_2'$
$p_D = \frac{1}{2}x_1' - x_2'$
$p_B = 1 - x_1' - x_2'$
$p_T = x_2'$

With these relationships the rate equations (A) and (B) can be expressed in terms of x_1' and x_2'.

$$r_1 = 6.23 \left[(1 - x_1' - x_2')^2 - \frac{(\frac{1}{2}x_1' - x_2')(\frac{1}{2}x_1' + x_2')}{0.312} \right] \tag{F}$$

$$r_2 = 3.61 \left[(1 - x_1' - x_2')(\frac{1}{2}x_1' - x_2') - \frac{x_2'(\frac{1}{2}x_1' + x_2')}{0.480} \right] \tag{G}$$

In theory Eqs. (F) and (G) can be substituted in the design equations (C) and (D) and values of exit conversions x_1' and x_2' computed corresponding to various values of V_R/F. Actually a difficulty arises which prevents this procedure

both x_1' and x_2' occur in Eq. (F) or (G), making the integration of Eq. (C) or (D) impossible. It is apparent that this difficulty is due to the fact that two chemical reactions are occurring simultaneously. If only the first reaction is considered, only x_1' is involved and direct integration of the design equation is possible. To obtain a concept of the method of approach for this type of reactor-design problem, the solution will first be carried out, making the assumption that just the first reaction is significant. This means that $x_2' = 0$.

Simplified Solution (reaction 2 assumed unimportant). Since $x_2' = 0$, Eq. (F) for r simplifies to

$$r = 6.23[(1 - x_1')^2 - 0.801(x_1')^2]$$

and involves only x_1'. Hence it is possible to substitute it in design Eq. (C) and integrate directly.

$$\frac{V}{F} = \frac{1}{6.23} \int_0^{x_1'} \frac{dx_1'}{(1 - x_1')^2 - 0.801(x_1')^2} = \frac{1}{6.23} \int_0^{x_1'} \frac{dx_1'}{(1 - 0.105x_1')(1 - 1.895x_1')}$$

$$\frac{V}{F} = \frac{0.559}{6.23} \ln \left(\frac{1 - 0.105x_1'}{1 - 1.895x_1'} \right) \tag{H}$$

Table 6-8 gives the values of V_R/F, corresponding to successive values of x_1' obtained by substituting in Eq. (H). A particular V_R/F figure represents the

TABLE 6-8

x_1', lb moles C_6H_6 decomposed/ lb mole feed	$\dfrac{V_R}{F}$, cu ft/(lb mole feed)(hr)	Space velocity hr^{-1}
0.0	0	∞
0.1	0.0179	21,200
0.2	0.0409	9,280
0.3	0.0725	5,230
0.4	0.123	3,080
0.5	0.260	1,460
0.52	0.382	990
0.528†	∞	0

† Equilibrium conditions.

ratio of volume of reactor to feed rate necessary to give the corresponding conversion. The space velocity (per hour) is related to V_R/F in the following way,

$$\text{Space velocity SV} = \frac{\text{volumetric feed rate}}{\text{volume of reactor}} = \frac{F_{vF}}{V_R}$$

or

$$\text{SV} = \frac{v_F}{V_R/F} \tag{I}$$

where v_F is the volume per mole of the feed. If the basis for measuring this volume is taken as 60°F and 1 atm pressure (standard conditions for gas volumes) and benzene behaves as a perfect gas at these conditions,

$$v_F = \frac{RT}{P} = \frac{10.73(400 + 60)}{14.7}$$
$$= 379 \text{ cu ft/lb mole}$$

The third column in Table 6-8 shows the space velocities from Eq. (I) with $v_F = 379$. Figure 6-9 is a plot of the space-velocity–conversion data given in the table. The equilibrium conversion is 52.8 per cent, as that is the value corresponding to infinite time. The same result could have been obtained by using

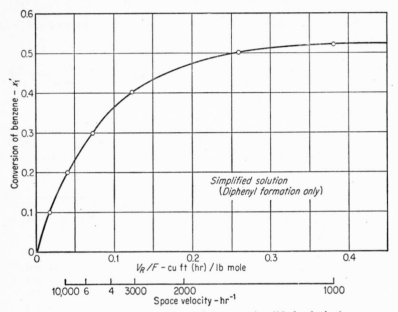

FIG. 6-9. Dehydrogenation of benzene (simplified solution).

the equilibrium constant $K_1 = 0.312$ to compute the equilibrium yield by the method described in Chap. 2. The space velocity is related to the time the reaction gases remain in the reactor (i.e., the contact time). In this isothermal problem the contact time would be equal to the reciprocal of a space velocity based upon v_F measured at 1400°F. Thus according to Table 6-8 a contact time of $\frac{1}{990}(530/1,860)$ hr, or about 1.0 sec, would be required to obtain a conversion of 52 per cent. The V_R/F data shown in Table 6-8 can be used to determine the reactor volume V_R required for any conversion x_1' at a given feed rate F. This calculation will be carried out for a feed of 10,000 lb/hr when the more accurate V_R/F vs. x' results are obtained in the following treatment, where both reactions 1 and 2 are taken into account.

General Solution (both reactions 1 and 2 considered). The rate equations (F) and (G) and the design equations (C) and (D) provide the means for determining x_1' and x_2' as a function of V_R/F. As direct integration is not possible, it is necessary to rewrite (C) and (D) in difference form and accomplish the integration by a stepwise numerical approach. Thus in a small element of volume ΔV the conversions $\Delta x_1'$ and $\Delta x_2'$ are

$$\Delta x_1' = \frac{\Delta V_R}{F} r_{1_a} = \Delta \left(\frac{V_R}{F}\right) r_{1_a} \tag{C'}$$

$$\Delta x_2' = \frac{V_R}{F} r_{2_a} = \Delta \left(\frac{V_R}{F}\right) r_{2_a} \tag{D'}$$

where r_{1_a} and r_{2_a} are average values of the rate for the conversion range x_1' to $x_1' + \Delta x_1'$ and x_2' to $x_2' + \Delta x_2'$.

The method of solution of (C') and (D') will be illustrated by starting at the entrance to the reactor, where x_1' and x_2' are both zero, and carrying out several stepwise calculations.

The initial rates of reaction r_{1_0} and r_{2_0} are given by Eqs. (F) and (G) with $x_1' = x_2' = 0$.

$$r_{1_0} = 6.23(1 - 0) = 6.23 \text{ lb moles } C_6H_6 \text{ converted}/(hr)(cu\ ft)$$
$$r_{2_0} = 3.61 \times 0 = 0$$

Choose an interval of $\Delta(V_R/F) = 0.005$ cu ft/(lb mole feed)(hr).
If the initial rates are assumed to be constant over the interval of

$$\Delta(V_R/F) = 0.005$$

the conversions at the end of the interval are, according to Eqs. (C') and (D'),

$$x_1' = 0 + 0.005 \times 6.23 = 0.03115$$
$$x_2' = 0 + 0.005 \times 0 = 0$$

Now more accurate values of r_{1_a} and r_{2_a} can be obtained by substituting these values of the conversion in the rate equations.

$$r_1' = 6.23 \left[(1 - 0.03115)^2 - \frac{1}{4} \frac{0.03115^2}{0.312} \right] = 6.23 \times 0.938 = 5.84$$

$$r_2' = 3.61 \left[(1 - 0.03115) \frac{0.03115}{2} - 0 \right] = 0.0544$$

The average values of the rates in the first increment of $\Delta(V_R/F)$ may be taken as the arithmetic average of the rates entering and leaving the increment; i.e.,

$$r_{1_a} = \frac{r_{1_0} + r_{1_1}}{2} = \frac{6.23 + 5.84}{2} = 6.04$$

$$r_{2_a} = \frac{r_{2_0} + r_{2_1}}{2} = \frac{0 + 0.054}{2} = 0.0272$$

Using these revised values of the average rates, the conversions at the end of the first increment are, again according to Eqs. (C') and (D'),

$$x_{1_1}' = 0 + 0.005 \times 6.04 = 0.0302$$
$$x_{2_1}' = 0 + 0.005 \times 0.0272 = 0.000136$$

Proceeding to the second increment of $\Delta(V_R/F)$, the computations can be speeded up by anticipating the average rates in the increment, rather than by using the values entering the increment. Estimate that the average rates will be

$$r_{1_a} = 6.04 - (6.23 - 5.84) = 5.65$$
$$r_{2_a} = 0.0272 + (0.0544 - 0) = 0.0816$$

Using these values, the conversion occurring within the second increment is given by Eqs. (C') and (D').

$$\Delta x_1' = 0.005 \times 5.65 = 0.0282$$

and
$$x_{1_2}' = x_{1_1}' + \Delta x_1' = 0.0302 + 0.0282 = 0.0584$$
$$\Delta x_2' = 0.005 \times 0.0816 = 0.000408$$
$$x_{2_2}' = 0.000136 + 0.000408 = 0.000544$$

The estimated values of the average rates can be checked by evaluating rates at the beginning and end of the increment.

At the end of the increment

$$r_{1_2} = 6.23 \left[(1 - 0.0584 - 0.0005)^2 - \left(\frac{0.0584}{2} - 0.0005 \right) \left(\frac{0.0584}{2} + 0.0005 \right) \frac{1}{0.312} \right]$$

$$= 6.23 \times 0.883 = 5.50$$

$$r_{2_2} = 3.61 \left[(1 - 0.0584 - 0.0005) \left(\frac{0.0584}{2} - 0.0005 \right) - 0.000544 \left(\frac{0.0584}{2} + 0.0005 \right) \frac{1}{0.480} \right]$$

$$= 3.61 \times 0.0270 = 0.0975$$

At the beginning of the increment

$$r_{1_1} = 6.23 \left[(1 - 0.0302 - 0.0001)^2 - \left(\frac{0.0302}{2} - 0.0001 \right) \left(\frac{0.0302}{2} + 0.0001 \right) \frac{1}{0.312} \right]$$

$$= 5.86$$

$$r_{2_1} = 3.61 \left[(1 - 0.0302 - 0.0001) \left(\frac{0.0302}{2} - 0.0001 \right) - 0.000136 \left(\frac{0.0302}{2} + 0.0001 \right) \frac{1}{0.480} \right]$$

$$= 0.0529$$

The average rates are

$$r_{1_a} = \frac{r_{1_1} + r_{1_2}}{2} = \frac{5.86 + 5.50}{2} = 5.68 \qquad \text{vs. 5.65 estimated}$$

$$r_{2_a} = \frac{r_{2_1} + r_{2_2}}{2} = \frac{0.0529 + 0.0975}{2} = 0.0752 \qquad \text{vs. 0.0816 estimated}$$

The comparison with the estimated average rates is sufficiently close that a second calculation is unnecessary. The final values for the conversion leaving the second increment ($V_R/F = 0.005 + 0.005 = 0.01$) will be

$$x'_{1_2} = 0.0302 + 0.005 \times 5.68 = 0.0586$$
$$x'_{2_2} = 0.000136 + 0.005 \times 0.0752 = 0.000512$$

This stepwise procedure can be repeated until any desired value of $x'_1 + x'_2$ is reached. The results from 0 to equilibrium are shown in Table 6-9 and Fig. 6-10. The required relationship between total conversion of benzene and space velocity is given in columns 2 and 5. As in Table 6-8 the space velocity is based upon the feed volume measured at 60°F and 1 atmosphere pressure.

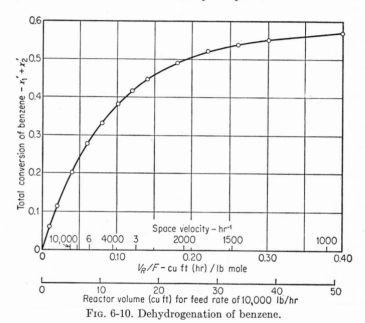

FIG. 6-10. Dehydrogenation of benzene.

It is also required to determine the reactor volume required to process 10,000 lb/hr of benzene. This may be computed from the V_R/F data in the table. For example, for a total conversion of 41.7 per cent, $V_R/F = 0.12$, and the reactor volume is

$$V_R = 0.12F = 0.12\frac{10,000}{78}$$
$$= 15.4 \text{ cu ft}$$

If a 4-in.-ID tubular reactor were used, a length of about 175 ft would be required. The complete curve of volume vs. total conversion is also shown in Fig. 6-10.

The equilibrium conversion of $49.6 + 9.1 = 58.7$ per cent and the equilibrium composition are shown as the values corresponding to $V_R/F = \infty$. These results could also have been obtained from Eqs. (F) and (G). Thus at equilibrium $r_1 = r_2 = 0$, and

$$(1 - x_1' - x_2')^2 = \frac{(\frac{1}{2}x_1' - x_2')(\frac{1}{2}x_1' + x_2')}{0.312}$$

and
$$(1 - x_1' - x_2')(\frac{1}{2}x_1' - x_2') = \frac{x_2'(\frac{1}{2}x_1' + x_2')}{0.480}$$

Simultaneous solution of these two equations leads to values of $x_1' = 0.496$ and $x_2' = 0.091$ as shown in Table 6-9.

TABLE 6-9. CONVERSION VS. V_R/F FOR THE DEHYDROGENATION OF BENZENE

$\dfrac{V_R}{F}$	Space velocity hr^{-1}	x_1'	x_2'	Total conversion, $x_1' + x_2'$	Composition of mixture (molal)			
					C_6H_6	$C_{12}H_{10}$	$C_{18}H_{14}$	H_2
0	∞	0	0	0	1.000	0	0	0
0.005	75,800	0.0302	0.00014	0.0303	0.970	0.0150	0.00014	0.0152
0.010	37,900	0.0586	0.00051	0.0591	0.941	0.0288	0.00051	0.0298
0.020	18,950	0.1105	0.00184	0.112	0.888	0.0534	0.00184	0.0571
0.040	9,500	0.197	0.0062	0.203	0.797	0.0923	0.0062	0.1047
0.060	6,320	0.264	0.0119	0.276	0.724	0.1201	0.0119	0.1439
0.080	4,740	0.316	0.0180	0.334	0.666	0.140	0.0180	0.176
0.100	3,790	0.356	0.0242	0.380	0.620	0.154	0.0242	0.202
0.120	3,160	0.387	0.0302	0.417	0.583	0.163	0.0302	0.224
0.140	2,710	0.411	0.0359	0.447	0.533	0.170	0.0359	0.241
0.180	2,110	0.445	0.0459	0.491	0.509	0.177	0.0459	0.268
0.220	1,720	0.468	0.0549	0.523	0.477	0.179	0.0549	0.289
0.260	1,460	0.478	0.0617	0.540	0.460	0.177	0.0617	0.301
0.300	1,260	0.485	0.0673	0.552	0.448	0.175	0.0673	0.310
0.400	950	0.494	0.0773	0.571	0.429	0.170	0.0773	0.324
∞ †	0	0.496	0.091	0.587	0.413	0.157	0.091	0.339

† Equilibrium conditions.

The rates of each reaction as a function of V_R/F are shown in Fig. 6-11. In both cases the rates fall off toward zero as V_R/F approaches high values. The rate of reaction 2 also approaches zero at very low values of V_R/F because diphenyl is not present in the benzene entering the reactor.

The last four columns in Table 6-9 give the composition of the reaction mixture. With a fixed feed rate the increasing V_R/F values correspond to moving through the reactor, i.e., increasing reactor volume. Hence these columns show how the composition varies with position in the reactor. It is observed that the mole fraction benzene decreases continuously as the reaction mixture proceeds through the reactor, while the diphenyl content reaches a maximum at a V_R/F value of about 0.22. This may be explained by the fact that diphenyl is produced by reaction 1 and disappears by reaction 2. At low conversions the rate of reaction 2 is small, but at high conversion this rate becomes greater than that of the first reaction, so that diphenyl is destroyed more rapidly than it is formed.

Example 6-4 illustrates the design procedure for a homogeneous flow reactor operating at constant temperature and pressure.   When the pressure is not constant and when the rate of reaction varies significantly with the pressure, the pressure drop in the reactor must be taken into account.   The method of accomplishing this involves no new principles or procedures.   Comparing such a case with Example 6-4, the differences are as follows:

1. The effect of pressure on the rate of reaction must be accounted for, i.e., rate equations (A) and (B) would be used rather than (F) and (G), which are based upon 1 atm pressure.

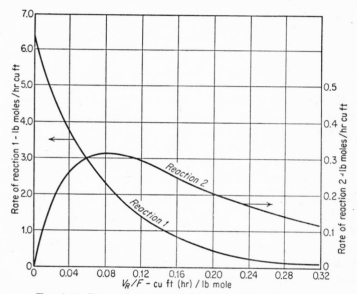

FIG. 6-11. Rates of reaction, dehydrogenation of benzene.

2. The same stepwise numerical procedure is applicable, except that the pressure at any point in the reactor must be computed and the appropriate value used in Eqs. (A) and (B) to estimate average rates of reaction.

The changes in pressure are due to friction, potential-energy changes, and kinetic-energy changes in the flow process in the reactor.   Hence the pressure drop may be computed from Bernoulli's equation, using suitable auxiliary relationships, such as the Fanning equation for the friction. Since the pressure drop is rather small for flow in empty pipes, which is the usual case for homogeneous reactors, the effect of pressure sometimes may be neglected.   However, this is not invariably the case.   Thermal cracking of hydrocarbons is accomplished by passing the fluid through pipes which may reach several hundred feet in total length.   In such instances the pressure drop may be of the order of 100 psi at an absolute pressure of 500 psia, corresponding to a 20 per cent change from entrance to exit of the reactor.

6-3. Nonisothermal Design (Tubular Flow). It is not always possible or desirable to operate a commercial-scale reactor at a constant temperature. High heats of reaction or poor heat-transfer rates may prevent isothermal operation. In addition the equilibrium yield, rate, or both may be more favorable if the heat of reaction is absorbed by the reaction mixture rather than transferred completely to the surroundings.

When the temperature varies in the flow reactor, the rate equation must include the temperature effect before the design can be accomplished. In comparison with the isothermal case (Example 6-4) Eqs. (A) and (B) must show the effect of temperature before they can be used for nonisothermal conditions. If the temperature is known in each part of the reactor, it can be substituted in the rate equations and then the numerical procedure of integrating the design equations is the same as used in Example 6-4. The temperature as a function of V_R is determined by an energy balance around the reactor. This can be written in general form as follows:

$$r \, dV_R(-\Delta H) - dQ_s' = \sum_{i=1}^{i=n} m_i c_{p_i} \, dt \qquad (6\text{-}3)$$

The first term represents the rate at which energy is evolved in the reactor volume dV_R as a result of the heat of reaction. The second term is the rate of transfer of energy from the element, by heat transfer to the surroundings. The term on the right represents the effect of this net rate of addition of energy on the temperature t of the reaction mixture. The coefficient $\Sigma m_i c_{p_i}$ is the total heat capacity per unit time of the material flowing through the volume increment. The mass rate of flow of any one component is m_i.

The heat transferred to the surroundings will depend upon the over-all heat-transfer coefficient U and the mean temperature difference $(t - t_s)_m$ between the surroundings and the reaction mixture. If A_R represents the heat-transfer area per unit length of reactor (dz),

$$dQ_s' = U A_R (t - t_s)_m \, dz$$

If A_c represents the cross-sectional area, Eq. (6-3) becomes

$$r A_c \, dz(-\Delta H) - U A_R (t - t_s)_m \, dz = \sum_{i=1}^{i=n} m_i c_{p_i} \, dt \qquad (6\text{-}4)$$

By noting that $r \, dV_R = F \, dx'$ the energy balance can be written so that all reference to the rate or kinetics of the reaction is eliminated. Thus

Eq. (6-4) may be expressed in the following way:

$$F \, dx'(-\Delta H) - U A_R(t - t_s)_m \, dz = \sum_{i=1}^{i=n} m_i c_{p_i} \, dt \qquad (6\text{-}5)$$

The energy balances expressed in the form of Eqs. (6-4) and (6-5) are valid for any tubular flow reactor, provided steady-state conditions are obtained and provided radial (perpendicular to direction of flow) temperature variations are negligible. This last requirement means that the reaction mixture at any longitudinal position in the reactor can be assumed to be at an average temperature t.

If the operation is adiabatic, the heat exchange with the surroundings is zero and the energy balance reduces to

$$F \, dx'(-\Delta H) = \Sigma m_i c_{p_i} \, dt \qquad (6\text{-}6)$$

It is observed that this equation for an adiabatic reactor is completely independent of the reactor size and the reaction rate, in that it may be integrated separately to give a relationship between the temperature and conversion. Then the design equation can be integrated without simultaneous consideration of the energy balance.

On the other hand, for reactors where the heat-transfer dQ'_s is important the temperature is a function of the reactor length z as well as the conversion, as indicated by Eq. (6-5). Under these conditions the design equation and energy-balance expression must be integrated simultaneously by stepwise numerical methods. It may be noted that these same conclusions were valid for batch reactors and were illustrated in Example 5-3, with the variable time replacing the reactor length.

The methods of designing adiabatic and nonisothermal tubular reactors will be illustrated by considering the substitution reaction between propylene and chlorine to give allyl chloride. The reaction is important commercially because allyl chloride is a useful starting material for production of such substances as allyl alcohol, cyclopropane, epichlorohydrin, trichloropropane, and allyl isothiocyanate.

Because of competing side reactions, particularly the additive chlorination to give dichloropropane, it is advantageous to operate at essentially constant temperature as well as adiabatically. This may be accomplished by constructing the reactor in a form of tank to which reactants are continuously added at a low temperature and products continuously withdrawn at a high temperature. In this case the excess thermal energy leaving in the products over that supplied with the reactants is equivalent to the heat of chemical reaction. However, to indicate the type of calculations involved in tubular nonisothermal reactors, a long-tube nonadiabatic reactor involving considerable temperature change will be considered first (Example 6-5).   Then, after the general subject of tank-type reactors has been discussed, the constant-temperature adiabatic reactor used commercially will be taken up (Example 6-6).

Example 6-5.   It is proposed to design a pilot plant for the production of allyl chloride.   The reactants will consist of 4 moles of propylene per mole of chlorine and will enter the reactor at 200°C.   The reactor will be a vertical tube, 2 in. ID. If the combined feed rate is 0.85 lb moles/hr, determine the conversion to allyl chloride as a function of tube length.   The pressure may be assumed constant and equal to 29.4 psia.

The reactants will be preheated separately to 200°C and mixed at the entrance to the reactor.   At this low temperature explosion difficulties on mixing are not serious.   The reactor will be jacketed with boiling ethylene glycol so that the inside-wall temperature will be constant and equal to 200°C.   The inside-heat-transfer coefficient may be taken as 5.0 Btu/(hr)(sq ft)(°F).

ADDITIONAL DATA AND NOTES.   The basic development work for the allyl chloride process has been reported by Groll and Hearne[1] and Fairbairn, Cheney, and Cherniavsky.[2]   It was found that the three chief reactions were as follows:
1. Allyl chloride formation,

$$Cl_2 + C_3H_6 \rightarrow CH_2=CH-CH_2Cl + HCl$$

2. Substitution to 1,2-dichloropropane,

$$Cl_2 + C_3H_6 \rightarrow CH_2Cl-CHCl-CH_3$$

3. Further chlorination of allyl chloride to 1,3-dichloropropene,

$$Cl_2 + CH_2=CH-CH_2Cl \rightarrow CHCl=CH-CH_2Cl + HCl$$

In order to simplify the kinetic treatment of the problem, only the first two reactions will be considered.   The heats of reaction (in calories per gram mole) available are:

	273°K	355°K
Reaction 1, ΔH........	−26,800	−26,700
Reaction 2, ΔH........	−44,100	−44,000

The molal-heat capacities will be assumed constant and equal to the values given in Table 6-10.

TABLE 6-10

c_p, Btu/(lb mole)(°R)

Propylene (g)................. 25.3
Chlorine (g).................. 8.6
Hydrogen chloride (g)......... 7.2
Allyl chloride (g)............. 28.0
1,2-dichloropropane (g)........ 30.7

[1] *Ind. Eng. Chem.*, **31**:1530 (1939).
[2] *Chem. Eng. Prog.*, **43**:280 (1947).

No information is published for the rate-of-reaction equations, although it is known that reaction 2 takes place at temperatures as low as 100°C, while reaction 1 has an insignificant rate below 200°C. As the temperature increases above 200°C, the rate of reaction 1 increases rapidly, until at 500°C it is several times as fast as that of reaction 2. From this general information and some published data on the effect of residence time and temperature on the conversion the following rate equations[1] are proposed:

Reaction 1: $r_1 = 206,000e^{-27,200/RT}p_p p_{Cl}$

Reaction 2: $r_2 = 11.7e^{-6,860/RT}p_p p_{Cl}$

where r_1, $r_2 = $ lb moles Cl_2 converted/(hr)(cu ft)

$T = °R$

$p_p = $ partial pressure C_3H_6, atm

$p_{Cl} = $ partial pressure Cl_2, atm

Solution. Since there will be heat transfer from the reaction gases to the glycol jacket, the temperature in the reactor will depend upon the length z and the design calculations have to be carried out by the stepwise integration of the rate and energy equations. As in Example 6-4 the conversion resulting from each of the two simultaneous reactions must be obtained separately. Defining the conversion, moles of chlorine reacted per pound mole of total feed, as x_1' for reaction 1 and x_2' for 2, the design equations are

$$r_1 \, dV_R = F \, dx_1'$$
$$r_2 \, dV_R = F \, dx_2'$$

or, in difference form,

$$\Delta x_1' = r_{1_{av}} \Delta \left(\frac{V_R}{F} \right) \qquad \text{(A)}$$

$$\Delta x_2' = r_{2_{av}} \Delta \left(\frac{V_R}{F} \right) \qquad \text{(B)}$$

The energy balance defining the temperature is given by either Eq. (6-4) or Eq. (6-5). Choosing the former and writing it also in difference form,

$$\Sigma m_i c_{p_i} \Delta t = -(r_{1_{av}} \Delta H_1 + r_{2_{av}} \Delta H_2) A_c \Delta z + U(t_s - t)_m A_R \Delta z \qquad \text{(C)}$$

Along with the rate expressions these three equations can be used to determine x_1', x_2', and t as a function of V_R/F, or reactor length. The reactor length is related to the volume of reactor by the expression $zA_c = V_R$; so

$$\frac{V_R}{F} = \frac{zA_c}{F}$$

or, in difference form,

$$\Delta \left(\frac{V_R}{F} \right) = \frac{A_c}{F} \Delta z \qquad \text{(D)}$$

[1] Insufficient data are available in the literature to determine the order of the reactions. The second-order irreversible functions as well as the numerical values suggested by the equations are unverified assumptions.

This last relationship may be used to eliminate either Δz or $\Delta(V_R/F)$ from Eqs. (A) to (C). The choice depends upon whether reactor length z or V_R/F is chosen to be the independent variable. If the former is taken, expressions (A) and (B) become,

$$\Delta x_1' = r_{1av} \frac{A_c}{F} \Delta z \qquad (A')$$

$$\Delta x_2' = r_{2av} \frac{A_c}{F} \Delta z \qquad (B')$$

The solution procedure will be as follows:

1. From a knowledge of the initial conversion ($x_1' = 0$, $x_2' = 0$) and temperature (200°C) the rates r_1 and r_2 entering the reactor can be computed.

2. Then an increment of reactor length is arbitrarily chosen. The smaller this increment, the more accurate will be the solution (and the more time-consuming the calculations).

3. For the chosen Δz first estimates of the conversion occurring within the increment can be obtained from Eqs. (A') and (B'). To do this, it is convenient to assume that the average values of the rates r_{1av} and r_{2av} are equal to the initial values evaluated in step 1.

4. The change in temperature, Δt, within the increment can be determined from Eq. (C). In making this calculation an estimate of the mean temperature difference $(t_s - t)_m$ in the increment is required in order to evaluate the heat-loss term. Once Δt has been computed, the estimate of $(t_s - t)_m$ can be checked. Hence, a trial-and error calculation is necessary in order to evaluate Δt.

5. From the conversion and temperature at the end of the first increment, as determined in steps 3 and 4, the rate of reaction can be computed at this position in the reactor. Then steps 3 and 4 can be repeated, using values for r_{1av} and r_{2av} based upon arithmetic average values of the rates at the beginning and end of the increment. This, in turn, will give more precise values of the conversion and temperature at the end of the first increment and permit a third estimate of the average values of the rates. If this third estimate agrees with the second, the next increment of reactor length is chosen and the procedure repeated.

The steps will be illustrated by carrying out the numerical calculations for the first two increments. The rate equations should be converted to a form involving the conversions rather than partial pressures. Four moles of propylene per mole of chlorine enter the reactor. Then at a point where the conversions are x_1' and x_2', the moles of each component will be as follows:

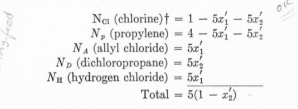

$$N_{Cl} \text{ (chlorine)}\dagger = 1 - 5x_1' - 5x_2'$$
$$N_P \text{ (propylene)} = 4 - 5x_1' - 5x_2'$$
$$N_A \text{ (allyl chloride)} = 5x_1'$$
$$N_D \text{ (dichloropropane)} = 5x_2'$$
$$N_H \text{ (hydrogen chloride)} = 5x_1'$$
$$\text{Total} = 5(1 - x_2')$$

† The coefficient 5 appears in this equation because x' is the conversion based upon 1 mole of total feed. Note that the maximum value for the sum of x_1' and x_2' is 0.2, as this corresponds to complete conversion of the chlorine to either allyl chloride or dichloropropane.

Assuming that all the components behave as perfect gases at $p_t = 29.4$ psia, the partial pressures of chlorine and propylene (in atmospheres) are given by

$$p_p = \frac{29.4}{14.7} \frac{4 - 5x_1' - 5x_2'}{5 - 5x_2'} = 2 \times \frac{0.8 - x_1' - x_2'}{1 - x_2'}$$

$$p_{Cl} = \frac{29.4}{14.7} \frac{1 - 5x_1' - 5x_2'}{5 - 5x_2'} = 2 \times \frac{0.2 - x_1' - x_2'}{1 - x_2'}$$

These expressions can be substituted in the rate equations stated in the problem to relate the rates to the conversions and the temperature. The results are

$$r_1 = 824{,}000e^{-13{,}700/T} \frac{(0.8 - x_1' - x_2')(0.2 - x_1' - x_2')}{(1 - x_2')^2} \tag{E}$$

and

$$r_2 = 46.8e^{-3{,}460/T} \frac{(0.8 - x_1' - x_2')(0.2 - x_1' - x_2')}{(1 - x_2')^2} \tag{F}$$

Equations (A') to (F) can be employed to carry out the previously enumerated steps in the solution.

1. The rates of reaction at the reactor entrance are given by Eqs. (E) and (F), with $T = (200 + 273) \times 1.8 = 852°$R and $x_1' = x_2' = 0$.

$$r_1 = 824{,}000e^{-16.1} \times 0.16$$
$$= 0.0135 \text{ lb mole/(hr)(cu ft)}$$
$$r_2 = 46.8e^{-4.06} \times 0.16$$
$$= 0.129 \text{ lb mole/(hr)(cu ft)}$$

2. Choose an increment of reactor length, $\Delta z = 4.0$ ft.

3. Assuming that the rates computed in step 1 are average values for the increment, the first estimates of the conversion in the increment are given by Eqs. (A') and (B').

$$A_c = \frac{\pi}{4}\left(\frac{2}{12}\right)^2$$
$$= 0.0218 \text{ sq ft}$$
$$\frac{A_c}{F} = \frac{0.0218}{0.85} = 0.0257$$
$$\Delta x_1' = 0.0135 \times 0.0257 \times 4.0 = 0.0014$$
$$x_1' = 0 + 0.0014 = 0.0014$$

In a similar manner for the second reaction

$$\Delta x_2' = 0.129 \times 0.0257 \times 4.0 = 0.0133$$
$$x_2' = 0 + 0.0133 = 0.0133$$

4. To use Eq. (C) for estimating Δt for the increment, it is necessary to know ΔH_1, ΔH_2, t_s, A_R, A_c, U, $\Sigma m_i c_{p_i}$, and $(t_s - t)_m$. The heat-of-reaction data given

are for low temperatures but show little change with temperature. Hence ΔH_1 and ΔH_2 will be assumed constant.

$$\Delta H_1 = -26{,}700 \times 1.8$$
$$= -48{,}000 \text{ Btu/lb mole}$$
$$\Delta H_2 = -44{,}000 \times 1.8$$
$$= -79{,}200 \text{ Btu/lb mole}$$
$$T_s = (200 + 273) \times 1.8$$
$$= 852°\text{R}$$
$$A_R = \pi D \times 1 = \tfrac{2}{12} \times 1 \times \pi$$
$$= 0.524 \text{ sq ft/ft length}$$
$$A_c = 0.0218 \text{ sq ft}$$
$$h = 5 \text{ Btu/(hr)(sq ft)(°F)}†$$

$\Sigma m_i c_{p_i}$ is the heat capacity per unit time of the reaction mixture. Since the conversion is small during the first increment, this heat capacity is essentially that of the chlorine and propylene in the feed to the reactor,

$$\Sigma m_i c_{p_i} = \frac{0.85}{5} \times 8.6 + \frac{4}{5} \times 0.85 \times 25.3$$
$$= 0.85 \times 21.8 = 18.5 \text{ Btu/(hr)(°F)}$$

If the mean temperature difference $(t_s - t)_m$ for the first increment is estimated to be $-20°\text{F}$,

$$18.5\,\Delta t = -(0.0135 \times -48{,}000 + 0.129 \times -79{,}200) \times 0.0218 \times 4$$
$$+ 5 \times -20 \times 0.524 \times 4$$
$$\Delta t = \frac{946 - 210}{18.5}$$
$$= 40°\text{F}$$

$T_1 =$ temperature at end of first increment $= 852 + 40$
$$= 892°\text{R}$$

$t_s - t$ at entrance $= 0$
$t_s - t$ at end of increment $= 852 - 892$
$$= -40°\text{F}$$

$$(t_s - t)_m = \frac{0 + (-40)}{2}$$
$$= -20° \quad \text{vs. } -20° \text{ assumed}$$
$$t_1 = 852 + 40$$
$$= 892°\text{R}$$

5. At the end of the first increment, the first estimate of the conversions and temperature is

$$x_1' = 0.0014$$
$$x_2' = 0.0133$$
$$t_1 = 852 + 40$$
$$= 892°\text{R}$$

† Since the inside-wall temperature is known, the heat transfer with the surroundings can be evaluated from the expression $h(t_s - t)_m A_R \,\Delta z$, where h is the inside-film

Substitution of these conditions in rate equations (E) and (F) yields

$$r_1 = 0.0256$$
$$r_2 = 0.143$$

A second, and more accurate, estimate of the average values of the rates for the first increment can now be made.

$$r_{1av} = \frac{0.0135 + 0.0256}{2} = 0.0195$$

$$r_{2av} = \frac{0.129 + 0.143}{2} = 0.136$$

A second estimate of the conversion occurring in the increment is obtained from these rates and Eqs. (A') and (B').

$$\Delta x_1' = 0.0195 \times 0.0257 \times 4.0 = 0.0020$$
$$x_1' = 0 + 0.0020 = 0.0020$$
$$\Delta x_2' = 0.136 \times 0.0257 \times 4.0 = 0.0140$$
$$x_2' = 0 + 0.0140 = 0.0140$$

The second estimate of Δt is determined from Eq. (C), as in step 4.

$$18.5\,\Delta t = -(0.0195 \times -48,000 + 0.136 \times -79,200) \times 0.0218 \times 4$$
$$+ 5 \times -20 \times 0.524 \times 4$$

$$\Delta t = 41°F$$
$$T_1 = 852 + 41$$
$$= 893°R$$

At the revised values of x_1', x_2', and t (at the end of the first increment) the rates are

$$r_1 = 0.0258$$
$$r_2 = 0.144$$

Since these values are essentially unchanged from the previous estimate, the average rates will also be the same and no further calculations for this increment are necessary.

For the second increment choose again $\Delta z = 4$ ft, and estimate the average rates to be

$$r_{1av} = 0.032$$
$$r_{2av} = 0.15$$

Then from Eqs. (A') and (B'),

$$\Delta x_1' = 0.032 \times 0.0257 \times 4 = 0.0033$$
$$x_1' = 0.0020 + 0.0033 = 0.0053$$
$$\Delta x_2' = 0.15 \times 0.0257 \times 4.0 = 0.0154$$
$$x_2' = 0.0140 + 0.0154 = 0.0294$$

---

coefficient and t_s is the inside-wall surface temperature. The over-all coefficient U is not needed in this case.

From Eq. (C), estimating $(t_s - t)_m = -55°F$,

$$18.5 \Delta t = -(0.032 \times -48,000 + 0.15 \times -79,200) \times 0.0218 \times 4$$
$$+ 5 \times -55 \times 0.524 \times 4$$

$$\Delta t = 32°F$$
$$T_2 = 893 + 32$$
$$= 925°R$$

The estimated $(t_s - t)_m$ for the second increment can be checked by evaluating the temperature difference at the beginning and end of the increment.

$$t_s - t = 852 - 893$$
$$= -41°F \quad \text{beginning of increment}$$
$$t_s - t = 852 - 925$$
$$= -73°F$$
$$(t_s - t)_m = -57°F \quad \text{vs.} \ -55°F \ \text{assumed}$$

The conversions and temperature, according to the first estimate, at the end of the second increment are

$$x_1' = 0.0053$$
$$x_2' = 0.0294$$
$$T_2 = 925°R$$

Using these quantities in the rate equations,

$$r_1 = 0.0400$$
$$r_2 = 0.145$$

A second estimate of the average rates during the increment is given by the expressions

$$r_{1\text{av}} = \frac{0.0258 + 0.0400}{2} = 0.0329$$

$$r_{2\text{av}} = \frac{0.144 + 0.145}{2} = 0.144$$

Since these values are close to the first estimates, additional rate calculations for the increment are unnecessary. The revised conversion values leaving the increment are

$$x_1' = 0.0020 + 0.0329 \times 0.0257 \times 4.0 = 0.0054$$
$$x_2' = 0.0140 + 0.144 \times 0.0257 \times 4.0 = 0.0288$$

The revised temperature is given by the equation

$$\Sigma m_i c_{p_i} \Delta t = -(0.0329 \times -48,000 + 0.144 \times -79,200) \times 0.0218 \times 4$$
$$+ 5 \times -57 \times 0.524 \times 4$$

Since the total conversion is becoming significant at the end of the second increment, it may be necessary to evaluate $\Sigma m_i c_{p_i}$ using the actual mixture existing in the reactor rather than assuming it equal to that for the feed. The rate of flow of each component at the end of the second increment will be

Allyl chloride $= Fx_1' = 0.85 \times 0.0054 = 0.0046$ moles/hr
Dichloropropane $= Fx_2' = 0.85 \times 0.0288 = 0.0245$
$\leftarrow$ Chlorine $= F(0.2 - x_1' - x_2') = 0.85 \times 0.1658 = 0.1410$
Propylene $= F(0.8 - x_1' - x_2') = 0.85 \times 0.7658 = 0.6510$
HCl $= Fx_1' = 0.85 \times 0.0054 = 0.0046$

$\Sigma m_i c_{p_i} = 0.0046 \times 28 + 0.0245 \times 30.7 + 0.1410 \times 8.6$
$+ 0.6510 \times 25.3 + 0.0046 \times 7.2$

$= 18.6$ Btu/(hr)(°R)

This result turns out to be not appreciably different from that based upon the feed but will become so when the conversion reaches larger values. Hence

$$\Delta t = \frac{536}{18.6}$$
$$= 29°F$$

and the revised temperature leaving the increment is

$$T_2 = 893 + 29$$
$$= 922°R$$

The results of these calculations indicate two trends. First, the rate of reaction 1 is relatively low with respect to reaction 2 at low temperatures but increases rapidly with temperature (from 0.0258 at the end of the first increment to 0.0400 at the end of the second), while that of reaction 2 is not very sensitive to temperature changes. This conclusion, considered by itself, would suggest that there would be some conversion to dichloropropane at the beginning of the reactor. However, as the heat of reaction raised the temperature, the reaction to allyl chloride would become increasingly important. The second trend is the increase in heat-transfer rate to the surroundings with an increase in reactor length. This is due to the increase in $(t - t_s)_m$. Its effect is to combat the rise in temperature due to the exothermic nature of the reactions and results ultimately in a decrease in temperature with reactor length. This point is reached when the heat transferred from the reactor tube to the surroundings is greater than the heat evolved from the reactions and would show up in the calculations in the form of a negative Δt determined from Eq. (C). From the results of additional incremental calculations (Fig. 6.12 and Table 6-11) it is observed that the point at which the temperature starts to decrease is about 18 ft from the entrance to the reactor. The temperature vs. length profile has a maximum value at this point and has the shape shown in Fig. 6-13.

This maximum temperature occurs at too low a level for the rate of reaction 1 to become large with respect to that of reaction 2. Therefore the conversion to allyl chloride never reaches a high value, most of the reaction being to the dichloropropane. A reactor of this type is not well suited for the production of allyl chloride. An adiabatic reactor would eliminate the maximum in the temperature vs. reactor-length curve and would result in higher temperatures. This in turn would favor the production of allyl chloride at the expense of reaction 2. The

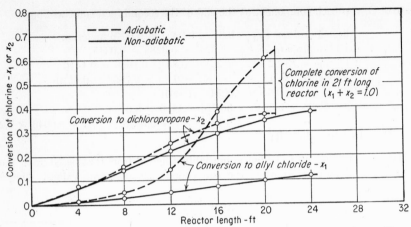

FIG. 6-12. Conversion curves, tubular reactor for allyl chloride production. (Example 6-5.)

only change in the calculations for such an adiabatic case is that the term $U(t_s - t)_m A_r \Delta z$ would be zero. For comparison purposes the temperature and conversion results for such an adiabatic reactor are also shown on Figs. 6-12 and 6-13.

TABLE 6-11. CONVERSION VS. REACTOR LENGTH FOR CHLORINATION OF PROPYLENE

Reactor volume, cu ft	Reactor length, ft	Conversion per mole of feed			Temp, °R	Conversion per mole of Cl₂		
		x_1'	x_2'	Total		x_1	x_2	Total
0	0	0.0	0.0	0.0	852	0.0	0.0	0.0
0.087	4	0.0020	0.0140	0.0160	893	0.0100	0.070	0.080
0.174	8	0.0054	0.0288	0.0342	922	0.0270	0.145	0.172
0.261	12	0.0098	0.0435	0.0533	940	0.0490	0.217	0.266
0.349	16	0.0147	0.0575	0.0723	949	0.0735	0.287	0.361
0.436	20	0.0193	0.0698	0.0891	949	0.0964	0.349	0.445
Adiabatic Operation								
0	0	0.0	0.0	0.0	852	0.0	0.0	0.0
0.087	4	0.0023	0.0144	0.0167	905	0.0115	0.0720	0.0835
0.174	8	0.0088	0.0315	0.0403	981	0.0440	0.157	0.201
0.261	12	0.0283	0.0505	0.0788	1,093	0.142	0.252	0.394
0.349	16	0.0779	0.0667	0.1446	1,261	0.389	0.334	0.723
0.436	20	0.1204	0.0739	0.1943	1,380	0.602	0.369	0.971

Even adiabatic operation results in the formation of considerable amounts of the undesirable dichloropropane. This occurs in the first part of the reactor, where the temperature of the flowing mixture is low. The low-temperature sec-

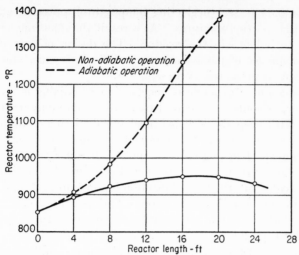

FIG. 6-13. Temperature profiles in tubular reactor, production of allyl chloride. (Example 6-5.)

tion can be eliminated by using a tank reactor operated under isothermal adiabatic conditions. This type of equipment is considered in the next section.

TANK FLOW REACTORS[1]

In the flow reactors considered up to this point it has been supposed that no mixing occurs in the direction of flow. This assumption is justified in any vessel where the forced velocity in the direction of flow is large with respect to secondary mixing velocities, due to entrance-velocity gradients, natural convection, or turbulent diffusion. In reactors consisting of long tubes, such as those studied in Examples 6-2 to 6-5, the velocity in the direction of flow is usually high enough to prevent appreciable mixing along the length of the tube.[2] In large-diameter (several feet) reactors longitudinal mixing is still not significant as long as the rate of movement in the direction of flow is high.

On the other hand, when the reactor consists of a vessel whose diameter is of the same order of magnitude as its length and when the flow rate is low, considerable mixing may occur. For example, suppose a reactor 10 ft long and 5 ft in diameter has a 1-in.-ID inlet line. If the velocity in the inlet line is 100 ft/sec, that in the reactor proper will be only

---

[1] This is the third type discussed in the classification in Chap. 4 and illustrated in Fig. 4-1B.

[2] Note, however, that in all such homogeneous reactors complete radial mixing (mixing across the tube, perpendicular to the direction of flow) has been assumed. This assumption would not be valid in streamline flow but is reasonable under turbulent-flow conditions in long, small-diameter tubes.

$100 \ (\frac{1}{60})^2$ or 0.03 ft/sec (neglecting temperature, pressure, and volume changes of the reaction mixture). As a result the inlet line will act as a jet causing turbulence in the reactor. The design of a reactor under these circumstances of partial mixing is difficult because the extent of mixing cannot be predicted at present.

The most common example of reactors where mixing is important is the tank-flow, or continuous-stirred-tank, type commonly used for liquid systems.[1] With properly designed mechanical stirring equipment essentially complete mixing can be obtained. Under these conditions the reactor-design problem is greatly simplified, because the mixing results in uniform composition, temperature, and pressure throughout the reactor. This means that the rate of reaction is constant and that the design equations do not require integration. This is true regardless of the mechanism of the reaction and may be expressed in the simple manner illustrated by Eq. (4-12).

In summary, satisfactory design methods are available for conditions of no longitudinal mixing (as illustrated in the previous examples of tubular flow reactors) and also for conditions of complete mixing as will be shown in Examples 6-6 to 6-8. For partial mixing, design procedures have yet to be developed.

6-4. Comparison of Tank Flow and Tubular Flow Reactors. The tank flow reactor has certain advantages because of the uniform temperature, pressure, and composition attained as a result of mixing. First of all it is possible to operate such a reactor under isothermal conditions even when the heat of reaction is high—an impossibility in a long, tubular type. When operation within a small temperature range is desired, for example, in order to minimize side reactions or avoid unfavorable rates, the opportunity for isothermal operation at the optimum temperature is a real advantage. Thus in the manufacture of allyl chloride considered in Example 6-5 the tube-type reactor results in the production of considerable amounts of undesirable dichloropropane because the temperature is low in part of the reactor. In the tank type equipment considered in Example 6-6 this disadvantage is overcome by isothermal operation at an optimum temperature level.

Stirred-tank reactors, by virtue of their large volumes (and therefore large V_B/F values) represent an economical method of providing for a long residence time. This combined with the isothermal nature of the reactor permits operation at the optimum temperature for a long reaction time.

Against these advantages are a number of adverse features. Efficient stirred-tank reactors are difficult to construct for gaseous systems because

---

[1] The terms tank flow and continuous stirred tank are both used to designate the steady-state tank-type reactor.

of the mixing problem.   Fixed baffles and mechanical stirrers can be used, but these do not ensure complete mixing in gaseous-reaction mixtures. Hence stirred-tank equipment is generally restricted to liquid systems, although the allyl chloride reactor is an exception.

For high-pressure reactions it is usually necessary, because of cost considerations, to use small-diameter tubular reactors rather than tank types. To operate the latter at high pressures requires a large wall thickness and also necessitates complex sealing arrangements for the mixer shaft. These factors increase both initial and maintenance costs.

The rate of heat transfer per unit mass of reaction mixture is generally lower in the conventional tank-type than in a small-diameter tubular reactor.   Two factors are primarily responsible: (1) a lower ratio of surface area (available for heat transfer) to volume in the tank reactors; (2) lower heat-transfer coefficients.   In instances where the heat of reaction is high it may be desirable for this reason to use a tubular reactor. For example, in the thermal cracking of hydrocarbons it is necessary to supply significant amounts of thermal energy at an elevated temperature level.   This would be difficult to accomplish with a large-diameter reactor because of the limited external heat-transfer surface (per unit mass of reaction mixture) and the low coefficient of heat transfer from the oil in the tank to the tank wall.   In the tubular reactors (pipe stills) used in industry the coefficient of heat transfer can be increased by forcing the oil through the tubes at a high velocity.   It is also apparent that severe difficulties would arise in attempting to provide for efficient stirring under cracking conditions (600 to 900°F, 300 to 800 psia).   It is possible to approach the complete-mixing characteristic of a tank-type reactor in other equipment than a tank-shaped vessel.   For example, a tubular loop operated at high circulation rates can give complete mixing in a small-diameter tube.   In shape this reactor is similar to a tubular flow reactor, and high rates of heat transfer can be attained.   By introducing small solid particles, free to move, a type is obtained in which there is considerable mixing.   Such fluidized-bed reactors also give greatly improved heat-transfer coefficients between the fluid and the wall.

Finally it should be noted that in stirred-tank equipment the reaction occurs at a rate determined by the composition close to that of the exit stream from the reactor.   If mixing is complete, the composition in the reactor is the same as that in the exit stream.   Since the rate generally decreases with the extent of conversion, the tank reactor operates at the lowest point in the range between the high rate corresponding to the composition in the reactor feed and the low rate corresponding to the exit composition.   In the tubular type maximum advantage is taken of the high rates corresponding to low conversions in the first part of the reactor. Practically, this means that the tank reactor would have to have a larger volume for a given feed rate (i.e., larger V_B/F value). Of course, this reasoning does not take into account the effects of side reactions or temperature variations. These may offset this disadvantage of the tank reactor, as illustrated in the production of allyl chloride. Also, the total volume required in a tank flow reactor can be reduced by using several small units in series.

The points that have been discussed indicate why stirred-tank flow reactors have been used mainly for liquid-phase reaction systems at low or medium pressures. They can be used when the heat of reaction is high, but only if the temperature level obtained in their isothermal operation is satisfactory from other points of view. In general if the reactions involved are endothermic and a high temperature is required, tubular reactors are indicated. On the other hand, a tank type may frequently be employed for a highly exothermic reaction. For example, the production of hexamethylenetetramine by reacting ammonia and formaldehyde (in aqueous solution) is highly exothermic, but the rate of reaction is rapid and 100 per cent conversion is possible over a range of temperature of at least 80 to 100°C. Hence, by adjusting the rate of feed and reactor volume, it is possible to add the feed at 20°C and remove enough heat to maintain the reaction mixture at below 100°C.

Denbigh and coworkers in a series of papers[1] have discussed the advantages and disadvantages of continuous-stirred-tank reactors, especially in comparison with batch-operated tank reactors. In another paper Stead, Page, and Denbigh[2] describe experimental techniques for evaluating rate equations from stirred-tank data.

6-5. Design Procedures for Single Tank Flow Reactors. The design concepts for tank flow reactors were developed in Sec. 4-4 and resulted in Eq. (4-12). As written there and repeated as Eq. (6-7), the feed and conversion can be expressed in either mass or molal units.

$$F(x'_E - x'_F) = rV_B \qquad (6\text{-}7)$$

where F = total feed rate, mass/unit time (also, F equals exit mass rate)
$\quad x'$ = conversion of reactant, mass of reactant/mass of total feed (the subscript F refers to feed stream and E to exit stream)
$\quad r$ = constant rate of reaction at uniform temperature, pressure, and composition of reaction mixture [the rate is based upon same reactant as the conversion and has the units (mass of reactant converted)/(unit volume)(unit time)]

---

[1] K. G. Denbigh, *Trans. Faraday Soc.*, **40**:352 (1944), **43**:648 (1947). K. G. Denbigh, M. Hicks, and F. M. Page, *Trans. Faraday Soc.*, **44**:479 (1948).

[2] B. Stead, F. M. Page, and K. G. Denbigh, *Discussions Faraday Soc.*, (2):263 (1947).

It has been mentioned that tank flow or continuous-stirred-tank reactors are most commonly employed for liquid systems. In such cases the density changes are often negligible so that the feed and exit flow rates are equal in volume as well as in mass units. Then Eq. (6-7) can be written in a simple form in terms of the concentrations (moles per volume) of reactant in feed and exit streams. The volumetric flow rate of feed and exit stream is Fv_F, where F is the molal flow rate and v_F the volume of the feed per mole. [The moles of reactant entering per unit time is $(Fv_F)C_F$, and leaving, $Fv_F C_E$.] Then, according to Eq. (4-1),

$$(Fv_F)C_F - (Fv_F)C_E = rV_B$$

or
$$C_F - C_E = \frac{rV_B}{Fv_F} \tag{6-8}$$

Eldridge and Piret[1] have developed design equations based upon constant density for single and multiple tank flow reactors.

Equation (6-8) gives the exit concentration C_E as a function of the reactor volume. The ratio V_B/Fv_F is the holdup time in the reactor and has the physical meaning of the average time a slug of liquid is in the vessel. The reciprocal, Fv_F/V_B is the familiar space velocity as defined by Eq. (4-13).

When the temperature in the reactor is the same as that of the entering reactants, Eq. (6-7) [or Eq. (6-8) for constant-density liquid systems] can be used directly to determine the reactor volume required to obtain a given conversion x'_E. This will be true when (1) the heat of reaction is negligible with respect to the heat capacity of the reactor contents or (2) where the heat of reaction is significant but the heat-transfer rate with the surroundings is sufficient to balance the heat of reaction.

When neither of these conditions is fulfilled, an energy balance must be made over the system in order to determine the reaction temperature and, therefore, the value of the rate that is to be used in Eq. (6-7). If t_1 represents the temperature of the entering reactants and t_2 that of the reaction mixture, the energy balance may be written

$$\Sigma c_{p_i}F_i(t_1 - t_0) + rV_B(-\Delta H_0) = \Sigma m_i c_{p_i}(t_2 - t_0) + UA(t_2 - t_s)_m \tag{6-9}$$

The left-hand term represents the thermal energy added in the feed above an arbitrary base temperature t_0; the second term[2] gives the energy evolved as a result of the heat of reaction. The right-hand terms represent the energy removed from the system. The first is the

[1] J. W. Eldridge and E. L. Piret, *Chem. Eng. Prog.*, **46**:290 (1950).
[2] The minus sign preceding ΔH_0 is necessary, because ΔH_0 represents the energy absorbed by the reaction, not the energy evolved. Note that ΔH_0 is the heat of reaction at t_0.

energy removed with the products leaving the system.[1]   The second represents the heat transfer from the reactor to the surroundings.

The summation terms in the equation correspond to the heat capacity per hour of the feed and the products; F_i is the mass feed rate of component i in the feed and m_i the mass rate of product i leaving the reactor. The surroundings temperature is t_s, and U and A are the heat-transfer coefficient and area.

Equation (6-9) may be simplified by choosing the base temperature t_0 equal to the feed temperature t_1 or reactor temperature t_2, since each choice eliminates one term of the equation.   If t_0 is chosen equal to t_2, the necessity of evaluating $\Sigma m_i c_{p_i}$ is avoided, and the energy balance becomes

$$\Sigma c_{p_i} F_i(t_1 - t_2) + r V_B(-\Delta H) = U A(t_2 - t_s)_m \qquad (6\text{-}10)$$

Equations (6-7) and (6-10) are sufficient to complete the design of the reactor, i.e., to determine the exit temperature and the reactor volume required for a given conversion. As Eq. (6-10) is written, a trial-and-error solution of the two equations is necessary, since the unknown volume and temperature are both involved in each equation.   However, if Eq. (6-7) is used to eliminate the term $r V_B$, a simultaneous solution is avoided.[2]   Thus Eq. (6-10) may be written

$$\Sigma c_{p_i} F_i(t_1 - t_2) + F(x'_E - x'_F)(-\Delta H) = U A(t_2 - t_s)_m \qquad (6\text{-}11)$$

This expression can be solved directly for the exit temperature t_2 from a knowledge of the conversion required in the reactor.   Then the rate r can be evaluated at this temperature t_2 and used in Eq. (6-7) to compute the reactor volume.

On the other hand, if the reactor volume is known and the exit conversion x'_E is the desired quantity, a trial-and-error simultaneous solution of the design equation and energy balance is required regardless of the form of the energy balance.   However, it is still more convenient to use Eq. (6-11) rather than (6-10).   A method of approach is to assume a series of exit conversion values, x'_E, and compute the corresponding exit temperatures t_2 from Eq. (6-11).   Then for each x'_E and t_2 evaluate r, and use it in Eq. (6-7) to determine a reactor volume.   When the computed volume agrees with the known volume, the temperature and conversion are correct.   This variation of the design problem would be encountered when the performance of an existing reactor is to be predicted.

Numerical illustrations of stirred-tank flow reactors are illustrated in Examples 6-6 and 6-7.

[1] The reaction-mixture temperature t_2 is equal to the temperature of the exit stream because of the assumption of complete mixing.

[2] When only one reaction occurs.   With reversible, simultaneous, or consecutive reactions a simultaneous solution may be required.

Example 6-6. Consider the design of a tank-type flow reactor for the production of allyl chloride from propylene, using the reaction-rate data given in Example 6-5. In order to compare the different types of reactors for this case, the same feed condition will be employed: total rate = 0.85 mole/hr, temperature = 200°C, pressure = 29.4 psia; molal ratio of propylene to chlorine = 4.0.

The equipment should be insulated so that the operation is essentially adiabatic. Also, suitable baffles and entrance nozzles will be used so that the contents of the reactor, though gaseous, will be of uniform temperature, pressure, and composition.

Using the heats of reaction and heat capacities given in Example 6-5, determine the conversion of chlorine to allyl chloride expected for a range of sizes of reactor (i.e., reactor volumes).

Solution. The rate of each reaction (allyl chloride and dichloropropane formation) will be a constant and should be evaluated at the temperature and composition of the stream leaving the reactor. To determine this temperature, the energy balance Eq. (6-11) will be employed. Since the operation is adiabatic and the entering conversion zero, this expression may be written

$$\Sigma F_i c_{p_i}(t_1 - t_2) + F[x_1'(-\Delta H_1) + x_2'(-\Delta H_2)] = 0 \qquad (A)$$

where x_1' and x_2' refer to exit conversions for reactions 1 and 2.

If only one reaction were involved (for example, if $x_2' = 0$), this energy balance could be used to calculate an exit temperature t_2 for a series of arbitrarily chosen conversions x_1'. Then each value of x_1' would fix a rate r_1. These rates, substituted in the design equation (6-7), would give the required reactor volumes corresponding to the conversions. In the present case the procedure is complicated by the existence of the two simultaneous reactions. Two equations of the form of (6-7) must be satisfied, i.e.,

$$x_1' - 0 = r_1 \frac{V_B}{F} \qquad (B)$$

$$x_2' - 0 = r_2 \frac{V_B}{F} \qquad (C)$$

The rate expressions are obtained by substituting $T_2 = t_2 + 460$ for the temperature in Eqs. (E) and (F) of Example 6-5,

$$r_1 = 824,000 e^{-13,700/T_2} \frac{(0.8 - x_1' - x_2')(0.2 - x_1' - x_2')}{(1 - x_2')^2} \qquad (D)$$

$$r_2 = 46.8 e^{-3,460/T_2} \frac{(0.8 - x_1' - x_2')(0.2 - x_1' - x_2')}{(1 - x_2')^2} \qquad (E)$$

The essence of the problem is the solution of the five equations (A), (B), (C), (D), and (E) for the five unknowns x_1', x_2', t_2, r_1, and r_2 at different values of the reactor volume V_B. One procedure which is not tedious is to choose a value of t_2. Then from the ratio of Eqs. (B) and (C), using (D) and (E) for r_1 and r_2, obtain the ratio of the conversions x_1'/x_2'. Employing this ratio in Eq. (A) will give separate values for each conversion. Finally the corresponding reactor volume can be obtained from either Eq. (B) or Eq. (C). This approach will be illustrated by including the numerical calculations for an exit temperature of 1302°R (450°C),

$$\frac{x_1'}{x_2'} = \frac{r_1}{r_2} = \frac{824,000e^{-13,700/1,302}}{46.8e^{-3,460/1,302}} = 6.77$$

Using this ratio in Eq. (A), and noting that the hourly heat capacity of the feed $\Sigma F_i c_{p_i}$ was determined as 18.5 Btu/(hr)(°F) in Example 6-5,

$$18.5(t_1 - t_2) + 0.85(6.77x_2' \times 48,000 + x_2' \times 79,200) = 0$$
$$18.5(852 - 1,302) + 343,000x_2' = 0$$
$$x_2' = 0.0243$$
$$x_1' = 6.77 \times 0.0243 = 0.164$$

Since the feed rate is 0.85 lb moles/hr, the reactor volume required for these conversions is, from Eq. (B),

$$0.164 = \frac{V_B}{0.85} 824,000e^{-13,700/1,302} \frac{(0.8 - 0.164 - 0.024)(0.2 - 0.164 - 0.024)}{(1 - 0.0243)^2}$$

$$V_B = \frac{0.164 \times 0.85}{0.167}$$
$$= 0.83 \text{ cu ft}$$

The corresponding values of the conversions and volume for other temperatures are summarized in Table 6-12. In comparing the results with those of Example

TABLE 6-12. CONVERSION VS. REACTOR VOLUME FOR ADIABATIC TANK REACTOR: ALLYL CHLORIDE PRODUCTION

Reactor (and exit) temp		Conversion/mole of feed		Conversion of chlorine in feed		Reactor vol., cu ft
°R	°C	x_1'	x_2'	x_1	x_2	
960	260	0.0098	0.0237	0.049	0.119	0.12
1032	300	0.0282	0.0324	0.14	0.162	0.15
1122	350	0.0660	0.0341	0.33	0.171	0.18
1212	400	0.114	0.0298	0.57	0.149	0.24
1257	425	0.138	0.0273	0.69	0.136	0.34
1302	450	0.164	0.0243	0.82	0.121	0.83

6-5 it is seen that the adiabatic tank reactor is better adapted to the production of allyl chloride than the tubular type. In the latter equipment considerable dichloropropane is formed in the initial sections of the reactor, where the temperature is relatively low. This is avoided in the adiabatic tank reactor by operating at a constant temperature high enough to favor allyl chloride rather than dichloropropane formation. For example, if the adiabatic tank reactor is operated at 450°C, 0.164 × 5 × 100, or 82 per cent, of the chlorine is converted to allyl chloride and 0.0243 × 5 × 100, or 12.1 per cent, converted to dichloropropane. The total conversion is $(0.0243 + 0.164) \times 5 \times 100$, or 94.1 per cent. In the adiabatic tubular reactor of Example 6-5 the products contained much greater amounts of dichloropropane for all reactor volumes. These conclusions are summarized in Fig. 6-14 where the fraction of the chlorine converted to each product is shown plotted vs. reactor volume for both the tubular and the tank reactor.

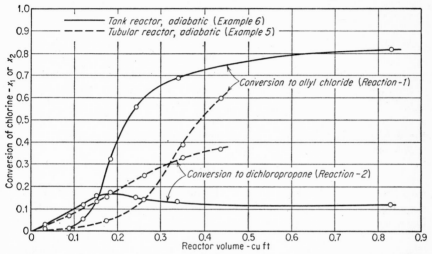

FIG. 6-14. Comparison of tubular and tank reactors for allyl chloride production.

Example 6-7. Eldridge and Piret[1] have investigated the hydrolysis of acetic anhydride in stirred-tank flow reactors of about 1,800 cc volume at temperatures from 15 to 40°C. Their experimental results for several volumetric feed rates Fv_F are shown in Table 6-13.

TABLE 6-13

Entering anhydride conc., C_F, moles/cc	Volumetric feed rate, Fv_F, cc/min	% hydrolysis of anhydride	Temp, °C
2.1×10^{-4}	378	25.8	15
1.4×10^{-4}	582	33.1	25
1.37×10^{-4}	395	40.8	25
1.08×10^{-4}	555	15.3	10
0.52×10^{-4}	490	16.4	10
0.95×10^{-4}	575	55.0	40
0.925×10^{-4}	540	55.7	40
1.87×10^{-4}	500	58.3	40
2.02×10^{-4}	88.5	88.2	40

[1] Loc. cit.

Independent determination of the rate of reaction by these investigators, from other experiments in batch-operated reactors resulted in the following first-order equations:

At 10°C
$$r = 0.0567C, \text{ g moles}/(\text{cc})(\text{min})$$

At 15°C
$$r = 0.0806C, \text{ g moles}/(\text{cc})(\text{min})$$

At 25°C
$$r = 0.1580C, \text{ g moles}/(\text{cc})(\text{min})$$

At 40°C
$$r = 0.380C, \text{ g moles}/(\text{cc})(\text{min})$$

where C = acetic anhydride concentration in gram moles per cubic centimeter.

For each run compute the per cent hydrolysis, and compare with the observed value given in the table of data. In all cases the feed temperature was the same as the temperature of the reaction mixture. Since the concentrations are low, the density of the solution may be assumed constant with little error.

Solution. The hydrolysis reaction,

$$(\text{CH}_3\text{CO})_2\text{O} + \text{H}_2\text{O} \rightarrow 2\text{CH}_3\text{COOH}$$

would be expected to be second-order. In this case, in which dilute aqueous solutions were employed, the water concentration is essentially constant so that a first-order equation is satisfactory.

Since the process is isothermal, an energy balance need not be employed. Also, Eq. (6-8) is applicable because the reaction mixture is a constant-density liquid phase.

Substituting the rate equation $r = kC$ into Eq. (6-8)[1] and solving the resulting expression for the exit concentration C_E,

$$C_E = \frac{C_F}{1 + k(V_B/Fv_F)} = \frac{C_F}{1 + k\theta'}$$

where θ' is the holdup time.

The fraction of the anhydride hydrolyzed is equal to $(C_F - C_E)/C_F$; so

$$\text{Fraction hydrolyzed} = 1 - \frac{C_E}{C_F} = 1 - \frac{1}{1 + k\theta'} \qquad (A)$$

Equation (A) can be employed to determine the per cent hydrolyzed (or conversion) from θ' and the reaction-rate constant. Thus, for the first set of data in the table, at 15°C,

$$k = 0.0806 \text{ min}^{-1}$$

$$\theta' = \frac{1,800}{378} \text{ min}$$

$$k\theta' = 0.0806 \frac{1,800}{378} = 0.384 \text{ (dimensionless)}$$

[1] Note that this concentration of anhydride in the rate equation is the same as the exit concentration C in Eq. (6-8), because of mixing.

Substitution in Eq. (A) gives

$$\text{Fraction hydrolyzed} = 1 - \frac{1}{1 + 0.384}$$
$$= 0.277, \text{ or } 27.7\%$$

This agrees reasonably well with the experimental value of 25.8 per cent. Table 6-14 shows the results of similar calculations for the other sets of data.

TABLE 6-14

Vol. feed rate, cc/min	% hydrolysis	
	Experimental	Calculated from Eq. (A)
378	25.8	27.7
582	33.1	32.8
395	40.8	41.8
555	15.3	15.5
490	16.4	17.2
575	55.0	54.4
540	55.7	55.9
500	58.3	57.8
88.5	88.2	88.5

The computed values are based upon the concept of complete mixing and, hence, upon the assumption of uniform composition and temperature throughout the mass. The agreement between the calculated results and the experimental ones is a measure of the validity of the complete mixing assumption. Tests with successively less stirring can be used to study the level of agitation required for complete mixing. MacDonald and Piret[1] have made such studies for a first-order reaction system.

6-6. Tank Flow Reactors in Series. In some cases it may be desirable to use more than one stirred-tank reactor operating in series, the exit stream from the first constituting the feed to the second, etc. The design problem to determine the final exit concentration or conversion can be solved by consecutive application of Eq. (6-8) to each reactor, starting with the first. Eldridge and Piret[2] have derived equations which may be solved algebraically for the final concentration for a number of types of rate expressions and for systems of reversible, consecutive, and simultaneous reactions. Graphical procedures were also developed. These are advantageous for a series of reactors when the rate equation is simple. The types of calculations involved are illustrated for the simple case of a first-order reaction in Example 6-8 by extending the results of Example 6-7.

[1] R. W. MacDonald and E. L. Piret, *Chem. Eng. Prog.*, **47**:363 (1951).
[2] *Loc. cit.*

Example 6-8. Acetic anhydride is to be hydrolyzed in three stirred-tank reactors operated in series. Suppose that each has a volume of 1,800 cc, that the temperature is constant and equal to 25°C, and that the feed rate to the first reactor is 582 cc/min. Compute the per cent hydrolysis accomplished in the three reactors.

Solution. From the results of Example 6-7 the fraction hydrolyzed in the stream leaving the first reactor is 0.328. If the anhydride concentration leaving the first reactor is designated as C_1 and that leaving the second is C_2, Eq. (6-8) applied to the second reactor becomes

$$C_1 - C_2 = r_2\theta_2'$$

In other words, the same equation as used for the first reactor can be used for the second with C_F replaced by C_1, C_E replaced by C_2, and r_1 by r_2. Hence Eq. (A) of Example 6-7 is applicable for the second reactor if it is written as follows:

$$\frac{C_1 - C_2}{C_1} = \text{fraction hydrolyzed in reactor 2} = 1 - \frac{1}{1 + k\theta_2'}$$

Since $\theta_2' = \theta_1'$, the fraction hydrolyzed in the second reactor will be 0.328. Therefore the following equations may be written for the three reactors:

$$\frac{C_F - C_1}{C_F} = 0.328 \qquad C_1 = (1 - 0.331)C_F = 0.672C_F$$

$$\frac{C_1 - C_2}{C_1} = 0.328 \qquad C_2 = 0.672C_1$$

$$\frac{C_2 - C_3}{C_2} = 0.328 \qquad C_3 = 0.672C_2$$

The total fraction hydrolyzed in all reactors is given by the expression

$$\frac{C_F - C_3}{C_F} = 1 - \frac{0.672C_2}{C_F} = 1 - \frac{0.672 \times 0.672 \times 0.672C_F}{C_F}$$
$$= 1 - 0.672^3 = 1 - 0.303$$
$$= 0.697, \text{ or } 69.7\%$$

Eldridge and Piret developed the following general equation for a series of n reactors in which a first-order irreversible reaction occurs:

$$\text{Fraction converted} = 1 - \frac{1}{[1 + k(\theta')_1][1 + k(\theta')_2] \cdots [1 + k(\theta')_n]}$$

In the present example this equation reduces to

$$\text{Fraction hydrolyzed} = 1 - \frac{1}{[1 + k(\theta')]^3}$$
$$= 1 - \frac{1}{1.489^3} = 1 - 0.672^3 = 0.697$$

as before.

NOMENCLATURE

A_c Cross-sectional area of tubular reactor

A_R Heat-transfer area/unit length of tubular reactor

F Feed rate

F_i Feed rate of component i

h Inside-heat-transfer coefficient for tubular reactor

ΔH Heat of reaction (ΔH_0 applies at t_0)

n Number of components in a reaction mixture

m_i Mass rate of flow of component i at any point in a tubular reactor or leaving a tank reactor

p Partial pressure

Q_s' Heat-transfer rate from the reactor to the surroundings

v_F Volume/mole of feed

V_B Volume of tank reactor

V_R Volume of tubular reactor

t Temperature; t_1, t_2 entering and exit values, respectively

T Absolute temperature

y Mole fraction in gas phase

θ' Holdup, or average residence, time in tank flow reactors

E, F Subscripts to denote exit and entering values, respectively, of the conversion in a tank-flow reactor

PROBLEMS

1. The production of carbon disulfide from methane and sulfur vapor can be carried out homogeneously, or with a solid catalyst. Also, some solid materials act as a poison retarding the reaction.

The following data were obtained on a flow basis at a constant temperature of 625°C and with an initial reactants ratio of 1 mole of CH_4 to 2.0 moles of sulfur vapor (considered as S_2). The first set of data were obtained with the reactor empty (effective volume 67.0 ml), while the second set were obtained after packing the reactor with a granular material (7-mesh) which reduced the void volume to 35.2 ml. Was the granular material acting as a catalyst or poison in this case?

Set	Run	Feed rate, g moles/hr		Product rate, CS_2 g moles/hr	Conversion of methane
		CH_4	S_2		
1	1	0.417	0.834	0.0531	0.127
	2	0.238	0.476	0.0391	0.164
	3	0.119	0.238	0.0312	0.262
2	1	0.119	0.238	0.0204	0.171
	2	0.178	0.357	0.0220	0.123

2. Butadiene and steam (0.5 mole of steam per mole of butadiene) are fed to a tubular flow reactor which operates at 1180°F and a constant pressure of 1 atm. The reactor is noncatalytic.

Considering only the reversible polymerization reaction to the dimer, determine: (a) the length of 4-in.-ID reactor required to obtain a conversion of 40 per cent of the butadiene with a total feed rate of 20 lb moles/hr; (b) the space velocity, measured as liters per hour of feed gas (at 1180°F and 1 atm) divided by the reactor volume in liters, required to obtain a conversion of 40 per cent.

The polymerization reaction is second-order and has a specific reaction-rate constant given by the following equation:

$$\log k = -\frac{5,470}{T} + 8.063$$

$$k = \text{g moles } C_4H_6 \text{ polymerized}/(\text{liter})(\text{hr})(\text{atm})^2$$
$$T = °K$$

The reverse (depolymerization) reaction is first-order. The equilibrium constant for the polymerization reaction is given by the expression

$$-R \ln K = -\frac{34,825}{T} + 5.968 + 11.075 \log T + 10^{-4}T - 1.288 \times 10^{-6}T^2$$

At 1180°F (911°K) the value of K from the preceding equation is 1.27.

3. (a) A mixture of butenes and steam is to be thermally (noncatalytically) cracked in a tubular flow reactor at the constant temperature of 1200°F and constant pressure of 1.0 atm. While the feed consists of a number of different butenes[1] and the products vary from coke to butadiene, the rate of reaction may be adequately represented by a first-order mechanism as follows:

$$r_1 = \frac{\delta}{\rho_B} k_1 p_4$$
$$\log k_1 = -\frac{60,000}{4.575T} + 15.27$$

The rate was determined experimentally in a reactor packed with inert quartz chips, and the reactor to be designed in this problem will also be so packed.

$r_1 = \text{g moles butenes cracked}/(\text{g quartz chips})(\text{hr})$
$\delta = \text{void fraction} = 0.40$
$\rho_B = \text{bulk density of bed packed with quartz chips} = 1,100 \text{ g/liter}$
$p_4 = \text{partial pressure of butenes, atm}$
$T = °K$

The ratio of steam to butenes entering the reactor will be 10:1.0 on a molal basis. Under these conditions the change in number of moles during the course of the reaction can be neglected.

Determine the conversion as a function of size of reactor. Also, prepare a plot having two abscissas [(1) pounds of quartz chips per pound moles of butene feed per hour; (2) space velocity defined as cubic feet per hour of feed at 1200°F divided by the void volume in cubic feet] and one ordinate (the conversion of butenes). Cover a range of values of the first abscissa of 0 to 3,000.

What total volume of reactor would be required to obtain a 20 per cent conversion with a butenes feed rate of 5 lb moles/hr?

(b) In this case the feed will consist of 10 moles of steam per mole of total hydrocarbons. The hydrocarbon fraction is 60 mole per cent butenes and 40 mole per cent butadiene. Consider that the butadiene may undergo two reactions, cracking and polymerization to the dimer. The rate data for these are as follows:

[1] See *Chem. Eng. Prog.*, **44**:229 (1948).

Cracking:
$$r_2 = \frac{\delta}{\rho_B} k_2 p_4''$$

$$\log k_2 = -\frac{30,000}{4.575T} + 7.241$$

Polymerization to the dimer:[1] $r_3 = \dfrac{\delta}{\rho_B} k_3 (p_4'')^2$

$$\log k_3 = -\frac{25,000}{4.575T} + 8.063$$

where r_2 = g moles butadiene cracked/(g of quartz chips)(hr)
   p_4'' = partial pressure of butadiene, atm
   r_3 = g moles butadiene polymerized/(g of quartz chips)(hr)
Determine the conversion of butenes and that of butadiene as a function of W/F from 0 to 3,000 lb chips/(lb mole feed)(hr).

Assume that the total number of moles is constant, and neglect all reactions except those mentioned.

4. Benzene is to be chlorinated in the liquid phase in a kettle-type reactor operated on a steady-state basis. Liquid benzene is added continuously; the liquid product and gaseous hydrogen chloride are continuously removed. The chlorine gas is bubbled continuously into the liquid-reaction mixture in the kettle.

The rate of reaction may be assumed large enough so that there is no unreacted chlorine in the reaction products. Also, the concentration of chlorine in the reaction mixture will be small. The hydrogen chloride concentration in the reaction is likewise small. The density of the liquid mixture may be assumed constant.

At the constant operating temperature of 55°C the significant reactions are the three substitution ones leading to mono-, di-, and trichlorobenzene. Each reaction is second-order and irreversible. The rate constants for each case are designated as follows:

k_1:
$$C_6H_6 + Cl_2 \rightarrow C_6H_5Cl_1 + HCl$$
k_2:
$$C_6H_5Cl + Cl_2 \rightarrow C_6H_4Cl_2 + HCl$$
k_3:
$$C_6H_4Cl_2 + Cl_2 \rightarrow C_6H_3Cl_3 + HCl$$

It was noted in Chap. 3 that, at 55°C, the ratios of the rate constants are

$$\frac{k_1}{k_2} = 8.0$$

$$\frac{k_2}{k_3} = 30$$

Under the proposed operating conditions, the composition of the liquid product will be constant for any one run. Different products will be obtained for different ratios of benzene and chlorine fed to the reactor. Compute the composition of the liquid product for the case where 1.4 moles of chlorine per mole of benzene are fed to the reactor.

5. Reconsider Prob. 4 for the case where, instead of a single reactor, a two-reactor system is used. The liquid stream enters the first reactor (as pure benzene), flows from the first to the second, and finally the product is withdrawn from the second reactor. Gaseous hydrogen chloride is withdrawn from each reactor.

Plot the composition of the product vs. moles of total chlorine added per mole of benzene. Cover a range of the latter variable from 0 to 2.5.

One-half the total chlorine is added to each reactor.

[1] This reaction is reversible, but neglect the reverse reaction in this instance.

CHAPTER 7

SEMIBATCH REACTORS

The semibatch reactor has been defined in Chap. 4 (Fig. 4-1C) as a tank type, operated on a non-steady-state, or transient, basis. Semi batch behavior occurs whenever a tank flow reactor is started up, when its operating conditions are changed from one steady state to another or when it is shut down, for then the properties of the system change with respect to time. Purging processes in which an inert material is added to the tank reactor can also be classified in the semibatch division.

In addition to these applications arising from short-period deviations from steady-state operation the semibatch reactor is used for its own particular characteristics. For example, it is sometimes advantageous to add all of one reactant initially and then the other continuously. In certain instances this modified procedure has advantages over ordinary batch operation. In systems with a high heat of reaction the energy evolution (or absorption) can be controlled by regulating the rate of addition of one of the reactants. In this way the disadvantage of batch reactors due to their poor heat-transfer characteristics can be partially eliminated. As mentioned in Chap. 4, this form of semibatch operation also allows for a degree of control of concentration of the reaction mixture, and hence rate of reaction, that is not possible in batch or flow reactors. Another illustration occurs when the reactants are all initially in the vessel, but one of the products is continuously removed. An example is the removal of water, by boiling, in esterification reactions. In this instance the advantage gained is an increased rate due to (1) the removal of one of the products of a reversible reaction and (2) increased concentrations of reactants.

The design equations for semibatch operation are complicated because each of the four terms in the general material balance [Eq. (4-1)] may be significant. The feed and withdrawal streams from the reactor cause changes in the composition and volume of the reaction mixture in addition to the changes due to the reaction itself. These variations so affect the rate that the design equations cannot be integrated analytically except for first- or zero-order reactions and isothermal conditions. A

186

in the case of other examples of tank reactors complete mixing must be assumed in order to handle the design problem in a quantitative fashion.

7-1. Isothermal Design. The design equation may be formulated in terms of the amount of the specific reactant which is used to measure the rate of reaction. Thus the rate of addition of reactant A in the feed stream will be $F_1 z_1$, where F is the mass feed rate and z the weight fraction.[1] Writing the other three terms in Eq. (4-1) in a similar way leads to the result

$$F_1 z_1 - F_2 z_2 - r V_B = \frac{M_A \, d(V_B C_2)}{d\theta} \tag{7-1}$$

Allowance must be made for the rate of feed $F_1 z_1$ and withdrawal $F_2 z_2$ to be different. The subscripts 1 and 2 are used to indicate this possibility. The term on the right represents the rate of accumulation of reactant A in the reactor contents. M_A is the molecular weight of A, and C_2 is the molal concentration of A in the mixture. The assumption of complete mixing means that this concentration corresponds to the weight fraction z in the exit stream.

Equation (7-1) cannot be integrated analytically, in the general case where F_1, z_1, F_2, z_2, r, V_B, and ρ can all vary with time. However, an important case will be considered in which assumptions are made concerning the constancy of the density, temperature, rates of flow, and the form of the rate equation.

The general equation can always be integrated numerically. Such procedures will be illustrated for an example in which there is a feed stream but no product withdrawn from the reactor.

Constant-density First-order Reactions. Piret and Mason[2,3] have reviewed the subject of transient conditions in tank flow reactors, under the conditions of constant flow rates, constant temperature, constant density, and first-order rate equations. From a practical point of view these conditions are reasonable in many of the semibatch operations that correspond to starting up and shutting down of steady-state reactors.

The assumption of constant density permits the use of the term concentration to account fully for changes in amount of reactant. Also, constant density, along with constant flow rates, means that the reactor volume V_B will remain constant. Under these restrictions Eq. (7-1) may be written

$$(F v_F) C_1 - (F v_F) C_2 - r V_B = V_B \frac{dC_2}{d\theta} \tag{7-2}$$

[1] Equally satisfactory would be to define F as the molal rate and z_A as the mole fraction A.

[2] D. R. Mason and E. L. Piret, *Ind. Eng. Chem.*, **42**:817 (1950).

[3] D. R. Mason and E. L. Piret, *Ind. Eng. Chem.*, **43**:1210 (1951).

(Fv_F) is the constant volumetric flow rate through the reactor. Equation (7-2) may be rearranged as follows:

$$\frac{dC_2}{d\theta} + \frac{Fv_F}{V_B} C_2 + r = \frac{Fv_F}{V_B} C_1 \qquad \boxed{R = KCC_2} \qquad (7\text{-}3)$$

The quantity V_B/Fv_F is the holdup time in the reactor and has been designated previously as θ'. If the rate may be expressed in a first-order form and the temperature is constant, Eq. (7-3) is a linear differential equation which can be integrated analytically.   In terms of θ' it may be written

$$\frac{dC_2}{d\theta} + \left(\frac{1}{\theta'} + k\right) C_2 = \frac{C_1}{\theta'} \qquad (7\text{-}4)$$

where k is the first-order rate constant.   Mason and Piret have developed solutions of Eq. (7-4) for both single reactors and when the equation is applied to each reactor vessel in a multistage system.   The Laplace-transform method is used to solve the differential equations applying to a variety of transient conditions for the starting up and shutting down of tank flow reactors.

The application of Eq. (7-4) is illustrated for a single reactor with a constant feed composition in the example that follows:

Example 7-1. Acetic anhydride is hydrolyzed at 40°C in a semibatch system operated by initially charging the stirred-tank reactor with 10 liters of an aqueous solution containing 0.50×10^{-4} g mole of anhydride per cubic centimeter.   The vessel is heated to 40°C, and at that time a feed solution containing 3.0×10^{-4} g mole of anhydride per cubic centimeter is added at the rate of 2 liters/min. Product is withdrawn at the same rate.   The solution density may be assumed constant, and the reaction is kinetically first-order with the following rate equation:

$$r = kC_2, \text{ g moles/(cc)(min)} \dagger$$
$$k = 0.380 \text{ min}^{-1}$$

Determine the concentration of the solution leaving the reactor as a function of time.

Solution.   Equation (7-4) is applicable, and in this case C_1/θ' is a constant.

$$\theta' = \frac{V_B}{Fv_F} = \frac{10,000 \text{ cc}}{2,000 \text{ cc}}$$
$$= 5 \text{ min}$$
$$\frac{C_1}{\theta'} = \frac{3.00 \times 10^{-4}}{5}$$
$$= 6 \times 10^{-5} \text{ g mole/(cc)(min)}$$
$$\frac{1}{\theta'} + k = \tfrac{1}{5} + 0.380$$
$$= 0.580 \text{ min}^{-1}$$

† Data taken from Example 6-7.

The integrated solution of Eq. (7-4) is

$$C_2 = \frac{C_1}{\theta'} \frac{1}{1/\theta' + k} + Ae^{-(1/\theta'+k)\theta}$$

where A is a constant of integration. It may be obtained by noting that, at $\theta = 0$, $C_2 = 0.50 \times 10^{-4}$.

$$A = 0.50 \times 10^{-4} - \frac{C_1}{\theta'} \frac{1}{1/\theta' + k}$$

$$= 0.50 \times 10^{-4} - \frac{6 \times 10^{-5}}{0.580} = -5.34 \times 10^{-5}$$

Then the final expression for the product concentration is

$$C_2 = \frac{6 \times 10^{-5}}{0.580} - 5.34 \times 10^{-5}e^{-0.58\theta}$$

$$= 10.3 \times 10^{-5} - 5.34 \times 10^{-5}e^{-0.58\theta}$$

Table 7-1 shows values of C_2 for increasing time measured from the instant of

TABLE 7-1

Time, θ, min	Exit anhydride conc., C_2, g moles/cc
0	5×10^{-5}
1	7.35×10^{-5}
2	8.67×10^{-5}
3	9.40×10^{-5}
5	10.0×10^{-5}
∞	10.3×10^{-5}

addition of the feed stream. These results indicate that after 5 min the reactor is operating very close to steady-state conditions; i.e., the exit concentration is close to that predicted at infinite time. This latter value could also be obtained directly from Eq. (6-8) for tank flow reactors.

$$C_F - C_E = C_1 - C_2 = \frac{rV_B}{Fv_F} = 0.380C_2\theta'$$

$$C_1 - C_2 = 0.380 \times 5 \times C_2$$

$$C_2 = \frac{C_1}{1 + 1.90} = \frac{3 \times 10^{-4}}{2.90}$$

$$= 10.3 \times 10^{-5} \text{ g mole/cc}$$

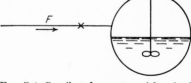

Fig. 7-1. Semibatch reactor with a feed but no withdrawal stream.

Non-first-order Reactions. Figure 7-1 shows a special type of semibatch system in which there is a continuous feed, no withdrawal of product, and a mass m_{0_A} of component A initially in the reactor. The application of Eq. (7-1) will be considered for a reactor of this type when the rate equation is not first-order and when the density of the reaction mixture is not necessarily constant. Isothermal operation is taken up here and the nonisothermal case in the next section.

Since there is no exit stream, Eq. (7-1) takes the following form:

$$F_1 z_{1_A} - rV_B = M_A \frac{d(V_B C_{2_A})}{d\theta} \tag{7-5}$$

The rate r could be expressed in terms of the concentrations of the reactants and this equation integrated numerically for any rate function. However, in this case the concept of a conversion has meaning, and concentration can be expressed in terms of this variable.[1] Define x at any θ as the ratio of the amount of reactant A converted to the total amount of A added up to that time. Then the concentration of A in the reactor will be related to x as follows:

$$C_{2_A} = \frac{(m_{0_A} + F_1 z_{1_A} \theta)(1 - x)}{M_A V_B} \tag{7-6}$$

and $$d(C_{2_A} V_B) = \frac{1}{M_A} \left[-(m_{0_A} + F_1 z_{1_A} \theta)\, dx + (1 - x) F_1 z_{1_A}\, d\theta \right]$$

Substituting this expression into Eq. (7-5) and simplifying lead to the result

$$F_1 z_{1_A} x\, d\theta + (m_{0_A} + F_1 z_{1_A} \theta)\, dx = rV_B\, d\theta \tag{7-7}$$

This is the desired design expression from which the conversion may be computed at any time for this form of semibatch reactor.

Note that, if reactant A were not present in both the initial charge and the feed stream, one of the two terms on the left side of the equation would disappear. Thus if there were no reactant A in the feed stream, the design equation would simplify to

$$m_{0_A}\, dx = V_B r\, d\theta \tag{7-8}$$

This result is identical with Eq. (5-2) for batch reactors. If no A were present in the initial charge to the reactor, the expression would become

$$F_1 z_{1_A}(x\, d\theta + \theta\, dx) = V_B r\, d\theta \tag{7-9}$$

The reactor volume varies with time and may be written

$$V_B = V_0 + \int \left(\frac{dV_B}{d\theta} \right) d\theta \tag{7-10}$$

The initial volume V_0 is equal to m_0/ρ_0, where ρ_0 is the density of the initial mass m_0.

In general, the volume will change owing to changes in both the mass

---

[1] When there are both feed and exit streams, conversion is not a useful concept, because the amount of material to base the definition of conversion upon is not clear.

and the density of the reaction mixture. However, for most systems density changes will be small. With this restriction

$$\frac{dV_B}{d\theta} = \frac{F}{\rho}$$

and Eq. (7-10) gives the simple result

$$V_B = V_0 + \frac{F}{\rho}\,\theta \qquad (7\text{-}11)$$

The rate of reaction is the other quantity that must be expressed in terms of x and θ before the design equation can be integrated. The rate may be expressed formally (for isothermal operation)

$$r = f(C_A, C_B, \ldots) \qquad (7\text{-}12)$$

where $A, B, \ldots$ are reactants and products. The conversion is related to the concentration (moles per volume) of A and B by Eq. (7-6) and by the expression

$$C_B = \frac{(1/M_B)(m_{0_B} + F_1 z_{1_B}\theta) - xb(m_{0_A} + F_1 z_{1_A}\theta)(1/M_A)}{V_B} \qquad (7\text{-}13)$$

In Eq. (7-13) the first term in the numerator represents the total moles of component B added up to time θ (z_{1_B} = weight fraction B in the incoming stream), and the second represents the moles of B reacted at the conversion x (b = moles of B used per mole of A; for example, if the reaction is $A + 2B \rightarrow C + D$, $b = 2$). Similar equations can be written for each product of the reaction. Combination of these expressions for C_A, C_B, $\ldots$ with Eq. (7-12) gives the rate r as a function of x and θ.

In theory the design equation (7-7) can now be integrated by substitution in it of the expressions for V_B and r. However, it is apparent that the functions are sufficiently complicated to prevent analytical integration in most cases. It is worthwhile at this point to note again the reason for the complicated nature of Eqs. (7-6) and (7-13). It is due entirely to the fact that there is a stream entering the reactor. For simple batch operation $F_1 = 0$, and V_B is constant (for the restriction of constant density).

The general method of approach for designing the reactor can be explained as follows:

1. The design equation (7-7) is first written in difference form,

$$(m_{0_A} + F_1 z_{1_A}\theta)\,\Delta x = [(V_B r)_a - F_1 z_{1_A} x_a]\,\Delta\theta \qquad (7\text{-}14)$$

and the value of Δx computed for a chosen time increment $\Delta\theta$. The average values of $V_B r$ and x for the first $\Delta\theta$ can be taken equal to the known values at $\theta = 0$, as a first estimate.

2. The reactor volume at time $\Delta\theta$ is computed from Eq. (7-11).

3. Using the conversion computed in step 1 and the reactor volume V_B from step 2, the concentrations at the end of the first time increment are determined from Eqs. (7-6) and (7-13).

4. The rate at the end of the first increment is then obtained from Eq. (7-12).

5. A second estimate of the average value of rV is determined from the known values at the beginning and end of the increment.

6. The design equation (7-7) is employed to calculate a second estimate of Δx.

7. This procedure is continued until the average values of rV_B do not change. Generally the second estimate is sufficient.

8. Second, third, etc., time increments are chosen and the process in steps 1 to 7 repeated.

It will be observed that these steps follow the same pattern as those employed in stepwise solutions of design equations for simple batch and flow reactors as illustrated in Chaps. 5 and 6. This is true because, from a mathematical viewpoint, the problem is the same regardless of the type of reactor. In each case all the quantities in the differential equation are functions of but two variables (conversion and reactor volume for the flow case and conversion and time for the batch).

Example 7-2. The esterification of acetic acid and ethyl alcohol is to be carried out in a semibatch tank reactor at a constant temperature of 100°C. The alcohol is added to the reactor initially as 400 lb of pure C_2H_5OH. An aqueous solution of acetic acid is then added at a rate of 3.92 lb/min for 120 min. The solution contains 42.6 per cent by weight acid. The density of the solution will increase during the course of the reaction, but to simplify the computations assume that it is constant and equal to that of water.

The reaction is reversible, and the specific rates may be taken as the same as those used in Example 5-2.

$$r = kC_H C_{OH} \qquad k = 4.76 \times 10^{-4} \text{ liter}/(\text{g mole})(\text{min})$$
$$r' = k'C_E C_W \qquad k' = 1.63 \times 10^{-4} \text{ liter}/(\text{g mole})(\text{min})$$
$$CH_3COOH + C_2H_5OH \rightleftharpoons CH_3COOC_2H_5 + H_2O$$

Compute the conversion of acetic acid to ester as a function of time from 0 min until the last amount of acid is added (120 min).

Solution. As the conversion is to be based upon the acetic acid and there is no acid in the initial charge to the reactor, the proper design equation is (7-9). Since the rate constants are in molal units, the concentrations will also be expressed in those units.

If C_H, C_{OH}, C_W, and C_E represent acid, alcohol, water, and ester, concentrations (in pound moles per cubic foot), equations similar to (7-6) and (7-13) are

$$C_H = \frac{F_1 z_{1H} \theta (1 - x)}{M_H V_B} \qquad \text{analogous to Eq. (7-6) with } m_A = 0$$

$$C_{OH} = \frac{\dfrac{1}{M_{OH}} m_{0OH} - x(F_1 z_{1H} \theta) \dfrac{1}{M_H}}{V_B} \qquad \text{analogous to Eq. (7-13) with } b = 1$$

per adding no more alcohol

$$C_W = \frac{(1/M_W)F_1 z_{1W}\theta + xF_1 z_{1H}\theta(1/M_H)}{V_B}$$

$$C_E = \frac{x(F_1 z_{1H}\theta)(1/M_H)}{V_B}$$

Substituting these expressions into the rate equations gives a relationship for the net rate of conversion of the acid in terms of x, θ, and V_B.

$$r = r - r' = \frac{k[F_1 z_{1H}\theta(1 - x)](m_{0OH}/M_{OH} - xF_1 z_{1H}\theta/M_H)}{M_H V_B^2}$$
$$- k' \frac{xF_1 z_{1H}\theta(F_1 z_{1W}\theta/M_W + xF_1 z_{1H}\theta/M_H)}{M_H V_B^2} \qquad (A)$$

where $F_1 = 3.92$ lb/min

$\qquad z_{1H} = 0.426$

$\qquad m_{0OH} = 400$ lb

$\qquad z_{1W} = 1 - 0.426 = 0.574$

$\qquad M_H = $ mol. wt acetic acid $= 60$

$\qquad M_{OH} = $ mol. wt ethyl alcohol $= 46$

$\qquad M_W = $ mol. wt water $= 18$

The rate constants expressed as cubic feet per pound mole per minute become

$$k = 4.76 \times 10^{-4} \frac{1}{28.32} \times 454 = 7.63 \times 10^{-3}$$

$$k' = 2.62 \times 10^{-3}$$

Substituting these results in Eq. (A) to obtain a working expression for the rate (pound moles per cubic foot per min),

$$r = \frac{1.28 \times 10^{-2}\theta(1 - x)(8.68 - 0.0278x\theta)}{60V_B^2} - \frac{4.37 \times 10^{-3}\theta^2 x(0.125 + 0.0278x)}{60V_B^2}$$

$$r = \frac{1}{V_B^2}[21.3 \times 10^{-5}\theta(1 - x)(8.68 - 0.0278x\theta)$$
$$- 7.13 \times 10^{-5}\theta^2 x(0.125 + 0.0278x)] \qquad (A')$$

Since the density is assumed constant, Eq. (7-11) is applicable and the reactor volume in cubic feet is

$$V_B = V_0 + \frac{F_1}{\rho}\theta = \frac{m_0 + F_1\theta}{\rho} = \frac{400 + 3.92\theta}{59.8} = 6.69 + 0.0655\theta \qquad (B)$$

Equation (7-9), in terms of numerical values, may be written

$$F_1 z_{1H}\theta\, dx = V_B r M_H\, d\theta - F_1 z_{1H} x\, d\theta$$
$$3.92 \times 0.426 \times \theta\, dx = V_B r \times 60\, d\theta - 3.92 \times 0.426 \times x\, d\theta$$

or
$$\theta\, dx = 35.9 V_B r\, d\theta - x\, d\theta$$

In difference form this expression becomes

$$\Delta(x\theta) = 35.9(V_B r)_a \, \Delta\theta \qquad\qquad (C)$$

Equations (C), (B), and (A') can now be employed to carry out a stepwise solution. Since the concentration equations have been combined with the rate equation in expression (A'), step 3 in the previously listed sequence can be omitted. The method of solution will be illustrated by following through the procedure step by step.

STEP 1. Choose an initial time increment of 5 min.

The initial volume $V_B = 6.69$ cu ft (based upon density of water at 100°C). The initial rate as computed from Eq. (A') is zero, since θ and x are both zero (i.e., at zero time there is no acid in the reactor). Hence, to obtain a reasonable estimate of $(rV_B)_a$ with which to start the computations, calculate r for an average $\theta = \frac{5}{2} = 2.5$ min.

$$r = \left(\frac{1}{6.69}\right)^2 [21.3 \times 10^{-5} \times 2.5(1-0)(8.68-0) - 0]$$
$$= 1.04 \times 10^{-4} \text{ lb mole/(cu ft)(min)}$$

Hence the first estimate of $(rV_B)_a$ is

$$(rV_B)_a = (1.04 \times 10^{-4}) \times 6.69 = 6.94 \times 10^{-4}$$

From Eq. (C),

$$\Delta(\theta x) = 35.9(6.94 \times 10^{-4}) \times 5 = 0.1250$$
$$\theta_1 x_1 - 0 = 0.1250$$

or
$$x_1 = 0 + 0.0250 = 0.0250$$

STEP 2. The reactor volume at the end of the first increment is given by Eq. (B),

$$V_{B_1} = 6.69 + 0.0655 \times 5$$
$$= 7.02 \text{ cu ft}$$

STEP 4. The rate at the end of the increment is obtained from Eq. (A'), with $x = 0.0250$, $\theta = 5$, and $V_B = 7.02$.

$$r = \left(\frac{1}{7.02}\right)^2 [21.3 \times 10^{-5} \times 5 \times 0.975(8.68 - 0.003)$$
$$- 7.13 \times 10^{-5} \times 0.625(0.125 + 0.0007)]$$
$$r = \frac{0.898 \times 10^{-2} - 0.56 \times 10^{-5}}{7.02^2} = 1.82 \times 10^{-4}$$

STEP 5. At end of increment, $rV_B = (1.82 \times 10^{-4}) \times 7.02 = 12.8 \times 10^{-4}$. At beginning of increment ($\theta = 0$), $rV_B = 0 \times 6.69 = 0$. Hence the second estimate of $(rV_B)_a$ is

$$(rV_B)_a = \frac{12.8 \times 10^{-4} + 0}{2} = 6.40 \times 10^{-4}$$

STEP 6. The second estimate of Δx is given by Eq. (C),

$$\Delta(\theta x) = 35.9(6.40 \times 10^{-4}) \times 5 = 0.115$$

STEP 7. Recalculation of $(rV_B)_a$ will not change the value of 6.40×10^{-4} significantly. Hence at the end of the first increment

$$x_1 = 0.0230$$
$$V_{B_1} = 7.02 \text{ cu ft}$$
$$r_1 = 1.82 \times 10^{-4} \text{ lb mole/(min)(cu ft)}$$
$$(rV_B)_1 = 12.8 \times 10^{-4}$$

For the second increment of 5 min estimate $(rV_B)_a = 18.0 \times 10^{-4}$. Then the first estimate of Δx is

$$\Delta(\theta x) = 35.9(18.0 \times 10^{-4}) \times 5 = 0.323$$
$$\theta_2 x_2 - \theta_1 x_1 = \theta_2 x_2 - 0.115 = 0.323$$
$$x_2 = 0.0115 + 0.0323 = 0.0438$$
$$V_B = 6.69 + 0.0655 \times 10$$
$$= 7.34 \text{ cu ft}$$

$$r = \frac{1}{7.34^2} (1.71 \times 10^{-2} - 0.004 \times 10^{-2}) = 3.18 \times 10^{-4}$$

$$(rV_B)_2 = 23.3 \times 10^{-4}$$

$$(rV_B)_a = \frac{(12.8 + 23.3) \times 10^{-4}}{2} = 18.1 \times 10^{-4}$$

Since this result is close to the first estimate of 18.0×10^{-4}, further calculations of the rate are unnecessary. At the end of the second increment ($\theta = 10$ min),

$$x_2 = 0.0115 + 0.0323 = 0.044$$
$$V_{B_2} = 7.34 \text{ cu ft}$$
$$r_2 = 3.18 \times 10^{-4}$$
$$(rV_B)_2 = 23.3 \times 10^{-4}$$

The results for the entire time interval 0 to 120 min, determined by continuing these stepwise calculations, are summarized in Table 7-2.[1]

Where reverse reactions are important, it has been mentioned that continuous removal of one or more of the products of the reaction will increase the conversion obtainable in a given time. Thus one reactant could be charged to the reactor, a second reactant added continuously, and one of the products withdrawn continuously.[2] This form of semibatch reactor can be treated by modifying the design equation (7-7), the

[1] It should be recognized that this solution of the problem is approximate because of the assumption of constant density of the reaction mixture. However, if density vs. composition data were available, the same stepwise method of calculation could be employed to obtain a more precise solution. The only difference would be that Eq. (B) would have to be modified to take into account density differences.

[2] This withdrawal might be accomplished by distillation, for example.

volume equation (7-10), and the expressions for the concentration, to take into account the withdrawal of material.

7-2. Nonisothermal Design. If the heat of reaction is not negligible, or if it is required to supply or remove thermal energy from the reactor, an energy balance must be included in order to solve semibatch-reactor problems. Owing to the assumption of complete mixing the temperature of the reactor contents will be uniform at any instant. However, this temperature may vary with time. The method of determining the conversion and temperature at any time will be treated for the specific type of semibatch reactor that has no product stream, i.e., the type illustrated in Fig. 7-1.

TABLE 7-2. SEMIBATCH-REACTOR DESIGN FOR ESTERIFICATION OF ACETIC
ACID WITH ETHYL ALCOHOL

Time, min	V_B, cu ft	Conversion of acid, x	Rate, r, lb moles acid reacted/(min)(cu ft)
0	6.69	0	0
5	7.02	0.023	1.82×10^{-4}
10	7.34	0.044	3.2×10^{-4}
20	8.00	0.081	5.2×10^{-4}
40	9.31	0.138	7.0×10^{-4}
60	10.6	0.178	7.3×10^{-4}
80	11.9	0.205	6.9×10^{-4}
100	13.2	0.224	6.3×10^{-4}
120	14.5	0.237	5.7×10^{-4}

Suppose that the temperature of the continuously added stream is t_F. The energy balance is a mathematical expression of the fact that the energy supplied by the heat of reaction and that in the incoming stream must either be absorbed by the reaction mixture or be transferred to the surroundings (i.e., cooling or heating surfaces). If the temperature of the reactor contents at any time θ is t, this expression may be written

$$\frac{-\Delta H}{M_A} r V_B \, d\theta + F_1 \, d\theta \, c_F(t_F - t) = m_t c \, dt + UA(t - t_s) \, d\theta \quad (7\text{-}15)$$

The first term represents the amount of energy supplied by the reaction in an element of time $d\theta$ (ΔH is the heat of reaction per mole and r the rate in mass units). The second represents the amount of energy that is introduced in the continuously added stream, above the reaction temperature t (c_F is the specific heat of the feed). The first term on the right is the part of the supplied energy that remains in the reaction mixture (c is the specific heat of the mixture, and m_t is its total mass, $m_0 + F_1\theta$). The last term represents the energy transferred to the surroundings in the time $d\theta$ (t_s = surroundings temperature; U = over-all heat-transfer coefficient between reaction mixture and surroundings; A = heat-transfer area).

If the reactor operates adiabatically, the last term on the right-hand side of the equation is zero. If the temperature of the stream F_1 is the same as that of the contents of the vessel, the second term on the left side disappears. Under the latter restriction the energy balance reduces to the same form that applies to ordinary batch-operated reactors, i.e., Eq. (5-5).

$$\frac{-\Delta H}{M_A} r V_B \, d\theta = m_t c \, dt + U A (t - t_s) \, d\theta \qquad (5\text{-}5)$$

Normally the feed rate F_1, the feed temperature t_F, and the surroundings temperature t_s are constants in Eq. (7-15). Under these circumstances the energy balance expresses how the temperature of the reaction mixture varies with time. In conjunction with the rate and design equations it can be solved for the conversion and temperature as a function of time by a numerical, stepwise process.

There are a number of means of controlling the temperature in semibatch reactors, suggested by the terms in the energy balance. For example, it may be desirable to maintain this temperature constant, as in the case of an exothermic reaction where a temperature rise beyond a certain level causes unfavorable side reactions. The restriction of a constant temperature eliminates the term $m_t c \, dt$, and the simplified result expresses the requirement placed on the heat-removal term $dQ_s = U A (t - t_s) \, d\theta$. Since the rate changes with time, Q_s likewise must be varied during the reaction in order to maintain the reaction temperature constant. The energy added in the stream F_1 may also be used to control the temperature. This can be carried out in two ways: (1) by varying the feed rate; (2) by changing the feed temperature.

In instances where the reaction rate is very fast and the permissible temperatures are limited, the factors that control the design of the reactor are the rate of energy exchange with the surroundings, the feed temperature, and the feed rate. Under these circumstances the solution of the design problem requires only the energy balance. The amount of material reacted in time $d\theta$ is the total amount of reactant in the feed stream, or $F_1 z_{1_A} \, d\theta$. Hence this quantity multiplied by $-\Delta H$ replaces the first term in Eq. (7-15), and the energy balance may be written

$$\frac{-\Delta H}{M_A} F_1 z_{1_A} \, d\theta + F_1 \, d\theta \, c_F (t_F - t) = m_t c \, dt + U A (t - t_s) \, d\theta$$

or

$$\frac{dt}{d\theta} = \frac{(-\Delta H / M_A) F_1 z_{1_A} + F_1 c_F (t_F - t) - U A (t - t_s)}{m_t c} \qquad (7\text{-}16)$$

Solution of this expression shows how the temperature varies with time for various combinations of feed rate, feed temperature, and heat exchange rate. The conversion obtained under such conditions is always the equilibrium value corresponding to the conditions at the end of the process. Its application to a practical problem is illustrated in Example 7-3.

Example 7-3. Hexamethylenetetramine (HMT) is to be produced in a semi-batch reactor by adding an aqueous ammonia solution (25 per cent by weight NH_3) at the rate of 2 gpm to an initial charge of 238 gal (at 25°C) of formalin solution containing 42 per cent by weight formaldehyde. The original temperature of the formalin solution is raised to 50°C in order to start the reaction. The temperature of the NH_4OH solution is 25°C.

The heat of reaction in the liquid phase may be assumed independent of temperature and concentration and taken as −960 Btu/lb of HMT. If the reactor can be operated at a temperature of 100°C, the rate of reaction is very fast in comparison with the rate of heat transfer with the surroundings. Higher temperatures than 100°C are not desirable because of vaporization and increase in pressure.

It is proposed to cool the reactor by internal coils through which water is passed. The over-all heat-transfer coefficient between the stirred reaction mixture and the cooling water will be 85 Btu/(hr)(sq ft)(°F). The water rate through the coils is such that its temperature varies but little, and an average value of 25°C may be used.

Calculate the length of 1-in.-OD tubing required for the cooling coils.

ADDITIONAL DATA AND NOTES

   Density of ammonia solution = 0.91 g/cc
   Density of formalin (42%) at 25°C = 1.10 g/cc
   Specific heat of reaction mixture (assume constant), c = 1.0 Btu/(lb)(°F)
   Specific heat of 25 wt % NH_3 solution, c_F = 1.0 Btu/(lb)(°F)

The rate of the reverse reaction is negligible.

Solution. Since the rate is very rapid and the reaction is irreversible, the ammonia in the inlet stream will be completely converted to HMT just as soon as it is added to the reactor. According to the reaction

$$4NH_3 + 6HCHO \rightarrow N_4(CH_2)_6 + 6H_2O$$

4 moles of ammonia are required for 6 moles of formaldehyde. Hence the total amount of ammonia required to react with all the charge of formalin solution will be

$$\text{Ammonia required} = \frac{238(8.33 \times 1.10) \times 0.42}{30} \frac{4}{6} \times 17$$

$$= 346 \text{ lb}$$

From the ammonia feed rate of 2 gpm the total time of reaction will be

$$\theta_t = \frac{346}{2(8.33 \times 0.91) \times 0.25}$$

$$= 91.3 \text{ min}$$

The heat-transfer surface is to be sufficient to prevent the temperature from exceeding 100°C. Hence, when $t = 100°C$, the change in temperature with time, or $dt/d\theta$ in Eq. (7-16), will be zero. However, at temperatures below 100°C the driving force $t - t_s$ will be insufficient to transfer enough energy to the cooling coils to maintain a constant temperature. Thus at the start of the addition of ammonia the first term in the numerator of Eq. (7-16), which is positive for an exothermic reaction, will be greater than the sum of the second and third terms, and the temperature of the reaction mixture will increase. From a practical point of view this heating-up period would be reduced to a minimum by shutting off the flow of cooling water until $t = 100°C$.

To determine the required heat-transfer area, Eq. (7-16) may be used with $dt/d\theta = 0$ and $t = 100°C$.

$$UA(t - t_s) = \frac{-\Delta H}{M_A} F_1 z_{1_A} + F_1 c_F (t_F - t)$$

$$85A(100 - 25) \times 1.8 = \frac{-\Delta H}{M_A} F_1 z_{1_A} + F_1 \times 1.0(25 - 100) \times 1.8 \qquad \text{(A)}$$

The heat of reaction $= -960$ Btu/lb HMT. On the basis of NH_3.

$$\frac{\Delta H}{M_A} = -\frac{960 \times 140}{4 \times 17}$$
$$= -1975 \text{ Btu/lb of } NH_3$$

The feed rate is
$$F_1 = 2 \times 60 \times 8.33 \times 0.91$$
$$= 910 \text{ lb/hr}$$
$$z_{1_A} = 0.25$$

Substituting these values in Eq. (A) and solving for the heat-transfer area,

$$A = \frac{910\,(1{,}975 \times 0.25 - 1 \times 75 \times 1.8)}{85 \times 75 \times 1.8}$$
$$= 28.3 \text{ sq ft}$$

If the heat-transfer coefficient of 85 is based upon the outside area of the tubes, the length of 1-in.-OD coil will be

$$L = \frac{28.3}{\pi D} = \frac{28.3 \times 12}{\pi}$$
$$= 108 \text{ ft}$$

An approximate size of the reactor can be obtained by noting that the total mass of mixture at the end of the process will be

$$910\,\frac{91.3}{60} + 238(8.33 \times 1.10) = 3{,}560 \text{ lb}$$

Assuming the density of the HMT solution to be 72 lb/cu ft, the minimum reactor volume is 50 cu ft. A cylindrical vessel 4 ft in diameter and 6 ft in height would provide 33 per cent excess capacity. If the 1-in. tubing were wound into a 3-ft-diameter coil, approximately 12 loops would be needed.

The length of time necessary to raise the reaction temperature from its initial value of 50°C to 100°C can be obtained by integrating Eq. (7-16). With the water rate shut off $UA(t - t_s)$ will be negligible, and the expression becomes

$$\int_{t_0}^{t} \frac{dt}{\dfrac{-\Delta H}{M_A} F_1 z_{1_A} + F_1 c_F (t_F - t)} = \int_{0}^{\theta} \frac{d\theta}{(m_0 + F_1 \theta)c}$$

where m_t has been replaced by $m_0 + F_1\theta$. If ΔH and c do not vary with temperature, this equation may be integrated to yield

$$-\frac{1}{F_1 c_F} \ln \frac{(-\Delta H/M_A)F_1 z_{1_A} + F_1 c_F(t_F - t)}{(-\Delta H/M_A)F_1 z_{1_A} + F_1 c_F(t_F - t_0)} = \frac{1}{F_1 c} \ln \frac{m_0 + F_1\theta}{m_0} \qquad (B)$$

Equation (B) expresses the temperature as a function of time during the heating period. Taking $t_0 = 50°C$, $t_F = 25°C$, and, expressing θ in hours, the time required for t to reach 100°C is given by

$$-\frac{1}{1 \times 910} \ln \frac{449{,}000 + 910 \times 1(25 - 100) \times 1.8}{449{,}999 + 910 \times 1(25 - 50) \times 1.8} = \frac{1}{910 \times 1} \ln \frac{2{,}180 + 910\theta}{2{,}180}$$

$$\ln(1 + 0.418\theta) = -\ln \frac{326{,}000}{408{,}000}$$

$$1 + 0.418\theta = 1.25$$

$$\theta = 0.60 \text{ hr, or } 36 \text{ min}$$

In summary, the reaction temperature would rise from 50°C to 100°C in 36 min after the ammonia feed is started, provided water is not run through the cooling coil. After 36 min the water flow would be started in order to maintain the reactor temperature at 100°C. After a total time of 93 min sufficient ammonia would have been added to convert all the formaldehyde to HMT.

NOMENCLATURE

A Heat-transfer area, semibatch reactor
C Concentration
c Specific heat of reaction mixture
c_F Specific heat of feed
F_1 Feed rate, mass per unit time
F_2 Withdrawal rate, mass per unit time
ΔH Heat of reaction
m_A Mass of component A in a mixture
m_t Total mass
m_0 Initial total mass
M Molecular weight
r rate of reaction in mass or molal units
t Reaction-mixture temperature
t_F Feed temperature
t_s Surroundings temperature
U Over-all heat-transfer coefficient between reaction mixture and surroundings
V_B Volume of semibatch reactor

V_0 Initial volume
v_F Volume of feed per unit mass
x Conversion
z Weight fraction of a component
z_1 Weight fraction in feed stream
z_2 Weight fraction in withdrawal stream
ρ Density of reaction mixture
ρ_0 Initial density
θ' Reaction time in semibatch reactor
θ' Holdup, or average residence, time in semibatch reactor with equal flow rates in and out ($\theta' = V_B/Fv_F$)

PROBLEMS

1. Repeat Example 7-1 in the text with the modification that the effluent from the first reactor is fed to the second. The second reactor originally contains 10 liters of an anhydride solution of concentration 0.50×10^{-4} g mole/cc. Product will be withdrawn from reactor 2 at a constant rate of 2 liters/min. Temperatures in both will be 40°C, and all other conditions will be the same as in Example 7-1.

a. Determine the concentration of anhydride in the solution leaving the second reactor from 0 time until steady-state conditions are reached.

b. Suppose that reactor 2 was originally empty and that its capacity is 10 liters. After it is filled, product is withdrawn at the rate of 2 liters/min. What would be the concentration of the first anhydride solution leaving the reactor?

2. Ethyl acetate is to be produced in a 100-gal reactor operated in the following manner:

a. The reactor originally holds 100 gal (at 100°C) of solution containing 20 per cent by weight ethanol and 35 per cent by weight acetic acid. Its density is 8.7 lb/gal. Assume that this value remains constant for all compositions.

b. The reactor is heated to 100°C and pure ethanol added at a rate of 2 gpm (17.4 lb/gal).

c. Solution is withdrawn at the same volumetric rate.

d. The temperature is maintained at 100°C in the reactor. At this level the rate data are as follows:

$$r = kC_H C_{OH} \qquad k = 4.76 \times 10^{-4} \text{ liter/(g mole)(min)}$$
$$r' = k'C_E C_W \qquad k' = 1.63 \times 10^{-4} \text{ liter/(g mole)(min)}$$

The subscripts H, OH, W, E refer to acid, alcohol, water, and ester. The concentrations are expressed in gram moles per liter. Determine the concentration of ester in the product stream for time values from 0 to 1 hr. What is the per cent conversion of the total amount of ethanol added?

Assume that no water is vaporized in the reactor.

3. Ethyl acetate is to be saponified by adding a 0.05-normal solution of sodium hydroxide continuously to a kettle containing the ethyl acetate.

The reactor is initially charged with 100 gal of an aqueous solution containing 10 g of ethyl acetate per liter. The sodium hydroxide solution is added at a rate of 1.0 gpm until stoichiometric amounts are present.

The reaction is relatively fast and irreversible, the specific-reaction rate being 92 liters/(g mole)(min) at 20°C. Assuming the contents of the kettle are well mixed, determine the concentration of unreacted ethyl acetate as a function of time. At what time will this concentration be a maximum?

CHAPTER 8

CATALYSIS

As kinetic information began to accumulate during the last century, it appeared that the rates of a number of reactions were influenced by the presence of a material which itself was unchanged during the process. In 1836 J. J. Berzelius[1] thoroughly reviewed these reactions and came to the conclusion that a "catalytic" force was in operation in such cases. Among the cases which he studied were the conversion of starch into sugar in the presence of acids, the decomposition of hydrogen peroxide in alkaline solutions, and the combination of hydrogen and oxygen on the surface of spongy platinum. In these three examples the acids, the alkaline ions, and the spongy platinum were the materials which increased the rate and yet were unchanged as the result of the reaction. Although the concept of a catalytic force proposed by Berzelius has now been discarded, the term *catalysis* is retained to describe all processes in which the rate of a reaction is influenced by a substance that remains chemically unaffected.

GENERAL CHARACTERISTICS

8-1. The Nature of Catalytic Reactions. Although the catalyst remains unchanged at the end of the process, there is no requirement that the material not take part in the reaction. Indeed, present-day theories attempting to explain the activity of catalysts postulate that the material does actively take part in the reaction. From the concept of the energy of activation developed in Chap. 3 the mechanism of catalysis would have to be such that the free energy of activation is lowered by the presence of the catalytic material. In other words, a catalyst is effective in increasing the rate of a reaction because it makes possible an alternative mechanism, each step of which has a lower free energy of activation than that for the uncatalyzed process. For example, in the case of the reaction between hydrogen and oxygen in the presence of spongy platinum this concept would suggest that hydrogen combines with the spongy platinum to form an intermediate substance, which reacts with oxygen to provide the final product and reproduce the catalyst.

---

[1] J. J. Berzelius, *Jahresber. Chem.*, **15**:237 (1836).

It is also required that this mechanism involving the platinum surface occur at a faster rate than the reaction between the hydrogen and oxygen alone. That is, the energies of activation for forming the intermediate compounds and for their decomposition into the products are lower than that for the homogeneous combination of hydrogen and oxygen.

In addition to the concept that the catalytic material is unchanged during reaction there are other important characteristics of catalytic reactions. The first is that a relatively small amount of catalyst can cause conversion of a large amount of the reactants. For example, Glasstone[1] points out that cupric ions in the concentration of 10^{-9}-normal appreciably increase the rate of the oxidation of sodium sulfide by oxygen. However, the idea that a small amount of the catalyst can cause a large amount of reaction does not mean that the catalyst concentration is unimportant. In fact, when the reaction does not involve a chain mechanism, it is generally true that the rate of the reaction is proportional to the concentration of the catalyst. This is perhaps most readily understood by considering the case of surface catalytic reactions. To continue with the example of hydrogen and oxygen and a spongy platinum catalyst, the extent of the surface of the platinum influences the rate of the reaction. Indeed, the rate is found to be directly proportional to the platinum surface. Similarly the hydrolysis of esters in an acid solution will depend upon the concentration of hydrogen ion acting as a catalyst.

A second property of a catalytic reaction is that the position of equilibrium in a reversible reaction is not changed by the presence of the catalyst. This conclusion has been verified experimentally in several instances. For example, the oxidation of sulfur dioxide by oxygen has been studied using three catalysts, platinum, ferric oxide, and vanadium pentoxide. In all three cases the equilibrium compositions were the same.

It was shown in Chap. 2 that the equilibrium constant of a chemical reaction is equal to the ratio of the reaction-velocity constants for the forward and reversed reactions. That is,

$$K = \frac{k}{k'} \tag{8-1}$$

If the equilibrium constant is unchanged by the presence of the catalyst, it is apparent that the ratio of the reaction-velocity constants for the forward and reverse reactions must be the same. Therefore the catalyst for promoting the forward direction must also be a catalyst for the reverse process. This has also been verified in the study of the oxidation of sulfur dioxide. Thus platinum, which is an effective catalyst for the

[1] S. Glasstone, "Textbook of Physical Chemistry," p. 1104, D. Van Nostrand Company, Inc., New York, 1940.

forward reaction, also has been found to speed up the decomposition of sulfur trioxide.

Examples have been observed of so-called negative catalysis where the rate is decreased by the catalyst. Indeed, the definition of catalysis in its general form suggests only that the material has an influence on the rate of reaction. Perhaps the most reasonable theory of negative catalysis has been developed for chain reactions. In these cases it is postulated that the catalyst breaks the reaction chains, or sequence of steps in the mechanism of the process. For example, nitric oxide reduces the rate of decomposition of acetaldehyde and ethyl ether. Apparently nitric oxide has the characteristic of combining with the free radicals involved in the reaction mechanism. The halogens, particularly iodine, also act as negative catalysts in certain homogeneous gaseous reactions. In the combination of hydrogen and oxygen, where a chain mechanism is probably involved, iodine presumably acts by destroying the radicals necessary for the propagation of the chains.

8-2. Classification of Catalytic Reactions. Catalytic reactions are conveniently divided into two main groups, depending upon whether the catalyst and the reaction mixture form a homogeneous phase. We have mentioned examples of both homogeneous and heterogeneous cases. The hydrolysis of an ester in an aqueous solution containing hydrogen ions is an example of homogeneous catalysis. On the other hand, the combination of hydrogen and oxygen to form water vapor in the presence of spongy platinum is heterogeneous since the platinum catalyst forms a separate phase from the reaction mixture. Heterogeneous catalysis need not involve only gas and solid phases. For example, in emulsion polymerization the reactants may be in the liquid phase and the catalyst in a solid phase or separate liquid phase.

One of the most common and important industrial examples of homogeneous catalysis is the gas-phase oxidation of sulfur dioxide involved in the chamber process for the manufacture of sulfuric acid. The direct combination of sulfur dioxide and oxygen in accordance with the following reaction

$$2SO_2 + O_2 \rightarrow 2SO_3$$

is a very slow process. However, termolecular reactions (combinations of three molecules of reactants) involving nitric oxide are well known and occur at reasonable velocities. On this basis, the most likely mechanism which has been proposed for the chamber process consists of the following two reactions:

1:          $2NO + O_2 \rightarrow 2NO_2$

2:          $NO_2 + SO_2 \rightarrow NO + SO_3$

Doubling the second and adding it to the first result in an over-all reaction equivalent to the noncatalytic combination of SO_2 with oxygen to form SO_3. The actual mechanisms involved in the chamber process are not definitely known, and the entire process may be quite complicated. However, the mechanism just proposed is probably involved and indicates how the presence of a catalyst, in this case NO, can result in two fairly fast reactions replacing a noncatalytic, slow step.

Homogeneous catalytic reactions can be subdivided into two classifications, gaseous and liquid. The chamber process for the manufacture of sulfuric acid is an example of the first. Homogeneous liquid catalytic reactions are numerous and used widely in industry. Most applications of this type are carried out in batch or continuous-tank-type reactors, such as the hydrolysis of organic esters in acid solutions and the nitration of aromatic liquids with nitric acid in the presence of sulfuric acid.

Reactions in the heterogeneous classification are of considerable significance to engineers. A few industrial applications of current importance are the oxidation of sulfur dioxide on vanadium pentoxide catalysts, the catalytic cracking of petroleum stocks using fixed or fluidized beds of solid catalysts, the oxidation of naphthalene to phthalic anhydride using vanadium pentoxide catalyst, and the manufacture of vinyl chloride by the reaction of acetylene and hydrogen chloride gas on a catalyst of mercuric chloride. In all these examples the reaction mixture is in the gas phase. There are other cases where the reaction mixture is either in both the gas and the liquid phase or in the latter alone. For example, a recently developed desulfurization process for the removal of mercaptans and sulfides from petroleum stocks involves the flow of a liquid-phase reaction mixture over a solid catalyst.

The study of catalysis in such heterogeneous cases is intimately connected with the subject of surface chemistry since surface processes play a dominant part in determining the kinetics of the reactions. The kinetics of this important class of reactions are discussed in Chap. 9, and the basic concepts of surface chemistry are considered in Sec. 8-4. However, before proceeding to these subjects it is worthwhile to consider a simple kinetic treatment of catalytic reactions which frequently may be applied to both homogeneous and heterogeneous cases.

8-3. Elementary Mechanism of Catalytic Reactions.[1] The concept that a catalyst provides an alternate mechanism for accomplishing a reaction, and that this alternate path is a more rapid one, has been developed in many individual cases. The common feature of this idea, in all instances, is that the catalyst and one or more of the reactants

[1] This presentation of a simple mechanism of catalysis follows closely the treatment of K. J. Laidler, "Kinetics and Catalysis," McGraw-Hill Book Company, Inc., New York, 1950.

form an intermediate complex, a loosely bound compound which is unstable. This complex then takes part in subsequent reactions which result in the final products and the regenerated catalyst.

Homogeneous catalysis can frequently be explained by using this concept. Applications of these ideas in homogeneous systems can be illustrated by reference to catalysis by acids and bases. In aqueous solutions acids and bases can increase the rate of hydrolysis of sugars, starch, and esters. The kinetics of the hydrolysis of ethyl acetate catalyzed by hydrochloric acid can be explained by the following mechanism:

1:    $CH_3COOC_2H_5 + H^+ \rightarrow CH_3COOC_2H_5[H^+]$

2:    $CH_3COOC_2H_5[H^+] + H_2O \rightarrow C_2H_5OH + H^+ + CH_3COOH$

For this catalytic reaction to be rapid with respect to the noncatalytic hydrolysis, the free energy of activation of steps 1 and 2 must each be less than the free energy of activation for the noncatalytic reaction,

$$CH_3COOC_2H_5 + H_2O \rightarrow CH_3COOH + C_2H_5OH$$

In a similar way the heterogeneous catalytic hydrogenation of ethylene on a solid catalyst might be represented by the following steps:

1:    $C_2H_4 + H_2[C] \rightarrow C_2H_4[C]H_2$ ΔF_1^*

2:    $C_2H_4[C]H_2 \rightarrow C_2H_6 + [C]$ ΔF_2^*

where [C] is the solid catalyst and $C_2H_4[C]H_2$ represents the complex formed between the reactants and the catalyst. In the second step the complex decomposes directly into the product and the catalyst.[1] The homogeneous reaction, according to the absolute theory of reaction rates discussed in Chap. 3, would be written

$$C_2H_4 + H_2 \xrightarrow{\Delta F^*} \underset{\text{Activated complex}}{C_2H_4 \cdot H_2} \rightarrow C_2H_6$$

where the free-energy change for the formation of the activated complex ΔF^* is the free energy of activation for the homogeneous reaction. The effectiveness of the catalyst is explained on the basis that the free energy of activation of each of the two steps in the catalytic mechanism, ΔF_1^* or ΔF_2^*, is less than ΔF^*.

ADSORPTION ON SOLID SURFACES

8-4. Surface Chemistry and Adsorption. We have seen that the effectiveness of solid surfaces in catalyzing heterogeneous reactions must be due to the interaction between reactants and the surface. Therefore

---

[1] In other more complicated cases the formation of the catalyst and products may require more than one reaction.

it is necessary to investigate how molecules of a fluid can attach themselves to solid surfaces. Even the most carefully polished surfaces are not smooth in a microscopic sense, but irregular with valleys and peaks alternating over the area. The areas of irregularity are particularly susceptible to the presence of residual-force fields. At these locations the surface atoms of the solid may attract other atoms or molecules in the surrounding gas or liquid phase.

Physical Adsorption. As the result of developments in the last few decades it is generally accepted that two main types of adsorption may occur. The first, called physical adsorption, is somewhat similar to the process of condensation. The forces attracting the fluid molecules to the solid surface are relatively weak, and the heat evolved during the adsorption process is of the same order of magnitude as the heat of condensation, that is, 1 to 20,000 cal/g mole. Since the forces of attraction between the fluid molecules and the surface atoms correspond to those assumed in the van der Waals equation of state of gases, this kind of process is frequently called van der Waals' adsorption. Equilibrium between the solid surface and the gas molecules is rapidly attained and easily reversible, because the energy requirements are small. Considered as a reaction, the energy of activation for physical adsorption must be small and in the neighborhood of 1000 cal/g mole. This result follows directly from the fact that the forces involved in physical adsorption are weak. Because of the small forces the energy states of adsorbed molecules are very similar to those of molecules in the gas phase. This in turn means the mechanism of reaction involving such adsorbed molecules cannot have activation energies much different from the corresponding homogeneous reaction. It is concluded that physical adsorption cannot explain the catalytic activity of solids for reactions between stable molecules, because there is no possibility of large reductions in activation energy. Reactions of atoms and free radicals at surfaces sometimes involve small activation energies. In these cases physical adsorption may play a role.

The effect of temperature on the extent of physical adsorption is such that the amount adsorbed decreases rapidly as the temperature is raised and is generally very small above the critical temperatures of the adsorbed component. This is further evidence that physical adsorption cannot play an important part in the actions catalyzed by solids. Thus such adsorption cannot account for the formation of intermediate products between reactants and solid catalysts where the reactant is a gas above the critical temperature. For example, the rate of oxidation of sulfur dioxide on a platinum catalyst is not appreciable below 300°C; yet this is considerably above the critical temperature of sulfur dioxide, 157°C, or oxygen, −119°C. Physical adsorption is not highly dependent upon the irregularities in the nature of the surface but is usually directly pro portional to the amount of surface. The extent of adsorption is no limited to a monomolecular layer on the solid surface, especially nea the condensation temperature. As the layers of molecules build up oi the solid surface, the process becomes progressively more like one o condensation.

While not of direct importance in surface catalysis of reactions of stabl molecules, physical-adsorption studies are valuable in determining th physical properties of solid catalysts. Thus the questions of surface are and pore-size distribution in porous catalysts can be answered fron physical-adsorption measurements. This aspect of physical adsorptioi is considered in Secs. 8-6 and 8-7.

Chemisorption. The second type of adsorption involves forces mucl stronger than in physical adsorption. According to Langmuir's pionee work[1] the adsorbed molecules are held to the surface by valence force of the same type as those occurring between atoms in molecules. Evi dence for these valence forces was presented by Langmuir in his worl with the adsorption of oxygen on tungsten. He observed that a stable oxide film was formed on the surface of tungsten wires in the presence of oxygen. This material was not the normal oxide WO_3, because it exhibited different chemical properties. However, analysis of the walls of the vessel holding the wire indicated WO_3 was given off from the wire surface on decomposition. This suggested the following type of process

$$3O_2 + 2W \rightarrow 2[W \cdot O_3]$$
$$2[W \cdot O_3] \rightarrow 2WO_3$$

where $[W \cdot O_3]$ represents the adsorption compound on the surface of the wire.

Further evidence for the theory that such adsorption involves valence bonds is found in the large heats of adsorption. Observed values are of the same magnitude as the heat of ordinary chemical reactions, that is, 10,000 to 100,000 cal/g mole, and much larger than the corresponding heats of physical adsorption.

Taylor[2] suggested the name chemisorption for describing and distin guishing this second type of combination of gas molecules with solid sur faces. Because of the high heat of adsorption the energy possessed by chemisorbed molecules can be considerably different from that of the molecules by themselves. Hence the energy of activation for reactions involving chemisorbed molecules can be considerably less than that for reactions involving the molecules alone. It is on this basis that chemi sorption offers an explanation for the catalytic effect of solid surfaces.

[1] I. Langmuir, *J. Am. Chem. Soc.*, **38**:221 (1916).
[2] H. S. Taylor, *J. Am. Chem. Soc.*, **53**:578 (1931).

Using the concept of such adsorption, an alternative mechanism can be postulated which may have a lower energy of activation in each step than that for the noncatalytic homogeneous process.

The term activated adsorption has also been commonly used to describe chemisorption, since the adsorbed molecules have received a considerable amount of energy and are now in a more activated, more energetic state. The free energy of activation is much greater than for physical adsorption, which means that the rate of the activated-adsorption process is slower than for the physical process. Thus activated adsorption is a slow process at low temperatures. On the other hand physical adsorption, owing to its similarity to simple condensation, is rapid at low temperatures. Hence at these temperature levels the quantity of material adsorbed is determined entirely by the physical process. The relationship between temperature and quantity adsorbed is as shown in the low-temperature range of Fig. 8-1. As the critical temperature of the component is exceeded, physical adsorption approaches a very low equilibrium value and equilibrium would be reached in a short time, because of the low energy of activation associated with the physical process. However, as the temperature is raised, the amount of activated adsorption becomes important, be-

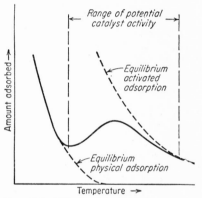

FIG. 8-1. Effect of temperature upon physical and activated adsorption.

cause the rate is high enough for significant quantities to be adsorbed in a reasonable amount of time. In an ordinary adsorption experiment involving the usual time periods the adsorption curve actually rises with increasing temperatures from the minimum value, as shown in Fig. 8-1 by the solid line. When the temperature is increased still further, the decreasing equilibrium value for activated adsorption begins to be significant and the quantity adsorbed passes through a maximum. At these high temperatures even the rate of the relatively slow activated process will be sufficient to give results closely approaching equilibrium. Hence the solid curve representing the amount adsorbed would approach the dotted equilibrium value for the activated adsorption process, as shown in the figure.

It has been explained that the effectiveness of solid catalysts for reactions of stable molecules is dependent upon chemisorption, while the physical process is not significant. Granting this, the temperature range over which a given catalyst is effective must coincide with the range where chemisorption of one or more of the reactants is appreciable. This is indicated on Fig. 8-1 by the dotted vertical lines. Therefore there is a definite relationship between the extent of chemisorption of a gas on a solid and that solid's effectiveness as a catalyst for reactions. For example, many metallic and metallic-oxide surfaces adsorb oxygen easily, and these materials are also found to be good catalysts for oxidation reactions.

An important feature of chemisorption is that its magnitude will not greatly exceed that corresponding to a monomolecular layer. This limitation is due to the fact that the valence forces holding the molecules on the surface diminish rapidly with distance. These forces become too small to form the adsorption compound when the distance from the surface becomes much greater than the usual bond distances.

It was Taylor's[1] concept that the irregularities on the surfaces of a solid lead to particular locations where unbalanced forces of the magnitude of valence forces are in existence. Taylor called these points activated centers. That catalytic surfaces can be highly irregular has been verified by examination in the case of ceramic-type catalysts. However, surface films produced by the condensation of evaporated metal have been shown to have significant catalytic activity, and in this case the irregularities in the surface are less extreme. Beeck and his coworkers[2] formulated catalytic activity, not in terms of active centers on the surface, but in terms of the normal properties of particular faces of the crystalline metals. These properties were assumed to stem from the geometric arrangement of the atoms in the several crystal faces. Regardless of the difficulties in explaining the activity of the solid catalyst surfaces, the concept of activated or chemisorption processes, involving large energies of activation, seems well established. The treatment of the kinetics of solid reactions in Chap. 9 will be developed on the basis of the validity of this concept.

8-5. Quantitative Treatment; Adsorption Isotherms. In order to develop the kinetics of solid catalytic reactions, it is necessary to have available an expression relating the rate and amount of adsorption to the partial pressure of the gas in contact with the adsorbed layer of the surface. At equilibrium and constant temperature this relationship between the pressure and the amount is known as the adsorption isotherm.

A thorough review of the theories of adsorption has recently been presented by Ries.[3] The modern developments are based upon the early work of Langmuir, Freundlich, and Polanyi. The results of both

[1] H. S. Taylor, *Am. Scientist*, **34**:553 (1946).

[2] O. Beeck, A. E. Smith, and A. Wheeler, *Proc. Roy. Soc. (London)*, **A177**:62 (1940).

[3] P. H. Emmett (ed.), "Catalysis," vol. I., chap. 1, Physical Adsorption, Reinhold Publishing Corporation, New York, 1954.

Freundlich and Polanyi, in their present state of development, are not suitable for chemisorption, and hence not useful as a steppingstone toward establishing the kinetics of solid catalytic reactions. Freundlich[1] proposed an empirical relationship for the isotherm,

$$v = \beta(p)^{1/n} \tag{8-2}$$

where v = volume of gas adsorbed
$\quad p$ = pressure of gas
$\quad \beta, n$ = specific constants for system of gas and surface
This equation has been found best suited for correlating experimental data in the region where there are several layers of adsorbed molecules. The Polanyi potential theory[2] originally supposed an adsorption layer several molecules in depth. It was an attempt to treat quantitatively the decrease in attractive forces between molecules and surface atoms as the number of layers increased.

Langmuir's treatment[3] was specifically for chemisorption and limited in its original form to a monomolecular layer. Hence it is the most suitable method upon which to base the kinetics of solid catalytic reactions. His derivations may be carried out by using as a measure of the amount adsorbed either the fraction of the surface covered or the concentration of the gas adsorbed on the surface. Both methods of procedure will be illustrated, although the second is the more useful for kinetic developments and will be used exclusively in Chap. 9.

Several assumptions are pertinent to the Langmuir treatment of the adsorption isotherm:

1. All the surface of the catalyst has the same activity for adsorption; i.e., it is a smooth surface. However, the concept of an irregular surface with active centers can be employed, if it is assumed that all the active centers have the same activity for adsorption and that the rest of the surface has none, or that an average activity can be used.

2. There is no interaction between adsorbed molecules. This means that the amount adsorbed has no effect on the rate of adsorption.

3. All the adsorption occurs by the same mechanism.

Langmuir considered that, in the system of a solid surface and a gas, the molecules of gas will be continually striking the surface and a fraction of these will adhere. However, because of their kinetic, rotational, and vibrational energy the more energetic molecules will be continually leaving the surface. An equilibrium will be established under steady-

[1] H. Freundlich, "Kapillarchemie," Akademische Verlagsgesellschaft m.b.H., Leipzig, 1923.
[2] M. Polanyi, *Verhandl. deut. physik. Ges.*, **18**:55 (1916); *Z. Elektrochem.*, **26**:370 (1920).
[3] *Loc. cit.; J. Am. Chem. Soc.*, **40**:1361 (1918).

state conditions such that the rate at which molecules strike the surface and remain for an appreciable length of time will be exactly balanced by the rate at which molecules detach themselves from the surface.

The rate of adsorption will be equal to the number of collisions, n_c, of gas molecules with the surface per second, multiplied by a factor F representing the fraction of the colliding molecules that adhere. At a fixed temperature the number of collisions will be proportional to the pressure p of the gas, and the fraction F will be constant. Hence the rate of adsorption per unit of bare surface will be $n_c F$. This is equal to kp, where k is a constant involving the fraction F and the proportionality between n_c and p.

Since the adsorption is limited to a monomolecular layer, the surface may be divided into two parts, the fraction θ covered by the monomolecular layer of adsorbed molecules and the fraction $1 - \theta$ which is bare. Since only those molecules striking the uncovered part of the surface can be adsorbed, the rate of adsorption per unit of *total* surface will be proportional to $1 - \theta$; that is,

$$r'_a = kp(1 - \theta) \tag{8-3}$$

The rate of desorption will be proportional to the fraction θ of covered surface and is given by the expression

$$r'_d = k'\theta \tag{8-4}$$

Equating the two rates at equilibrium and solving for the fraction of the surface that is covered,

$$\theta = \frac{kp}{k' + kp} = \frac{K_A p}{1 + K_A p} \tag{8-5}$$

where $K_A = k/k'$ = adsorption equilibrium constant.

The fraction covered is proportional to volume of gas adsorbed, since monomolecular adsorption is assumed. Hence Eq. (8-5), like the Freundlich expression [Eq. (8-2)], may be regarded as a relationship between the pressure of the gas and the volume adsorbed. The Brunauer-Emmett-Teller equation for determining surface areas from the amount adsorbed may be considered an extension of the Langmuir derivation to multilayer physical adsorption. The usefulness of the Brunauer-Emmett-Teller approach in studying catalytic surfaces is considered in Sec. 8-6.

The development of Eq. (8-5) has supposed a smooth surface such that all parts are equally effective for adsorption (assumption 1). If the adsorption occurs only on certain active centers, θ in the equations must be defined as the fraction of the active centers covered, not of the total surface. Similarly the bare surface would be only the fraction of the active centers that was unoccupied.

Langmuir himself proposed a more general equation than (8-5) for the case of a nonuniform surface where there were n_i adsorption sites of different activity. If each site had an adsorption equilibrium constant K_i, the fraction of the surface covered by all the sites was proposed to be

$$\theta = \sum_{i=1}^{i=n} \frac{K_i p}{1 + K_i p} \tag{8-6}$$

Because of the assumptions involved Langmuir's isotherm seldom fits experimental data in a satisfactory way. However, the basic concepts upon which it is based, the ideas of a dynamic equilibrium between rate of adsorption and desorption and a finite adsorption time, appear sound and are of great value in developing the kinetics of solid catalytic reactions. Laidler[1] has termed the Langmuir isotherm an ideal treatment, somewhat analogous to the ideal-gas law. Few systems follow the ideal law, but it serves as a foundation for building modifications to fit experimental results. A number of other isotherms have been proposed for quantitatively explaining chemisorption. These have been reviewed by Laidler.[2] He has summarized also the experimental information available for this type of adsorption.

For developing catalytic rate equations, it is convenient to adapt Eq (8-5) to a form involving surface concentrations rather than a fraction of the surface. Suppose that the total number of active centers, or adsorption sites, per unit area of catalyst is S. Also, suppose S_v is the number of vacant sites per unit area. The rate of adsorption, analogous to Eq. (8-3), will be proportional to the partial pressure of the gas and to S_v. If a molecule of gas A is adsorbed on one site s, according to the equation

$$A + s \rightarrow A \cdot s$$

the rate will be in units of molecules adsorbed per unit area of surface per unit time. It is given by the expression

$$r'_a = kpS_v \tag{8-7}$$

For practical purposes it is desirable to express the rate in terms of moles per unit mass of catalyst. If S_g represents the catalyst area per unit mass and N_0 the molecules per mole (Avogadro's number), such a rate is given by

$$r_a = r'_a \frac{S_g}{N_0} = kp \frac{S_v S_g}{N_0} \tag{8-8}$$

[1] Emmett, *op. cit.*, chap. 3, Chemisorption.
[2] *Ibid.*

The group $S_v S_g/N_0$ represents the number of vacant adsorption sites per unit mass of catalyst divided by Avogadro's number. This may be regarded as a molal surface concentration of adsorption sites per unit mass of catalyst and will be given the symbol C_v. Hence

$$r_a = kpC_v \tag{8-9}$$

where r_a = rate of adsorption in moles per unit time per unit mass of catalyst

p = pressure of gas at surface, atm

C_v = molal concentration of vacant adsorption sites per unit mass of catalyst

k = adsorption velocity constant, time^{-1} atm^{-1}

The rate of desorption from the surface is proportional to the concentration of adsorbed molecules. If this concentration is S_A molecules per unit area of catalyst, the molal surface concentration of sites occupied by A per unit mass may be defined by the expression

$$C_A = \frac{S_A S_g}{N_0} = \text{moles/unit mass of catalyst} \tag{8-10}$$

Hence the rate of desorption, r_d, is

$$r_d = k'C_A \tag{8-11}$$

At equilibrium, the rates will be the same. Equating Eqs. (8-9) and (8-11),

$$kpC_v = k'C_A$$
$$\frac{k}{k'} = K_A = \frac{C_A}{pC_v} \tag{8-12}$$

The ratio of the rate constants K_A is equal to the adsorption equilibrium constant for A on the catalyst surface.

Equation (8-12) and the usual form of the Langmuir adsorption isotherm [Eq. (8-5)] may be shown to be equivalent. Thus the concentration C_A of adsorbed A is proportional to the fraction of the surface covered, θ, while the concentration of vacant sites is proportional to the vacant fraction $1 - \theta$. Hence the ratio $C_A/C_v = \theta/(1 - \theta)$, so that Eq. (8-12) may be written

$$K_A = \frac{\theta}{p(1 - \theta)}$$

or

$$\theta = \frac{K_A p}{1 + K_A p}$$

This is identical with Eq. (8-5).

PHYSICAL PROPERTIES OF SOLID CATALYSTS

It has long been known that increasing the surface area of a solid has a pronounced effect on its ability to adsorb gases and hence on its activity as a catalyst. For example, if a small piece of Raney nickel (highly porous, with a large surface area) is held in the hand, the heat of adsorption is immediately felt. With the same weight of nonporous metal no heating effect is evident. This fact has led to the development of materials[1] with surface areas of as high as 1,000 sq m/g for use either directly as catalysts or as carriers to which the catalytic material can be added. However, until recent times no reliable method was available for measuring such areas. This made it impossible to study different materials for their catalytic activity alone, because the surface areas of the materials might not be the same. In general the relationship between area and catalytic activity had to be on a qualitative basis until a satisfactory method of surface measurement was developed.

The method finally developed is based upon the physical adsorption of gases on the solid at temperatures near the boiling point. Under these conditions adsorption of several layers of molecules on top of each other is possible. Identification of the amount adsorbed when one molecular layer is attained is sufficient to determine a quantity proportional, and perhaps very nearly equal, to the surface area. The historical steps in the development of the Brunauer-Emmett-Teller method[2] are clearly explained by Emmett.[3] There may be some uncertainty as to whether the numbers given by the method are exactly equal to the surface area. However, this is relatively unimportant since the procedure is standardized and results can be reproduced in different laboratories by different investigators. If, as Taylor[4] has proposed, the Brunauer-Emmett-Teller area measurement is included in all publications on solid catalysts, progress in the field would be significantly advanced.

Other properties of solid catalysts may also have an important effect on activity. For example, the surface of a porous catalyst may be very large but the pore size too small to permit the reactants to diffuse into the interior rapidly enough to use all the surface effectively. In addition the pore-size distribution in some instances may be significant. The remainder of this division of the chapter is devoted to a discussion of the measurement of these properties of solid catalysts.

[1] The size of the over-all particles varies from a few microns in the case of fluidized - bed catalysts up to fractions of an inch for fixed bed applications. Further details of size and shape are given in a later section on catalyst preparation.

[2] S. Brunauer, P. H. Emmett, and E. Teller, *J. Am. Chem. Soc.*, **60**:309 (1938).

[3] Emmett, *op. cit.*, vol. I, chap. 2.

[4] H. S. Taylor, *Am. Scientist*, **34**:553 (1946).

8-6. Surface-area Determination.　By surface area is meant the sum of the external, or outer, surface, plus the internal surface formed by walls of pores, cracks, and crevices in the porous material. Usually the inner part is of an order of magnitude greater than the outer surface. However, when carriers are used, the catalytic material may not, in some instances, impregnate all the interior surface of a porous catalyst carrier. In this case the catalyst surface will consist of the external area plus the part of the inner surface covered with catalytic material.　The Brunauer-Emmett-Teller method described in this section does not differentiate between the total surface and that covered by catalyst.

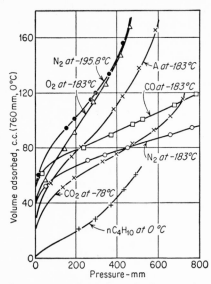

The experimental part of the surface determination requires an all-glass apparatus[1] for measuring the volume of gas adsorbed on a sample of the solid material. The apparatus operates at a low, but variable, pressure from nearly zero up to about 1 atm. Since physical adsorption is desired, the operating temperature is in the range of the normal boiling point. The data obtained are gas volumes at a series of pressures in the adsorption chamber. The observed volumes are corrected to cubic centimeters at 0°C and 1 atm, standard temperature and pressure (STP), and plotted vs. the pressure in millimeters, or the ratio of the pressure to the vapor pressure at the operating temperature. Typical results from

Fig. 8-2. Adsorption isotherms for various gases on a 0.606-g sample of silica gel. [*Reproduced by permission from "Catalysis," vol. I, by P. H. Emmett (ed.), Reinhold Publishing Corporation, New York, 1954.*]

Brunauer and Emmett's work[2] are shown in Fig. 8-2 for the adsorption of several gases on a 0.606-g sample of silica gel.

The curves in Fig. 8-2 are similar to the extent that at low pressures they rise more or less steeply, then flatten out for a linear section at intermediate pressures, and finally increase in slope at higher pressure levels. After careful analysis of many data it was concluded that the lower part

[1] For a complete description of apparatus and techniques see L. G. Toyner, "Scientific and Industrial Glass Blowing and Laboratory Techniques," Instruments Publishing Co., Pittsburgh, 1949. Also see S. Brunauer, "The Adsorption of Gases and Vapors," vol. 1, Princeton University Press, Princeton, N.J., 1943.

[2] S. Brunauer and P. H. Emmett, *J. Am. Chem. Soc.*, **59**:2682 (1937).

of the linear region corresponded to complete monomolecular adsorption. That is, at this point all the surface was covered with a layer of adsorbed gas one molecule thick, and the second layer had not yet accumulated. If this point could be located with precision, the volume of one layer of gas, v_m, could be read from the curve and the surface area evaluated. The Brunauer-Emmett-Teller method locates this point from an equation obtained by extending the Langmuir isotherm to apply to multilayer adsorption. The development is briefly summarized in the following way: Equation (8-5) can be written in terms of the volume adsorbed, v,

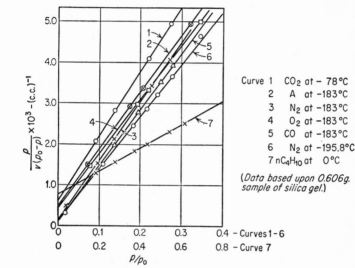

Curve 1 CO_2 at $- 78\,°C$
      2   A at $-183\,°C$
      3   N_2 at $-183\,°C$
      4   O_2 at $-183\,°C$
      5   CO at $-183\,°C$
      6   N_2 at $-195.8\,°C$
      7 nC_4H_{10} at $0\,°C$

(*Data based upon 0.606g. sample of silica gel.*)

FIG. 8-3. Plot of Brunauer-Emmett-Teller equation for data of Fig. 8-2. [*Reproduced by permission from "Catalysis," vol. I, by P. H. Emmett (ed.), Reinhold Publishing Corporation, New York, 1954.*]

by noting that the fraction covered, θ, is equal to the ratio of the actual volume adsorbed to the volume v_m required to cover completely the surface with a monomolecular layer. In other words,

$$\frac{v}{v_m} = \frac{Kp}{1 + Kp} \qquad (8\text{-}13)$$

This expression may be rearranged to read

$$\frac{p}{v} = \frac{1}{Kv_m} + \frac{p}{v_m} \qquad (8\text{-}14)$$

Brunauer, Emmett, and Teller,[1] by adapting this equation to apply to

[1] *Loc. cit.*

multilayer adsorption, arrived at the following result,

$$\frac{p}{v(p_0 - p)} = \frac{1}{v_m c} + \frac{(c-1)p}{c v_m p_0} \qquad (8\text{-}15)$$

where p_0 = saturation or vapor pressure

c = a constant for the particular temperature and gas-solid system

If physical adsorption data are in agreement with Eq. (8-15), a plot of $p/v(p_0 - p)$ vs. p/p_0 should give a straight line. The data of Fig. (8-2) are replotted in this fashion in Fig. (8-3), where they do follow a straight-line pattern. Of additional significance is the fact that such straight lines can be safely extrapolated to p/p_0 equal to zero. The intercept obtained from this extrapolation, along with the slope of the straight line, gives two equations from which v_m, and ultimately the surface area, can be obtained. These equations are

$$\text{Intercept (at } p/p_0 = 0\text{)}, \quad I = \frac{1}{v_m c} \qquad (8\text{-}16a)$$

$$\text{Slope, } m = \frac{c-1}{v_m c} \qquad (8\text{-}16b)$$

Solving them for the volume of gas corresponding to the monomolecular layer gives

$$v_m = \frac{1}{I + m} \qquad (8\text{-}17)$$

The volume v_m can be readily converted to the number of molecules adsorbed. However, to determine the absolute surface area, it is necessary to select a value for the area covered by one adsorbed molecule. If this area per molecule is α, the total surface area is given by the relation

$$S_g = \left[\frac{v_m N_0}{V_m} \right] \alpha \qquad (8\text{-}18)$$

where N_0 = Avogadro's number (6.02×10^{23} molecules/mole)

V_m = volume of 1 mole of gas at conditions of v_m

Since v_m is recorded at STP, V_m = 22,400 cc/g mole. The term in brackets represents the number of molecules adsorbed. If v_m is based upon a 1-g sample, the area is S_g, the total surface per gram of solid adsorbent.

The value of α has been the subject of considerable investigation. Emmett and Brunauer[1] proposed that α is the projected area of a molecule on the surface when the molecules are arranged in close two-dimensional packing. The result they obtained is slightly larger than that obtained

---

[1] P. H. Emmett and S. Brunauer, *J. Am. Chem. Soc.*, **59**:1553 (1937).

by assuming that the adsorbed molecules are spherical and their projected area on the surface is circular. The proposed equation is

$$\alpha = 1.09 \left[\frac{M}{N_0\rho} \right]^{\frac{2}{3}} \qquad (8\text{-}19)$$

where M = molecular weight
ρ = density of adsorbed molecules

The term in brackets represents the volume of one adsorbed molecule. The density is normally taken as that of the pure liquid at the temperature of the adsorption experiment. For example, for N_2 at $-195.8°C$, $\rho = 0.808$ g/cc.

In theory the adsorption measurements can be made with a number of different gases. However, it is found that even though the values of α calculated from Eq. (8-19) for each gas are used, the results are somewhat different (see Example 8-2). Therefore it has become customary to employ N_2 at its normal boiling point $(-195.8°C)$ as a standard procedure. The reason for the variation in areas obtained by using different gases is not well understood. Nevertheless, by carrying out the measurements with one gas at one temperature the results for different catalysts may be compared with confidence.

Using the value of ρ for N_2 at $-195.8°C$, the area per molecule from Eq. (8-19) is 16.2×10^{-16} sq cm, or 16.2 sq A. If this result is used in Eq. (8-18), along with the known values of N_0 and V_m, the area is

$$S_g = 4.35 \times 10^4 v_m \qquad \text{sq cm/g of solid adsorbent}$$

In the usual unit of area of square meters per gram the expression becomes

$$S_g = 4.35 v_m \qquad (8\text{-}20)$$

In using Eq. (8-20) it should be remembered that it is based upon adsorption measurements with N_2 at $-195.8°C$.

Values of the surface area range from less than 1 sq m/g for relatively nonporous substances up to several hundred for solids such as activated carbon and silica gel. Table 8-1 shows surface areas determined by the Brunauer-Emmett-Teller method for a number of common catalysts and carriers.

The calculations of surface areas from adsorption data are illustrated in Examples 8-1 and 8-2.

Example 8-1. From the Brunauer-Emmett-Teller plot in Fig. 8-3 estimate the surface area per gram of the silica gel. Use the data for adsorption of nitrogen at $-195.8°C$.

Solution. From Fig. 8-3, curve 6, the intercept on the ordinate is

$$I = 0.1 \times 10^{-3} \text{ cc}^{-1}$$

The slope of the curve is

$$m = \frac{(5.3 - 0.1) \times 10^{-3}}{0.4 - 0}$$
$$= 13 \times 10^{-3} \; cc^{-1}$$

These values of m and I may be substituted in Eq. (8-17) to obtain v_m.

$$v_m = \frac{10^3}{0.1 + 13} \frac{1}{0.606}$$
$$= 126 \; cc/g \; of \; catalyst$$

The factor 0.606 is introduced since the data in Fig. 8-3 are for a silica gel sample of 0.606 g, while v_m is the monomolecular volume per gram.

TABLE 8-1. SURFACE AREA, PORE VOLUME, AND MEAN PORE RADII FOR TYPICAL SOLID CATALYSTS[†]

Catalyst	Surface area, S_g, sq m/g	Pore volume, V_g, cc/g	Mean pore radius, A
1. Activated carbons......	500–1,500	0.6–0.8	10–20
2. Silica gels............	200–600	0.4	15–100
3. SiO$_2$ Al$_2$O$_3$ cracking catalysts.............	200–500	0.2–0.7	33–150
4. Activated clays........	150–225	0.4–0.52	100
5. Activated alumina......	175	0.39	45
6. Celite (Kieselguhr).....	4.2	1.1	11,000
7. Synthetic ammonia catalysts, Fe..........	....	0.12	200–1,000
8. Pumice...............	0.38		
9. Fused copper..........	0.23		

[†] Taken in part from A. Wheeler, "Advances in Catalysis," vol. III, pp. 250–326, Academic Press, Inc., New York, 1950.

For nitrogen at $-195.8°C$ Eq. (8-20) is applicable.

$$S_g = 4.35 \times 126$$
$$= 550 \; sq \; m/g$$

Example 8-2. For comparison purposes estimate the surface area of the silica gel by using the adsorption data for oxygen at $-183°C$. The density of the liquefied oxygen at $-183°C$ from the International Critical Tables is 1.14 g/cc.

Solution. First the area of an adsorbed molecule of O_2 must be calculated from Eq. (8-19).

$$\alpha = 1.09 \left(\frac{32}{6.02 \times 10^{23} \times 1.14} \right)^{\frac{2}{3}}$$
$$= 14.2 \times 10^{-16} \; sq \; cm$$

With this value of α the area equation [Eq. (8-18)] becomes

$$S_g = \frac{v_m \times 6.02 \times 10^{23}}{22,400} \times 14.2 \times 10^{-16}$$
$$= 3.8 \times 10^4 v_m \quad \text{sq cm/g}$$

From Fig. (8-3), curve 4,

$$I = 0.40 \times 10^{-3} \text{ cc}^{-1}$$
$$m = \frac{(5.4 - 0.4) \times 10^{-3}}{0.38 - 0}$$
$$= 13.2 \times 10^{-3} \text{ cc}^{-1}$$

Then the monomolecular volume per gram of silica gel is, from Eq. (8-17),

$$v_m = \frac{10^3}{0.4 + 13.2} \frac{1}{0.606}$$
$$= 122 \text{ cc/g of catalyst}$$

Finally, substituting this value of v_m in the area expression gives S_g.

$$S_g = 3.8 \times 10^4 \times 122$$
$$= 465 \times 10^4 \text{ sq cm/g, or } 465 \text{ sq m/g}$$

The difference in areas determined from the N_2 and O_2 data is somewhat larger than normally expected for these gases. The adsorption curve for N_2 at $-183°C$ gives a value in closer agreement with 550 sq m/g (see Prob. 1 at end of chapter).

8-7. Pore Size. While a large surface area indicates a high activity, it is not safe to compare catalysts entirely on the basis of surface areas per unit mass. This is because the interior surface of a porous catalyst may not be readily available for reaction. There are many possible reasons for this,[1] but one of the most important is that the size of the openings, or pores, into the interior of a catalyst particle may be too small to allow easy access of the reactants to the inner surface. Hence it is not enough to know the surface area of the catalyst. In order to be able to understand fully how reactions occur in pores, it is necessary to know, in addition, the average pore radius, perhaps the pore-size distribution, and a knowledge of how the pores are interconnected.

The surface area per gram, S_g, determined by the Brunauer-Emmett-Teller method can be used to determine the average pore diameter, provided the total pore volume is also known. If the pores are assumed to be cylindrical and V_g is the pore volume per gram of catalyst, equations can be written for both S_g and V_g in terms of the average radius $\bar{r}$,

$$m_p S_g = 2\pi\bar{r}(n\bar{L}) \tag{8-21}$$
$$m_p V_g = \pi\bar{r}^2(n\bar{L}) \tag{8-22}$$

[1] The effectiveness of internal surfaces is considered in connection with the kinetics of catalytic reactions in Chap. 9.

The quantities in parentheses represent the number of pores in a catalyst particle times the average pore length $\bar{L}$. The mass of one particle is m_p. Dividing these equations gives

$$\bar{r} = \frac{2V_g}{S_g} \tag{8-23}$$

In an excellent review of solid catalyst structure, Wheeler[1] has pointed out that this equation gives results which agree well with other measurements even though there are two major errors. The effect of surface roughness in the pores is not accounted for, since a smooth cylindrical shape is assumed. Also, intersections of pores would affect both the volume and the surface, and this has not been taken into consideration. Wheeler suggests that these opposing errors just about cancel each other.

The pore volume V_g can be estimated in a simple manner by boiling a weighed sample of catalyst in a liquid such as water. After the air in the pores has been displaced, the sample is superficially dried and weighed. The increase in weight divided by the density of the liquid gives the pore volume.

A more accurate procedure is the helium-mercury penetration method. The volume of helium displaced by a sample of catalyst is measured first. Then the helium is removed, and the volume of mercury displaced is measured. Since mercury will not fill the pores of most catalysts, the difference in volumes gives the pore volume of the catalyst sample.

The volume of helium displaced is a measure of the volume occupied by the solid material. From this and the weight of the sample the so-called chemical density, ρ_t, can be obtained. This is the density of the actual solid material in the catalyst. Then the void fraction, or porosity, δ_p, of the particle is available from the equation

$$\delta_p = \frac{\text{void, or pore volume, of particle}}{\text{total volume of particle}} = \frac{m_p V_g}{m_p V_g + m_p(1/\rho_t)}$$

$$\delta_p = \frac{V_g \rho_t}{V_g \rho_t + 1} \tag{8-24}$$

Hence from the helium-mercury method both the pore volume and the porosity of the catalyst particle can be determined. Values of δ_p are about 0.5, indicating that the particle is about half void space and half solid material. Since over-all void fractions δ in packed beds are about 0.4, a rule of thumb for a fixed-bed catalytic reactor is that about 30 per cent of the volume is pore space, 30 per cent solid catalyst and carrier, and 40 per cent void space between catalyst particles. Individual catalysts may show results considerably different from these average values.

Table 8-1 in the third and fourth columns gives typical pore volumes

---

[1] Emmett, *op. cit.*, vol. II, chap. 2.

and mean radii in angstroms (10^{-8} cm). The range 10 to 200 A includes most catalytic materials.

Measuring the pore-size distribution is a difficult problem. The larger-size pores can be measured by forcing mercury under pressure into the catalyst particle. This is called the mercury-porosimeter method.[1] Very high pressures are required to study pores less than 10 A in diameter. For small pores the capillary condensation of a condensable vapor in the pores can be used. Wheeler[2] has made a careful analysis of this method and its recent improvements.

Example 8-3. In an experiment to determine the pore volume, catalyst-particle porosity, and average pore radius the following data were obtained on a sample of activated silica (granular, 4-12 mesh size):
1. Mass of catalyst sample placed in chamber = 101.5 g.
2. Volume of helium displaced by sample = 45.1 cc.
3. Volume of mercury displaced by sample = 82.7.

From adsorption measurements and the Brunauer-Emmett-Teller equation the surface area of the gel is 560 sq m/g.

Calculate the required properties.

Solution. The volume of mercury displaced, minus the helium displacement volume, is the pore volume. Hence

$$V_g = \frac{82.7 - 45.1}{101.5}$$
$$= 0.371 \text{ cc/g}$$

The helium volume also is a measure of the density of the solid material in the catalyst. That is,

$$\rho_t = \frac{101.5}{45.1}$$
$$= 2.25 \text{ g/cc}$$

Substituting the value of V_g and ρ_t in Eq. (8-24) gives the porosity of the silica-gel particles,

$$\delta_p = \frac{0.371 \times 2.25}{0.371 \times 2.25 + 1} = 0.455$$

The average pore size is obtained from Eq. (8-23),

$$\bar{r} = \frac{2 \times 0.371}{560 \times 10^4}$$
$$= 13 \times 10^{-8} \text{ cm, or 13 A}$$

[1] H. L. Ritter and L. C. Drake, *Ind. Eng. Chem., Anal. Ed.*, **17**:787 (1945).
[2] Emmett, *op. cit.*, vol. II, chap. 2.

CATALYST PREPARATION AND GENERAL BEHAVIOR

Now that a brief treatment of the physical properties of solid catalysts has been presented, some attention should be given to methods of preparation. Also, the effect of physical characteristics on the activity of catalyst materials will be considered and catalyst life, poisons, promoters, and inhibitors discussed.

8-8. Preparation Methods. Experimental methods and techniques for catalyst manufacture are particularly important because chemical composition is not enough by itself to determine activity. The physical properties of surface area, pore size, particle size, and particle structure frequently exert a pronounced effect on the activity. These properties are determined to a large extent by the preparation procedure.

To begin with, a distinction should be drawn between preparations in which the entire material constitutes the catalyst and those in which the active ingredient is supported by an inert material, commonly called the carrier. The first kind of catalyst is usually made by precipitation, gel formation, or simple mixing of the components.

Precipitation. Precipitation provides a method of obtaining the solid material in a porous form. It consists, in a general way, of adding a precipitating agent to aqueous solutions of the desired components. Washing, drying, and sometimes calcination and activation are subsequent steps in the process. For example, a magnesium oxide catalyst can be prepared by precipitating the magnesium from nitrate solution by adding sodium carbonate. The precipitate of $MgCO_3$ is washed, dried, and calcined to obtain the oxide. Such variables as concentration of the aqueous solutions, temperature, and time of the drying and calcining steps may influence the surface area and pore structure of the final product. This explains the difficulty in reproducing catalysts and indicates the necessity of carefully following tested recipes. Of particular importance is the washing step to remove all traces of impurities, which may act as poisons.

Gel Formation. A special case of the precipitation method is the formation of a colloidal precipitate which gels. The steps in the process are essentially the same as for the usual precipitation procedure. Catalysts containing silica and alumina are especially suitable for preparation by gel formation since their precipitates are of a colloidal nature. Detailed techniques for producing catalysts through gel formation or ordinary precipitation are given by Ciapetta and Plank.[1]

Mixing of Catalyst Components. In some instances a porous material can be obtained by mixing the components with water, milling to the desired grain size, drying, and calcining. Finally such materials must be

---

[1] Emmett, *op. cit.*, vol. I, chap. 7.

ground and sieved to obtain the proper particle size. A mixed magnesium and calcium oxide catalyst can be prepared in this fashion. The carbonates are milled wet in a ball machine, extruded, dried, and the carbonates reduced by heating in an oven.

Preparation of Catalysts on Carriers. Materials such as silica gel and alumina have a very large surface area. Hence they serve as effective carriers for those catalytic materials which by themselves are difficult to produce in a highly porous form. Carriers are also of value as a means of obtaining a large surface area with a small amount of active material. This is important when expensive agents such as platinum, nickel, and silver are used. Berkman, Morrell and Egloff[1] have treated the subject of carriers in some detail.

The steps in the preparation of a catalyst impregnated on a carrier may include the following: (1) evacuating the carrier; (2) contacting the carrier with the impregnating solution; (3) removing the excess solution; (4) drying; (5) calcination and activation. For example, a nickel hydrogenation catalyst can be prepared on alumina by soaking the evacuated alumina particles with nickel nitrate solution, draining to remove the excess solution, and heating in an oven to decompose the nitrate to nickel oxide. The final step, reduction of the oxide to metallic nickel, is best carried out with the particles in place in the reactor by passing hydrogen through the equipment. Activation in place is necessary to prevent contamination with air and other gases which might react with, and poison, the reactive nickel.

In the example just described no precipitation was required. This is a desirable method of preparation, since thorough impregnation of all the interior surface of the carrier particles is relatively simple. On the other hand, if the solution used to soak the carrier contains potential poisons such as chlorides or sulfates, it may be necessary to precipitate the required constituent and wash out the possible poison.

Little work has been done on determining the optimum amount of catalyst that should be impregnated on a carrier. The amount of gas necessary to cover the surface with a monomolecular layer is available from adsorption measurements. The values of v_m determined from the Brunauer-Emmett-Teller equation [Eq. (8-15)] are generally within the range of 0.1 to 100 cc (STP)/g of catalyst. For N_2 these values correspond to a mass of 1.07×10^{-4} to 0.107 gram, or 0.01 to 10.7 per cent by weight of the carrier. It seems doubtful that more than a monomolecular layer would improve the catalyst performance. Since all parts of the surface are probably not active, less than a complete monomolecular layer is more reasonable. These calculations suggest that the amount of catalyst should be only a fraction of 1 per cent, or at most a few per cent of

[1] S. Berkman, J. C. Morrell, and G. Egloff, "Catalysis," Reinhold Publishing Corporation, New York, 1940.

the mass of the carrier. Platinum catalysts on an alumina carrier with as little as 0.1 to 0.5 per cent by weight platinum have shown good activity for oxidation of sulfur dioxide.

Miscellaneous Procedures. There are numerous special procedures for preparing specific catalysts. An illustration is Raney nickel, a porous material obtained by dissolving the aluminum out of an alloy of nickel and aluminum with an alkaline solution. Ciapetta and Plank[1] have described several of these special techniques.

8-9. Activity and Surface Area. The desirability of a catalytic material having a high surface area is readily understandable. If the activity of a catalyst for a specific reaction is defined as the amount of product produced per unit time per unit mass of catalyst, the activity will increase as S_g increases. However, the activity is frequently not directly proportional to the surface area. One reason, inaccessibility of interior surface due to small pore size, has already been mentioned. It has been found that a direct proportionality is more likely to exist in comparing different batches of the same catalyst with the same reaction. Under these limited conditions surface area is likely to be the only variable. When different catalysts are compared for the same reaction, S_g is not so good a measure of activity. One of the main reasons is based upon the concept that reaction occurs only on certain parts, active centers, of the surface. If the fractions of the total surface that contain active centers are different for different catalysts, then activity will not be proportional to the surface.

8-10. Catalyst Life, Catalyst Poisons. In some reaction systems the catalyst activity decreases so slowly that exchange for new material or regeneration is required only at yearly or longer intervals. Examples are synthetic ammonia catalysts and those containing metals such as platinum and silver. On the other hand, cracking catalysts require frequent regeneration. The decrease in activity is due to poisons, which will be defined here as substances, either in the reactants stream or produced by the reaction, which lower the activity of the catalyst. The frequent regeneration of cracking catalysts is necessary because of the deposition of one of the products, carbon, on the surface.

Poisons can be differentiated by means of the way in which they operate. Many summaries listing specific poisons and classifying groups of poisons are available.[2-4] The following arrangement has been taken in part from Innes.[5]

[1] Emmett, *op. cit.*, vol. I, chap. 7.

[2] Berkman, Morrell, and Egloff, *op. cit.*

[3] R. H. Griffith, "The Mechanism of Contact Catalysis," p. 93, Oxford University Press, New York, 1936.

[4] E. B. Maxted, *J. Soc. Chem. Ind. (London)*, **67**:93 (1948).

[5] Emmett, *op. cit.*, vol. I, chap. 6.

Deposited Poisons. Carbon deposition on catalysts used in the petroleum industry comes under this category. The carbon covers the active sites of the catalyst and may also partially plug the pore entrances. Both result in less active surface and decrease the activity. This type of poisoning is at least partially reversible, and regeneration can be accomplished by burning off the carbon with air. If the carbon is actually deposited as a high-boiling hydrocarbon, it may be possible to regenerate with steam.

Chemisorbed Poisons. Compounds of sulfur and other materials are frequently chemisorbed on nickel, copper, and platinum catalysts. The decline in activity of this type of poisoning stops when equilibrium is reached between the poison in the reactant stream and that on the catalyst surface. If the strength of the adsorption compound is low, the activity will be regained when the poison is removed from the reactants. If the adsorbed material is tightly held, the poisoning is more permanent. The mechanism appears to be one of covering the active sites, which could otherwise adsorb reactant molecules.

Selectivity Poisons. The selectivity of a solid surface for catalyzing one reaction with respect to another is not well understood. However, it is known that some materials in the reactant stream will adsorb on the surface and then catalyze other undesirable reactions, thus lowering the selectivity. The very small quantities of nickel, copper, iron, etc., in petroleum stocks may act as poisons in this way. When such stocks are cracked, the metals deposit on the catalyst and act as dehydrogenation catalysts. This results in increased yields of hydrogen and coke and lower yields of gasoline.

Stability Poisons. When water vapor is present in the sulfur dioxide–air mixture supplied to a platinum-alumina catalyst, a decrease in oxidation activity occurs. This type of poisoning is due to the effect of water on the structure of the alumina carrier. Temperature has a pronounced effect on stability poisoning. Sintering and localized melting may occur as the temperature is increased, and this, of course, changes the catalyst structure.

Diffusion Poisons. This kind of poisoning has already been mentioned in connection with carbon deposition on cracking catalysts. Blocking the pore mouths prevents the reactants from diffusing into the inner surface. Entrained solids in the reactants or fluids which can react with the catalyst, forming a solid residue, can cause this type of poisoning.

Table 8-2[1] lists poisons for various catalysts and reactions.

8-11. Promoters, Inhibitors. Innes[1] has defined a promoter as a substance, added to the catalyst during its preparation, which gives improved activity, selectivity, or stability, for the desired reaction. The promoter

[1] In part from W. B. Innes in Emmett, *op. cit.*, vol. 1, chap. 7, p. 306.

is present in small amount and by itself has little activity. There are various types of promoters, depending on how they act to improve the catalyst. Adding alumina to the iron synthetic ammonia catalyst increases the surface area and in this way increases the activity. Some promoters are also believed to increase the number of active centers and thus make the existing catalyst surface more active.

The published information on promoters is largely in the patent literature. Innes has summarized the data appearing from 1942 to 1952 in tabular form.

TABLE 8-2. POISONS FOR VARIOUS CATALYSTS†

Catalyst	Reaction	Type of poisoning	Poisons
Silica-alumina......	Cracking	Chemisorption Deposition Stability Selectivity	Organic bases Carbon, hydrocarbons Water Heavy metals
Nickel, platinum copper	Hydrogenation Dehydrogenation	Chemisorption	Compounds of S, Se, Te, P, As, Zn, halides, Hg, Pb, NH_3, C_2H_2, H_2S, Fe_2O_3, etc.
Cobalt.............	Hydrocracking	Chemisorption	NH_3, S, Se, Te, P
Silver.............	$C_2H_4 + O \rightarrow C_2H_4O$	Selectivity	CH_4, C_2H_6
Vanadium oxide....	Oxidation	Chemisorption	As
Iron...............	Ammonia synthesis Hydrogenation Oxidation	Chemisorption Chemisorption Chemisorption	O_2, H_2O, CO, S, C_2H_2 Bi, Se, Te, P, H_2O VSO_4, Bi

† In part from W. B. Innes in P. H. Emmett (ed.), "Catalysis," vol. 1, chap. 7, p. 306, Reinhold Publishing Corporation, New York, 1954.

An inhibitor is the opposite of a promoter. When added in small amounts during catalyst manufacture, it causes poorer activity, stability, or selectivity. Theoretically inhibitors can be useful for reducing the activity of a catalyst for an undesirable side reaction. Actually voluntary uses seem to be few.

The materials that are added to reactant streams to improve the performance of a catalyst are called accelerators. They are the counterparts of poisons. For example, steam added to the butene feed of a dehydrogenation reactor appeared to reduce the amount of coke formed and increase the yield of butadiene. The catalyst in this case was iron.[1]

[1] K. K. Kearly, *Ind. Eng. Chem.*, **42**:295 (1950).

NOMENCLATURE

C_v Molal concentration of vacant adsorption sites $= S_v S_g / N_0$
C_A Molal concentration of adsorbed $A = S_A S_g / N_0$
c Constant in Brunauer-Emmett-Teller equation [Eq. (8-15)]
I Intercept on Brunauer-Emmett-Teller plot (Fig. 8-3)
K_A Adsorption equilibrium constant for component A
$\bar{L}$ Mean pore length in a catalyst particle
M Molecular weight
m_p Mass of a single catalyst particle
n Number of pores of mean length $\bar{L}$ and $\bar{r}$ in a catalyst particle
N_0 Avogadro's number, 6.02×10^{23} molecules/mole
p Pressure of gas which is adsorbed on catalyst
p_0 Vapor pressure of gas at temperature of adsorption experiment
$\bar{r}$ Mean radius of pores in a catalyst particle
r_a Rate of adsorption, moles per unit mass of catalyst per unit time
r_d Rate of desorption
r_a' Rate of adsorption, molecules per unit surface of catalyst per unit time
r_d' Rate of desorption
S Total number of adsorption sites per unit area of catalyst
S_v Number of vacant sites per unit area
S_g Total surface area, external plus internal, per gram of catalyst
V_g Volume of interior pores/g of catalyst
V_m Volume at STP of 1 mole of gas (22,400 cc for a perfect gas)
v Volume at STP of gas adsorbed at a pressure p, per gram of catalyst
v_m Volume at STP of a monomolecular layer of gas, per gram of catalyst
α Projected area on the catalyst surface of one molecule of adsorbed gas, sq cm
β Constant in Freundlich adsorption isotherm
δ Void fraction for catalyst bed $=$ volume of void space between particles/total volume
δ_p Void fraction of a single catalyst particle, pore volume/volume of particle
θ Fraction of surface covered by adsorbed gas (in a monomolecular layer)
ρ Density of liquefied or solidified gas at temperatures of adsorption, g/cc
ρ_t Density of solid material in a catalyst particle $=$ mass of catalyst particle divided by volume of solid material in the particle

PROBLEMS

1. Figure 8-3, curve 3, is a Brunauer-Emmett-Teller plot for the adsorption data of N_2 at $-183°C$ on the sample of silica gel. The density of liquid N_2 at this temperature is 0.751 g/cc. Estimate the area of the silica gel in square meters per gram from these data, and compare with the results of Example 8-1.

2. The "point B" method of estimating surface areas was frequently used prior to the development of the Brunauer-Emmett-Teller approach. It involved choosing from an absorption diagram, such as Fig. 8-2, the point where the central linear section began. This procedure worked well for some systems, but it was extremely difficult, if not impossible, to select a reliable point B on an isotherm such as that shown for n-butane in Fig. 8-2.

On the other hand the Brunauer-Emmett-Teller method was found to be reasonably satisfactory for this type of isotherm. Demonstrate this by estimating the surface area of the silica-gel sample from the n-butane curve in Fig. 8-3 (multiply ordinate of n-butane curve by 10). The density of liquid butane at 0°C is 0.601 g/cc.

3. An 8.01-g sample of Glaucosil is studied with N_2 adsorption at $-$ 195.8°C. The following data are obtained:

Pressure, p, mm	Volume adsorbed, cc at STP
6	61
25	127
140	170
230	197
285	215
320	230
430	277
505	335

The vapor pressure of N_2 at -195.8°C is 1 atm. Estimate the surface area (square meters per gram) of the Glaucosil sample.

4. Low-temperature (-195.8°C) N_2 adsorption data were obtained for an Fe-Al$_2$O$_3$ ammonia catalyst. For a 50.4-g sample the results were:

Pressure, p, mm	Volume adsorbed, cc at STP
8	103
30	116
50	130
102	148
130	159
148	163
233	188
258	198
330	221
442	270
480	294
507	316
550	365

Estimate the surface area for this catalyst.

5. Drake and Ritter[1] give the chemical density of the solid material in an activated alumina particle as 3.675 g/cc. The density of the particle determined by mercury displacement is 1.547. The surface area by adsorption measurement is 175 sq m/g.

From this information compute the pore volume per gram, the porosity of the particles, and the mean pore radius.

The bulk density of a bed of the alumina particles in a 250-cc graduate is given as 0.81 g/cc. What fraction of the total volume of the bed is void space between the particles, and void space within the particles?

6. Two samples of silica-alumina cracking catalysts have particle densities of 1.126 and 0.962 g/cc determined by mercury displacement. The chemical density of the solid materials in each case is 2.37 g/cc. The first sample has a surface area of 467 sq m/g and the second 372 sq m/g. Which sample has the larger mean pore radius?

[1] *Loc. cit.*

CHAPTER 9

KINETICS OF SOLID CATALYTIC REACTIONS

With the background of adsorption information gained in Chap. 8 it is now feasible to consider the kinetics of catalytic reactions. The treatment will be limited to a study of rate equations for fluid-solid systems, i.e., reactions in which the reactants and products are fluids and the catalyst a solid. The industrial applications in this category are numerous and include the widely used fixed- and fluidized-bed reactors where the reactants (usually gaseous) are passed over the solid catalyst.

Because of the complex nature of gas-solid catalytic systems the theoretical developments must include a number of postulates. Some of these are subject to question. Also, the resulting rate expressions may be complicated and contain a number of arbitrary constants. For these reasons many engineers prefer to correlate catalytic rate data empirically, using conventional first- or second-order rate equations, either directly or with minor modications. For those who follow this procedure Secs. 9-4 to 9-7 will not be of significance. In these sections the Langmuir-Hinshelwood concepts of reactions between chemisorbed molecules are developed into over-all expressions for the rate in terms of measurable bulk concentrations. Two recent treatments[1,2] of this subject have provided background material for this chapter. The Hougen and Watson approach is most understandable to engineers. Hence their nomenclature of a concentration of adsorbed substance on the surface, rather than a fraction of the surface covered, has been used.

Regardless of the quantitative method of handling the reactions on the surface of the catalyst certain qualitative aspects of catalytic rates and the question of diffusion, both external and internal, must be considered. These topics are taken up in Secs. 9-1 to 9-3 and 9-8 to 9-11.

9-1. Steps in Fluid-Solid Catalytic Reactions. The reactants in the fluid phase must first reach the solid catalyst before surface effects can

[1] K. J. Laidler, in P. H. Emmett (ed.), "Catalysis," vol. I, chap. 3, Reinhold Publishing Corporation, New York, 1954.
[2] O. A. Hougen and K. M. Watson, "Chemical Process Principles," vol. III, McGraw-Hill Book Company, Inc., New York, 1949. See also K. M. Watson and coworkers, *Natl. Petroleum News, Tech. Secs.*, July, 1936, and O. A. Hougen, *Ind. Eng. Chem.*, **35**:529 (1943), for these authors' pioneer work in the field.

occur. Similarly, after the surface reaction the products must be transported to the fluid phase and carried away. These transport processes are involved in formulating over-all expressions for the rate of reaction. By over-all rate is meant the rate of conversion of reactants to products as measured in the fluid phase. Over-all rate expressions are in terms of concentrations or pressures in the bulk-fluid stream. In contrast, the surface rate of reaction is expressed in terms of concentrations of reactants and products on the catalyst surface.

In a general way, the over-all process in a fluid-solid catalytic system can be broken down into five steps:

1. Transport of the reactants from the bulk-fluid phase to the solid-fluid interface.

2. Adsorption of reactants (one or more) on the solid surface.

3. A surface reaction on the solid catalyst.

4. Desorption of products (one or more) from the surface to the fluid-solid interface.

5. Transport of the products from the interface to the bulk-fluid stream.

With porous catalysts internal diffusion through the pores of the catalyst may be involved as well as external diffusion (steps 1 and 5) in the fluid phase surrounding the catalyst particle. Some of the reactant molecules, for example, will not be adsorbed on the outer surface of the catalyst but will diffuse into the pores and be adsorbed and react on the internal pore surface. In such cases two additional steps should be added to the list: ($1a$) internal diffusion of reactants along the pores; ($5a$) internal diffusion of the products along the pores to the outer surface.

Processes 1 and 5 can be handled independently of the others. However, the internal-diffusion steps $1a$ and $5a$ cannot be separated from the surface reactions 2, 3 and 4. Conventionally they have been treated by basing the rate of reaction upon the total catalytic surface (internal and external). Then an effectiveness factor is introduced to take into account the additional diffusion resistance for the part of the reactants that react on the internal surface of the pores. This approach is not necessarily rigorous, because the kinetics of the reaction deep in the pores may not be the same as near the outer surface. Internal diffusion is taken up in Sec. 9-11.

The five processes take place in series. Therefore, under steady-state conditions, the rates of all the individual steps will be identical. The concept of a resistance can be associated with each of the five processes in series, as is done in treating a series heat-transfer process. In the case of heat transfer the rate through each resistance is given by the ratio of the driving force to the resistance, i.e.,

$$Q' = \frac{1}{R_i} \Delta t_i \qquad \frac{c_o - c_i}{R_1} + \frac{c_i - c_b}{R_2} \qquad (9\text{-}1)$$

where Δt_i = temperature difference across resistance R_i
$\qquad Q'$ = rate of heat flow

The driving force Δt_i is linear so that the sum of individual values equals the total temperature difference Δt. For this reason the heat flow may also be expressed by the equation

$$Q = \frac{\Delta t}{R_t} = U \, \Delta t \qquad (9\text{-}2)$$

The over-all heat-transfer coefficient U is equal to the reciprocal of the sum of the resistances

$$U = \frac{1}{R_t} = \frac{1}{\Sigma R_i} \qquad (9\text{-}3)$$

It would be desirable to be able to express the over-all *reaction* rate like Eq. (9-2), i.e., to state that the reaction rate is equal to the reciprocal of the sum of the resistances of each of the five listed steps multiplied by the over-all driving force. The advantage of this form arises in using the rate expression in the design of the reactor. If an over-all rate expression can be used, the design equation involves concentrations only in the bulk fluid, rather than interface values, and can more easily be integrated. For chemical reactions, except first-order ones, this cannot be done. The chief reason is that a rate equation in terms of a linear driving force cannot be written, in general, for process 3. In other words, equations like (9-1) cannot be written for step 3.[1] In the general case it is necessary to compute values of the concentrations at the interface as described in Sec. 9-2.

Fortunately, in many fluid-solid catalytic reactions the diffusion resistances of steps 1 and 5 are negligible and need not be considered in formulating the rate equation. When the resistances of steps 1 and 5 are small with respect to those for 2, 3, and 4, the concentrations at the interface are the same as in the bulk-fluid phase. Then only steps 2, 3, and 4 need be considered, and the over-all rate equation can be written in terms of properties in the bulk fluid. For any specific reaction this situation is more likely at high velocities of fluid past the catalyst surface and at low temperatures. It is at these conditions that the diffusion resistances would be diminished with respect to the reaction resistances. In addition to the effects of operating variables many catalytic chemical reac-

[1] Even for processes 1 and 5 the advantage of the linear equations is lost in formulating over-all rate equations, if the reaction involves more than one reactant or product.

tions are inherently slow with respect to the physical-diffusion process. Under these conditions also steps 1 and 5 may be neglected.

While less common, the other extreme can also exist. For example in batch reactors involving ionic reactions, the rate of mixing determines the over-all rate of reaction. When the reaction rate is very rapid, the physical diffusional processes control the over-all process and kinetics is not involved at all. Over-all rate equations for such cases can easily be written in terms of properties in the bulk fluid, as illustrated in Example 9-2.

In some instances the surface steps 2, 3, and 4 can be approximated by first-order rate equations. Then the driving force is linear for these steps. In addition if but one reactant and product is involved, an over-all rate expression analogous to Eq. (9-3) for heat transfer is possible. In these cases diffusion need not be negligible to be able to use an over-all rate equation in terms of bulk-fluid concentrations. Hurt[1] has developed the "height of a reactor unit" to apply in this situation. The equations for the over-all rate as developed by Hurt are given later in this chapter (Sec. 9-10).

9-2. Diffusion (External). The transport of reactants and products to and from the surface of the catalyst is by the mechanisms of molecular and turbulent diffusion. When the fluid velocities are large with respect to the solid, molecular diffusion will play a small role in determining the rate of mass transfer. This is the situation in fixed-bed reactors, where the mass velocity of fluid past the surface of catalyst particles is high. At the other extreme is the batch reactor with little or no provision made for agitation. In this case molecular diffusion may be the predominant transport process. This situation is to be avoided industrially because the molecular process is so slow that it greatly increases the time of reaction.

Mathematically the rate of mass transfer from a bulk-gas phase to the solid surface is described by the expression

$$N = k_g a(p_g - p_i) \tag{9-4}$$

where N = rate of mass transfer, g moles/(hr) (g of catalyst)

p_g = partial pressure of diffusing gas in bulk stream, atm

p_i = partial pressure of diffusing gas at solid surface, atm

k_g = diffusion-rate constant or coefficient, g moles/(hr)(atm)(sq cm)

a = external area of catalyst particle per unit mass, sq cm/g

For flow reactors, at steady-state conditions, the rate of reaction is equal to the rate of diffusion when both are expressed in terms of the

[1] D. M. Hurt, *Ind. Eng. Chem.*, **35**:522 (1943).

same component.   Hence Eq. (9-4) may be written

$$r = k_g a(p_g - p_i) \qquad (9\text{-}5)$$

Here r is the rate of reaction per unit mass of catalyst, the most desirable basis for solid catalytic reactions.

The diffusion-rate constant depends upon the nature of the diffusing component, turbulence conditions in the vicinity of the catalyst particle, and properties of the entire gas mixture.   Turbulence conditions vary with the type of reactor, and some experimental data are available for estimating k_g for different systems.   For example, Hougen and Wilkie,[1] Hurt,[2] Gamson,[3] and Ergun,[4] among others, have presented correlations of k_g for gases passing over fixed beds of solid particles.   Resnick and White[5] and Kettenring and Smith[6] give similar information for fluidized beds.

Once the diffusion coefficient is known, Eq. (9-5) can be employed to determine the difference in partial pressure between the bulk gas and the solid surface.   This value of $p_g - p_i$ determines the importance of step 1 in the list of five series processes constituting the over-all reaction.   For example, if $p_g - p_i$ is but a few per cent of p_g, diffusion resistances can be neglected.   Then bulk partial pressures can be used in studying the remaining processes 2, 3, and 4.   On the other hand, if $p_g - p_i$ is a large fraction of p_g, serious errors result unless interface values of partial pressure are employed in studying the surface processes.

For liquid-phase reaction mixtures Eq. (9-5) becomes

$$r = k_L a(C_g - C_i) \qquad (9\text{-}6)$$

where the driving force is expressed in concentrations and k_L is the corresponding liquid-phase diffusion coefficient.   Less is known about diffusivities in the liquid phase so that it is more difficult to predict satisfactory values for k_L than for k_g.

For water vapor diffusing from celite particles into air in a fixed-bed arrangement Hougen and Wilkie[7] obtained the following correlations for mass-transfer coefficients:

$$j_D = \frac{k_g M_m p_f}{G}\left(\frac{\mu}{\rho D}\right)^{\frac{2}{3}} = 0.989\left(\frac{d_p G}{\mu}\right)^{-0.41} \qquad (9\text{-}7)$$

$$j_D = \frac{k_g M_m p_f}{G}\left(\frac{\mu}{\rho D}\right)^{\frac{2}{3}} = 1.82\left(\frac{d_p G}{\mu}\right)^{-0.51} \qquad (9\text{-}8)$$

[1] O. A. Hougen and C. R. Wilkie, *Trans. Am. Inst. Chem. Engrs.*, **45**:445 (1945).

[2] *Loc. cit.*

[3] B. W. Gamson, *Chem. Eng. Progr.*, **47**:19 (1951).

[4] Sabri Ergun, *Chem. Eng. Progr.*, **48**:227 (1952).

[5] W. Resnick and R. R. White, *Chem. Eng. Progr.*, **45**:337 (1949).

[6] K. N. Kettenring and J. M. Smith, *Chem. Eng. Progr.*, **46**:139 (1950).

[7] *Loc. cit.*

The first expression applies for d_pG/μ greater than 350 and the second for lower Reynolds numbers. In these equations D is the molecular diffusivity, p_f the pressure film factor (analogous to the mean partial pressure of the inert gas in a single diffusing component in a stagnant gas), and M_m the mean molecular weight.

By combining Eq. (9-7) or (9-8) with Eq. (9-5) to eliminate k_g an expression for $p_g - p_i$ can be developed in terms of the rate of reaction r. This has been done by Yang and Hougen,[1] who then carried the problem further by developing convenient charts for estimating the value of $p_g - p_i$ at various levels of rate of reaction and mass velocity G.

Olson et al.[2] measured the rate of oxidation of sulfur dioxide at various mass velocities past the catalyst surface. Their results can be analyzed for the importance of diffusional resistances. Example 9-1 illustrates the method of using Eqs. (9-5) and (9-8) in an actual case.

Example 9-1. Determine the values of $p_i - p_g$ and p_g for sulfur trioxide from the following data obtained by Olson et al.:[2]

TABLE 9-1

Mean conversion of SO_2, x	Rate of reaction, g moles SO_2/(hr)(g of catalyst)	p_g, atm		
		SO_2	SO_3	O_2
0.1	0.0956	0.0603	0.0067	0.201
0.6	0.0189	0.0273	0.0409	0.187

The reactor consisted of a fixed bed of $\frac{1}{8}$- by $\frac{1}{8}$-in. cylindrical catalyst pellets through which the gases passed at a superficial mass velocity of 147 lb/(hr)(sq ft) and at a pressure of 790 mm. The temperature was 480°C, and the mixture entering the reactor contained 6.42 mole per cent SO_2 and 93.58 mole per cent air. In order to simplify the auxiliary calculations, compute physical properties on the basis of the reaction mixture being air alone. The error introduced by this assumption will be small because of the low concentrations involved.

The external area of the catalyst pellets was 5.12 sq ft/lb of material. The active material, platinum, covered only the external surface and a small section of the pores of the alumina carrier so that internal diffusion need not be considered.

Compute $p_i - p_g$ at each conversion level. Do the results indicate that diffusion resistance is important in this case? Would operation at a lower temperature decrease the relative importance of the diffusion resistances?

Solution. It is necessary first to determine the Reynolds number in order to decide which of Eqs. (9-7) and (9-8) to use.

[1] K. H. Yang and O. A. Hougen, *Chem. Eng. Progr.*, **46**:146 (1950).
[2] R. W. Olson, R. W. Schuler, and J. M. Smith, *Chem. Eng. Progr.*, **46**:614 (1950).

At 480°C the viscosity of air is about 0.09 lb/(hr)(ft).   The particle diameter to employ in Eq. (9-7) or Eq. (9-8) is the diameter of the sphere with the same area as that of the cylindrical pellets.   Hence πd_p^2 will equal the sum of the areas of the lateral and end surfaces of the cylinder.

$$\pi d_p^2 = \pi\, dL + 2\,\frac{\pi d^2}{4}$$

$$= \pi\,\frac{1}{96}\frac{1}{96} + \frac{2\pi}{4}\left(\frac{1}{96}\right)^2$$

$$d_p^2 = \tfrac{3}{2}(\tfrac{1}{96})^2\pi$$

$$d_p = 0.0128 \text{ ft}$$

The Reynolds number is

$$\frac{d_p G}{\mu} = \frac{0.0128 \times 147}{0.09} = 21$$

indicating that Eq. (9-8) should be used.

Combining Eqs. (9-5) and (9-8) to eliminate k_g yields the required expression for $p_i - p_g$.   Since sulfur trioxide, SO_3, is diffusing from the catalyst surface into the gas stream, Eq. (9-5) takes the form

$$r = k_g a(p_i - p_g)$$

The expression for $p_i - p_g$ is

$$p_i - p_g = \frac{M_m p_f r}{1.82 a G (d_p G/\mu)^{-0.51}}\left(\frac{\mu}{\rho D}\right)^{\frac{2}{3}} \tag{A}$$

In determining the Schmidt group, $\mu/\rho D$, the correct value for D would be the diffusivity of sulfur trioxide in a mixture of nitrogen, oxygen, and sulfur dioxide, in which O_2 and SO_2 would also be diffusing.   Hougen and Watson[1] and Wilkie[2] have proposed procedures for evaluating diffusivities in such complex systems. However, in this instance little error will be introduced by considering D the diffusivity of SO_3 in air.   This may be estimated from Gilliland's[3] equation

$$D_{AB} = 0.0043\,\frac{T^{\frac{3}{2}}}{p_t(V_A^{\frac{1}{3}} + V_B^{\frac{1}{3}})^2}\left(\frac{1}{M_A} + \frac{1}{M_B}\right)^{\frac{1}{2}} \tag{9-9}$$

where D_{AB} = diffusivity of A in B, sq cm/sec
    T = temperature, °K
M_A, M_B = molecular weights of A and B
    p_t = total pressure, atm
V_A, V_B = molecular volumes of A and B

[1] "Chemical Process Principles," vol. III, Kinetics and Catalysis, p. 977, John Wiley & Sons, Inc., New York, 1947.
[2] C. R. Wilkie, *Chem. Eng. Progr.*, **46**:95 (1950).
[3] E. R. Gilliland, *Ind. Eng. Chem.*, **26**:681 (1934).

The molecular volumes may be approximated from Table 9-2.

TABLE 9-2†

Molecular volumes of simple gases

H₂	14.3	SO₂	44.8
O₂	25.6	NO	23.6
N₂	31.2	N₂O	36.4
Air	29.9	NH₃	25.8
CO	30.7	H₂O	18.9
CO₂	34.0	H₂S	32.9

Atomic volumes for use in estimating molecular volumes

Bromine, Br	27.0	Oxygen in:	
Carbon	14.8	Aldehydes, ketones	7.4
Chloride, Cl	24.6	Methyl esters	9.1
Hydrogen	3.7	Methyl ethers	9.9
Sulfur, S	25.6	Higher esters and ethers	11.0
		Acids	12.0

† J. H. Arnold, *Ind. Eng. Chem.*, **22**:109 (1930).

The molecular volume of SO_3 may be estimated to be $25.6 + 3 \times 7.4 = 47.8$. Then, substituting numerical values in Eq. (9-9),

$$D_{SO_3\text{-air}} = 0.0043 \frac{(480 + 273)^{\frac{3}{2}}}{1.04[(47.8)^{\frac{1}{3}} + (29.9)^{\frac{1}{3}}]^2}\left(\frac{1}{80} + \frac{1}{28.9}\right)^{\frac{1}{2}}$$

$$= 0.412 \text{ sq cm/sec} = 1.60 \text{ sq ft/hr}$$

The density of air will be

$$\frac{28.9}{359}\frac{273}{480 + 273}\frac{790}{760} = 0.0304 \text{ lb/cu ft}$$

Then the Schmidt group is

$$\frac{\mu}{\rho D} = \frac{0.09}{0.0304 \times 1.60} = 1.85 \text{ (dimensionless)}$$

The mean molecular weight M_m refers to the average value of the bulk and interface gas. As with the other properties there will be little change across the film so that bulk values may be used. However, the molecular weight of the mixture is considerably different from that of pure air and may be easily computed. Hence M_m will be taken as the molecular weight of the bulk gas at each conversion level. For a conversion of 0.1:

	Partial pressure, atm	Mol. fraction	Mol. weight
SO_2	0.0603	0.0580	3.72
O_2	0.2006	0.1930	6.17
SO_3	0.0067	0.0064	0.51
N_2	0.7719	0.7426	20.78
Total	1.0395	1.0000	31.2

The mean molecular weight at a conversion of 0.60, computed in the same way, is 31.7.

The pressure film factor p_f has been developed by Hougen and Watson.[1] For equimolal diffusion p_f is equal to the total pressure. Since there is only a small change in moles in the SO_2 oxidation, and since the partial pressures of reactants and products are small anyway, p_f in this problem will be essentially the same as the total pressure.

The area per unit mass of catalyst is known to be 5.12 sq ft/lb, and the rate is 0.0956 g mole of $SO_2/(hr)(g$ of catalyst) at a conversion of 0.1. Since 1 mole of SO_3 is formed per mole of SO_2, the rate r in Eq. (A) is also 0.0956 lb moles $SO_3/(hr)(lb$ of catalyst).

In Eq. (A) the Schmidt and Reynolds numbers are dimensionless. If p_f is expressed in atmospheres, $p_i - p_g$ will also be in atmospheres, and the group $M_m r/1.82aG$ will be dimensionless.

Substituting the numerical values for a conversion of 0.1,

$$p_i - p_g = \frac{31.2 \times 1.04 \times 0.0956}{1.82 \times 5.12 \times 147} (21)^{0.51}(1.85)^{\frac{2}{3}}$$

$$p_i - p_g = 0.0161 \text{ atm}$$

At a conversion of 0.6

$$p_i - p_g = \frac{31.7 \times 1.04 \times 0.0189}{1.82 \times 5.12 \times 147} (21)^{0.51}(1.85)^{\frac{2}{3}}$$

$$p_i - p_g = 0.00323 \text{ atm}$$

Summarizing these results in tabular form:

Conversion	p_g, atm	$p_i - p_g$	p_i
0.1	0.0067	0.0161	0.0228
0.6	0.0409	0.0032	0.0441

The conditions of low mass velocity and high temperature were chosen to emphasize the importance of diffusion. The values of $p_i - p_g$ are large with respect to p_i, and using p_g values in place of p_i to study the rate of the surface

[1] "Chemical Process Principles," vol. III, p. 977, John Wiley & Sons, Inc., New York, 1947.

steps 2, 3, and 4 would result in serious errors. Operation at lower temperatures would decrease the rate of the surface processes and lessen the relative importance of the diffusion steps.

9-3. Diffusion Controlling. Example 9-1 illustrated an intermediate case where the diffusional resistances (steps 1 and 5) were neither controlling nor negligible. Before leaving diffusion, it is worthwhile to consider the formulation of the over-all rate equation when diffusion is controlling.

It has been mentioned that the diffusion-controlling case is infrequent and also that the kinetics of the reaction are not involved. This second statement is true because the diffusional resistances must be so much slower than the surface processes that the latter can be assumed to occur at equilibrium conditions. For a simple reaction where 1 mole of A is converted to 1 mole of B the over-all conversion may be divided into three series processes,

$$A(p_g) \rightarrow A(p_i) \rightarrow B(p_i) \rightarrow B(p_g)$$

The terms in parentheses represent the partial pressures of the component A or B in the bulk-gas phase (g) or at the catalyst surface (i). The reaction at the surface approaches equilibrium so that the pressures there are related by the surface equilibrium constant K_s,

$$K_s = \frac{p_{B_i}}{p_{A_i}} \tag{9-10}$$

The rate of reaction is given by Eq. (9-5) applied to the diffusion of either A or B as follows:

$$r = k_{g_A}(p_g - p_i)_A \tag{9-11}$$
$$r = k_{g_B}(p_i - p_g)_B \tag{9-12}$$

Solving each expression for the driving force and substituting the value of p_{B_i} from Eq. (9-10) yield

$$p_{g_A} - p_{i_A} = \frac{r}{k_{g_A}}$$

$$p_{i_A} - \frac{p_{g_B}}{K_s} = \frac{r}{k_{g_B}K_s}$$

Adding these two expressions and solving for the rate give

$$r = \frac{1}{1/k_{g_A} + 1/K_s k_{g_B}}\left(p_A - \frac{1}{K_s} p_B\right)_g \tag{9-13}$$

If K_g is considered an over-all diffusion coefficient, Eq. (9-13) may be written

$$r = K_g\left(p_A - \frac{1}{K_s} p_B\right)_g \tag{9-14}$$

in which

$$\frac{1}{K_g} = \frac{1}{k_{g_A}} + \frac{1}{K_s k_{g_B}}$$ (9-15)

Equation (9-14) is the desired rate expression in terms of bulk-stream values of the partial pressures. Equation (9-15) for the over-all diffusion coefficient in terms of the values for the individual diffusing components A and B is analogous to the relationship for the over-all absorption coefficient used in absorption-column design. This is expected because the two processes are of the same type. In absorption, equilibrium is assumed at the interface between phases, and the over-all coefficient is related to the individual film coefficients for the gas and liquid phases and to an equilibrium constant (Henry's-law constant). In the reaction case equilibrium is assumed at the catalyst surface, and Eq. (9-15) gives the over-all rate coefficient.

When more than one reactant or product is involved, the over-all rate equation does not take such a simple form. For example, if the reaction is

$$A + B \rightarrow C$$

the expression for r in terms of the bulk-stream partial pressures becomes a quadratic equation.

Example 9-2. Formulate an expression for the reaction rate of $A + B \rightarrow C$ in terms of bulk-phase partial pressures. Assume external diffusion resistances are controlling.

Solution. The sequence of diffusion of reactants, surface processes, and diffusion of product may be written

$$A \rightarrow A_i$$
$$+ \rightarrow C_i \rightarrow C$$
$$B \rightarrow B_i$$

Since the surface processes exert no control over the rate, they must occur at close to equilibrium conditions. Hence the partial pressures at the catalyst surface are related by the thermodynamic equilibrium constant for the reaction as follows:

$$K_s = \frac{p_{C_i}}{p_{A_i} p_{B_i}}$$

The rate of the reaction is controlled by the diffusion steps and may be written in terms of Eq. (9-5) for each component,

$$r = k_A(p_g - p_i)_A \quad \text{or} \quad p_{A_i} = p_{A_g} - \frac{r}{k_A}$$

$$r = k_B(p_g - p_i)_B \quad \text{or} \quad p_{B_i} = p_{B_g} - \frac{r}{k_B}$$

$$r = k_C(p_i - p_g)_C \quad \text{or} \quad p_{C_i} = p_{C_g} + \frac{r}{k_C}$$

It is required to obtain an expression for the rate in terms of the bulk partial pressures, i.e., to eliminate the p_i values from the rate equations. This is accomplished by substituting the equations for p_{C_i}, p_{B_i}, and p_{A_i} into the equilibrium expression, as follows:

$$p_{C_i} = K_s p_{A_i} p_{B_i}$$

$$p_{C_g} + \frac{r}{k_C} = K_s \left(p_{A_g} - \frac{r}{k_A} \right) \left(p_{B_g} - \frac{r}{k_B} \right)$$

This result is a quadratic equation in r. Solved explicitly for the rate, it yields

$$r = \frac{\beta}{2} \pm \frac{(\beta^2 - 4\gamma)^{\frac{1}{2}}}{2} \qquad (A)$$

where

$$\beta = \frac{p_{A_g} k_A + p_{B_g} k_B + k_A k_B / K_s k_C}{2} \qquad (B)$$

$$\gamma = \frac{(p_{A_g} k_A)(p_{B_g} k_B) - (k_A k_B / K_s)(p_{C_g})}{2} \qquad (C)$$

Equations (A), (B), and (C) constitute the solution for the rate in terms of bulk partial pressures, the diffusion-rate coefficients, and the equilibrium constant. It is apparent from this elementary example that for a bimolecular diffusion-controlling reaction the simple form of rate equation is lost.

9-4. Rates of Surface Processes. *Adsorption.* Steps 2, 3, and 4 of the over-all conversion of reactants to products, as described in Sec. 9-1, refer to surface processes. The methods and their limitations for developing rate expressions for these processes were set forth in Chap. 8. Thus the net rate of adsorption of gas A is the difference between the adsorption and desorption rates given by Eqs. (8-9) and (8-11).

$$r_A = k_A p_{A_i} C_v - k_A' C_A = k_A \left(p_{A_i} C_v - \frac{1}{K_A} C_A \right) \qquad (9\text{-}16)$$

In this equation p_{A_i} is the partial pressure of A in the gas phase at the catalyst surface. It is not equal to the partial pressure p_{A_g} in the bulk-gas stream unless diffusion resistances are negligible as explained in Sec. 9-2. If the resistance to adsorption is negligible with respect to other steps in the over-all conversion process, the concentration C_A of A on the catalyst surface may be assumed to be in equilibrium with the pressure of A in the gas phase. In other words, the net rate of adsorption from Eq. (9-16) approaches zero, and C_A is given by the expression

$$C_{A\text{equil}} = \frac{k}{k'} p_{A_i} C_v = K_A p_{A_i} C_v \qquad (9\text{-}17)$$

in which K_A designates the adsorption equilibrium constant for A.

Surface Reaction. The mechanism assumed for the surface process will depend upon the nature of the reaction. Suppose that the over-all reaction is of the following type:

$$A + B \rightarrow C \tag{9-18}$$

An immediate question arising concerning the surface process is whether the reaction is between an adsorbed molecule of A and a gaseous molecule of B at the surface or between absorbed molecules of both A and B on adjacent active centers. In the former case the process might be represented by the expression

$$A{\cdot}s + B \rightarrow C{\cdot}s \tag{9-19}$$

If the concentration of adsorbed C on the surface is C_C in moles per unit mass of catalyst, analogous to C_A, the net rate of this surface reaction would be

$$r_s = k_s C_A p_{B_i} - k_s' C_C = k_s \left(C_A p_{B_i} - \frac{1}{K_s} C_C \right) \tag{9-20}$$

This equation supposes that the rate of the forward reaction is proportional to the product of the concentration of A on the solid surface and the concentration of B in the gas phase (measured by p_{B_i}). Similarly the rate of the reverse process is proportional to the concentration of adsorbed product C on the surface.[1]

If the mechanism is a reaction between adsorbed A and adsorbed B, the process may be represented by the expression

$$A{\cdot}s + B{\cdot}s \rightarrow C{\cdot}s + s \tag{9-21}$$

In this case only those A molecules will react which are adsorbed on centers immediately adjacent to adsorbed B molecules. Hence the rate of the forward reaction should be proportional to the concentration of the pairs of adjacent centers occupied by A and B. The concentration of these pairs will be equal to C_A multiplied by the fraction of the adjacent centers occupied by B molecules. This fraction is proportional to the fraction of the total surface occupied by B molecules, i.e., to θ_B.[†] If C_t is defined, in an analogous fashion to C_A, as the molal concentration of total centers, then $\theta_B = C_B/C_t$. The rate of the forward reaction according to the mechanism of Eq. (9-21) will be

$$r = k_s C_A \frac{C_B}{C_t}$$

---

[1] This is one of the basic postulates of the Langmuir-Hinshelwood approach to kinetics of catalytic reactions referred to at the beginning of the chapter.

[†] This is strictly correct only if the fraction of the surface occupied by A molecules is small. It would be more accurate to postulate that the fraction of the adjacent centers occupied by B is equal to $\theta_B/1 - \theta_A$. For small values of θ_A the two results are the same.

The reverse rate is proportional to the pairs of centers formed by adsorbed C molecules and adjacent vacant centers. If C_v is the molal concentration of vacant centers, this reverse rate is

$$r'_s = k'_s C_C \frac{C_v}{C_t}$$

Combining these two expressions gives the net surface rate by the mechanism of Eq. (9-21),

$$r_s = \frac{1}{C_t}(k_s C_A C_B - k'_s C_C C_v) = \frac{k_s}{C_t}\left(C_A C_B - \frac{1}{K_s}C_C C_v\right) \quad (9\text{-}22)$$

Equations (9-19) and (9-21) are simply illustrative of those which might be written for the surface reaction between A and B to form C. There are other possibilities, but these two serve to show that different rate equations arise from the different mechanisms.[1] Experimental catalytic rate data can, in theory, be employed to determine the correct mechanism. However, this determination is made difficult by the fact that there are so many steps in the over-all process, i.e., the five steps listed in Sec. 9-1.

If the surface step has a negligible resistance with respect to the others, the process would occur at equilibrium and Eq. (9-20) or (9-22) could be used to relate the concentrations of the reactants and products on the catalyst surface. For example, if the chosen mechanism is Eq. (9-21), the concentration of the product C_C is given by Eq. (9-22) with $r_s = 0$; that is,

$$K_s = \left(\frac{C_v C_C}{C_A C_B}\right)_{equil} \quad (9\text{-}23)$$

where K_s (equal to k_s/k'_s) is the equilibrium constant for the surface reaction.

Desorption. The mechanism for the desorption of the product C may be represented by the expression

$$C \cdot s \rightarrow C + s$$

where C is the product in the gas phase at the catalyst surface. The rate of desorption will be analogous to Eq. (9-16) for the adsorption of A and may be written

$$r_d = k'_d C_C - k_d p_{C_i} C_v = -k_d\left(p_{C_i} C_v - \frac{1}{K_C}C_C\right) \quad (9\text{-}24)$$

9-5. Over-all Expression for the Rate. Equations have been considered for the rate of each of the five steps involved in the conversion of

---

[1] Another possibility would be a reaction between adsorbed B and gaseous A.

reactants to products in a gas-solid catalytic reaction. It is now desirable to see how they may be combined to formulate an over-all expression
for the rate in terms of partial pressures in the bulk-gas stream. To illustrate this, consider the case examined in the preceding section,

$$A + B \to C$$

and suppose that reaction occurs between adsorbed A and adsorbed B
on the catalyst. Under steady-state conditions the rates of each of the
series steps must be the same and equal to the rate of reaction r. The
rate equations, taken from the developments in the prior sections, are
summarized here:

1. Diffusion of reactants (equations from Sec. 9-2),

$$r = k_{g_A}a(p_g - p_i)_A \qquad (9\text{-}5A)[1]$$
$$r = k_{g_B}a(p_g - p_i)_B \qquad (9\text{-}5B)[1]$$

2. Adsorption of reactants (equations from Sec. 9-4),

$$r = k_A\left(p_{A_i}C_v - \frac{1}{K_A}C_A\right) \qquad (9\text{-}16A)$$

$$r = k_B\left(p_{B_i}C_v - \frac{1}{K_B}C_B\right) \qquad (9\text{-}16B)$$

3. Surface reaction [between adsorbed A and adsorbed B, Eq. (9-21)],

$$r = r_s = \frac{k_s}{C_t}\left(C_AC_B - \frac{1}{K_s}C_CC_v\right) \qquad (9\text{-}22)$$

4. Desorption of product (equation from Sec. 9-4),

$$r = -k_C\left(p_{C_i}C_v - \frac{1}{K_C}C_C\right) \qquad (9\text{-}24)$$

5. Diffusion of product (equation from Sec. 9-2),

$$r = -k_{g_c}a(p_g - p_i)_C \qquad (9\text{-}5C)$$

To obtain the over-all expression for the rate, it is necessary to elimi-
nate the surface potentials p_{A_i}, p_{B_i}, p_{C_i}, C_A, C_B, C_C, and C_v from these
equations. To illustrate the method of approach, note that Eq. (9-16A)
may be solved for C_A, yielding

$$C_A = K_A\left(p_{A_i}C_v - \frac{r}{k_A}\right) \qquad (9\text{-}25)$$

---

[1] For this case of 1 mole of A reacting with 1 mole of B the rates of diffusion of A and
B are identical. If the reaction were $A + 2D \to G$,

$$r = k_{g_A}a(p_g - p_i)_A = \tfrac{1}{2}k_{g_D}a(p_g - p_i)_D$$

Solving Eq. (9-5A) for p_{A_i} and substituting this in Eq. (9-25) give

$$C_A = K_A \left[\left(p_{A_g} - \frac{r}{k_{g_A}a} \right) C_v - \frac{r}{k_A} \right] \qquad (9\text{-}26)$$

In a similar fashion, equations for C_B and C_C in terms of p_{B_g} and p_{C_g} can be developed. They are

$$C_B = K_B \left[\left(p_{B_g} - \frac{r}{k_{g_B}a} \right) C_v - \frac{r}{k_B} \right] \qquad (9\text{-}27)$$

$$C_C = K_C \left[\left(p_{C_g} + \frac{r}{k_{g_C}a} \right) C_v + \frac{r}{k_C} \right] \qquad (9\text{-}28)$$

These expressions for C_A, C_B, C_C on the catalyst surface can be substituted in the surface-reaction equation [Eq. (9-22)] to eliminate these variables. The result is as follows:

$$r = \frac{k_s}{C_t} \left\{ K_A K_B \left[\left(p_{A_g} - \frac{r}{k_{g_A}a} \right) C_v - \frac{r}{k_A} \right] \left[\left(p_{B_g} - \frac{r}{k_{g_B}a} \right) C_v - \frac{r}{k_B} \right] \right.$$
$$\left. - \frac{K_C}{K_s} C_v \left[\left(p_{C_g} + \frac{r}{k_{g_C}a} \right) C_v + \frac{r}{k_C} \right] \right\} \qquad (9\text{-}29)$$

Equation (9-29) expresses the rate in terms of the partial pressures in the bulk stream and the various rate and equilibrium constants, except for the surface concentration (C_v) of the vacant active centers on the catalyst. The latter concentration can be related to C_t. In Chap. 8 the total number of active centers per unit area of catalyst was called S. The equivalent "molal" concentration of total active centers would be

$$C_t = \frac{SS_g}{N_b} \qquad (9\text{-}30)$$

This expression is exactly analogous to Eq. (8-10) defining C_A, the concentration of active sites occupied by A. Since the total number of active centers will be made up of those which are vacant, S_v, and those occupied by components A, B, and C,

$$S = S_v + S_A + S_B + S_C \qquad (9\text{-}31)$$

Using expressions like Eq. (9-30) to relate S and C, the total concentration is equal to

$$C_t = C_v + C_A + C_B + C_C \qquad (9\text{-}32)$$

Eliminating C_A, C_B, and C_C by applying Eqs. (9-26), (9-27), and (9-28) and solving for C_v give

$$C_v = \frac{C_t + r(K_A/k_A + K_B/k_B - K_C/k_C)}{1 + K_A \left(p_{A_g} - \frac{r}{k_{g_A}a} \right) + K_B \left(p_{B_g} - \frac{r}{k_{g_B}a} \right) + K_C \left(p_{C_g} + \frac{r}{k_{g_C}a} \right)} \qquad (9\text{-}33)$$

Equations (9-29) and (9-33) constitute the desired over-all expression for the rate r in terms of partial pressures in the bulk-gas stream. The 12 constants involved are the following:

$$k_s = \text{specific-reaction rate for the surface reaction (step 3)}$$

$$k_{g_A}a,\ k_{g_B}a,\ k_{g_C}a = \text{diffusion coefficients for } A, B, \text{ and } C \text{ per unit mass of catalyst}$$

$$k_A,\ k_B,\ k_C = \text{specific-reaction rates for the adsorption of } A, B, \text{ and } C$$

$$K_A,\ K_B,\ K_C = \text{adsorption equilibrium constants for } A, B, \text{ and } C$$

$$K_s = \text{equilibrium constant for the surface reaction}$$

$$C_t = \text{total molal concentration of active sites, or centers, on the catalyst (this is a characteristic property of the catalyst, independent of process variables; it depends primarily upon the catalyst material and method of preparation)}$$

Even for the simple reaction $A + B \rightarrow C$, it is evident that the over-all expression for the rate becomes unwieldy and involves numerous constants. With complex reaction systems the results become even more difficult to handle. This is a consequence of the impossibility of expressing the rate step as a simple product of a linear driving force divided by a resistance.

In order to obtain expressions which are not too complicated for practical use, it has been necessary to assume that the major resistance for the over-all process is concentrated in the diffusion steps (1 and 5), and but one of the surface processes (2, 3, 4).

The reason why the importance of diffusion can be taken into account is that experimental mass-transfer data are available to estimate the diffusion coefficients, that is, $k_{g_A}, k_{g_B}, k_{g_C}$. This permits determination of the partial pressures at the interface, p_i values, without recourse to the over-all expressions such as Eqs. (9-29) and (9-33). The method of doing this has been illustrated in Example 9-1. Such a procedure is not possible for the surface steps 2, 3, and 4, because the constants such as $k_A, k_B, k_C, k_s, K_A, K_B, K_C,$ and C_t cannot be evaluated from available data. Hence these constants must be determined from kinetic measurements using the over-all expressions such as Eqs. (9-29) and (9-33).

Supposing that the diffusion resistances are taken into account by the methods of Sec. 9-2 and p_i values are known, Eqs. (9-29) and (9-33) can be expressed in somewhat simpler form. Thus in the example in question it is not necessary to use Eqs. (9-5A), (9-5B), and (9-5C) to eliminate p_i values. The corresponding form of Eq. (9-29) is

$$r = \frac{k_s}{C_t} \left[K_A K_B \left(p_{A_i} C_v - \frac{r}{k_A} \right) \left(p_{B_i} C_v - \frac{r}{k_B} \right) - \frac{K_C}{K_s} C_v \left(p_{C_i} C_v + \frac{r}{k_C} \right) \right]$$

$$(9\text{-}29A)$$

Similarly, in terms of interface values of the partial pressures, Eq. (9-33) becomes

$$C_v = \frac{C_t + r(K_A/k_A + K_B/k_B - K_C/k_C)}{1 + K_A p_{A_i} + K_B p_{B_i} + K_C p_{C_i}} \qquad (9\text{-}33A)$$

Even these expressions, from which the diffusion resistances have been eliminated, are too complicated for practical use. Note that it would be necessary to evaluate a large number of constants from data of one type, i.e., kinetic measurements. Data are not available for an independent evaluation of specific adsorption rates or adsorption equilibrium constants. These factors explain more concretely the necessity for assuming that but one of the surface steps (2, 3, or 4) has a significant resistance.

The nature of the rate expression when each of the steps is separately assumed to control the surface processes is developed in Secs. 9-6 and 9-7.

9-6. Surface Reaction Controlling. If step 3 controls the surface processes, the concentrations C_A, C_B, and C_C will be those corresponding to equilibrium for the adsorption and desorption steps. Equation (9-17) gives the equilibrium value for C_A. Similar results for C_B and C_C are

$$C_{B_{\text{equil}}} = K_B p_{B_i} C_v \qquad (9\text{-}34)$$
$$C_{C_{\text{equil}}} = K_C p_{C_i} C_v \qquad (9\text{-}35)$$

Substituting these results in Eq. (9-22) for the surface rate gives

$$r = \frac{k_s}{C_t} \left[K_A K_B (p_{A_i} p_{B_i} C_v^2) - \frac{K_C}{K_s} p_{C_i} C_v^2 \right] \qquad (9\text{-}36)$$

The expression analogous to Eq. (9-33A) for C_v can be obtained by substituting the equilibrium values of C_A, C_B, and C_C in Eq. (9-32). The result is

$$C_v = \frac{C_t}{1 + K_A p_{A_i} + K_B p_{B_i} + K_C p_{C_i}} \qquad (9\text{-}37)$$

Now these two equations can be combined to obtain a relatively simple expression for the rate,

$$r = k_s C_t \frac{K_A K_B p_{A_i} p_{B_i} - (K_C/K_s) p_{C_i}}{(1 + K_A p_{A_i} + K_B p_{B_i} + K_C p_{C_i})^2} \qquad (9\text{-}38)$$

This result can be further reduced by noting the relationship between the several equilibrium constants K_A, K_B, K_C, and K_s. If the equilibrium constant for the homogeneous reaction is denoted by K,

$$K = \left(\frac{p_{C_i}}{p_{A_i}p_{B_i}}\right)_{\text{equil}} \tag{9-39}$$

This equilibrium constant is the conventional K for a homogeneous reaction computed from thermodynamic data as outlined in Chap. 2.[1] It may be related to the adsorption and surface-reaction equilibrium constants by the equilibrium equations for each of these processes, i.e., Eqs. (9-17), (9-34), and (9-35). Thus

$$K = \frac{C_C/K_C C_v}{(C_A/K_A C_v)(C_B/K_B C_v)} = \frac{K_A K_B}{K_C}\left(\frac{C_v C_C}{C_A C_B}\right)_{\text{equil}} \tag{9-40}$$

But according to Eq. (9-23) the bracketed group of surface concentrations in Eq. (9-40) is simply K_s. Hence

$$K = \frac{K_A K_B}{K_C} K_s \tag{9-41}$$

Substituting this relationship in Eq. (9-38) gives the final expression for the rate in terms of p_i values.

$$r = k_s C_t K_A K_B \frac{p_{A_i}p_{B_i} - (1/K)p_{C_i}}{(1 + K_A p_{A_i} + K_B p_{B_i} + K_C p_{C_i})^2} \tag{9-42}$$

It is well at this point to review the chief premises involved in Eq. (9-42).

1. It supposes that the surface reaction controls the rate of the three surface steps; i.e., it is based on the assumption that the adsorption and desorption steps have a negligible resistance with respect to the surface rate.

2. The equation applies to the simple reaction $A + B \rightarrow C$. Further, it was assumed that the mechanism of the surface reaction involved the combination of an adsorbed molecule of A and an adsorbed molecule of B.

3. The concepts of adsorption and kinetics used in obtaining Eq. (9-42) rest upon the Langmuir-Hinshelwood theories referred to earlier in the chapter.

It may be observed that Eq. (9-42) does not rule out the possible importance of diffusion steps 1 and 5, because it is written in terms of interfacial partial pressures. These p_i values may be computed from bulk partial pressures (p_g) as illustrated in Example 9-1.

The development of Eq. (9-42) has been carried out in detail to illustrate the methods employed. It is now desirable to consider briefly the

---

[1] It is supposed that the reaction mixture behaves as a perfect gas. This assumption will be made regarding thermodynamic behavior here in order not to complicate the kinetic problems.

form of the equations obtained when adsorption or desorption is assumed to control the surface processes.

9-7. Adsorption or Desorption Processes Controlling. Still retaining the simple reaction $A + B \rightarrow C$, suppose that the adsorption of A is the slow step. Then the adsorption of B, the surface reaction, and the desorption of C will occur at equilibrium. The rate can be formulated from the adsorption equation (9-16A). The value of C_A in this expression is obtained from the equilibrium equations for the surface rate [Eq. (9-23)], adsorption of B [Eq. (9-34)], and desorption of C [Eq. (9-35)]. Proceeding to do this,

$$C_A = \frac{C_v C_C}{K_s C_B} = \frac{C_v(K_C p_{C_i} C_v)}{K_s(K_B p_{B_i} C_v)} = \frac{C_v K_C p_{C_i}}{K_s K_B p_{B_i}}$$

From the relationship between the several equilibrium constants [Eq. (9-41)] the expression for C_A may be simplified to the form

$$C_A = \frac{K_A}{K} \frac{C_v p_{C_i}}{p_{B_i}} \tag{9-43}$$

Substituting this value of C_A in the rate-controlling equation (9-16A) gives

$$r = k_A C_v \left(p_{A_i} - \frac{1}{K} \frac{p_{C_i}}{p_{B_i}} \right) \tag{9-44}$$

The expression for C_v can be formulated from Eq. (9-32), the equilibrium values of C_B and C_C from Eqs. (9-34) and (9-35), and C_A from Eq. (9-43). With this expression for C_v substituted in Eq. (9-44) a final rate equation when adsorption of A controls the process is obtained. It is

Derive this eq $\rightarrow$
$$r = \frac{k_A C_t[p_{A_i} - (1/K)(p_{C_i}/p_{B_i})]}{1 + K_B p_{B_i} + (K_A/K)(p_{C_i}/p_{B_i}) + p_{C_i} K_C} \tag{9-45}$$

If, instead of adsorption, the rate of desorption of the product C controls the whole reaction, the expression for r should be formulated from Eq. (9-24). The adsorption and surface steps will occur at equilibrium conditions. Substituting the equilibrium values of C_C and C_v in Eq. (9-24) leads to the result

$$r = k_C C_t K \frac{p_{A_i} p_{B_i} - (1/K)p_{C_i}}{(1 + K_A p_{A_i} + K_B p_{B_i} + K_C K p_{A_i} p_{B_i} + K_{C_i} p_{C_i})} \tag{9-46}$$

9-8. Qualitative Analysis of Rate Equations. The procedure for developing rate expressions in terms of bulk gas properties according to the Langmuir–Hougen and Watson concepts has been illustrated for a simple reaction in Secs. 9-5 to 9-7. Hougen and Yang[1] have considered

[1] *Loc. cit.*

a number of different kinds of reactions and mechanisms and examined the results when adsorption, desorption, or surface reaction is controlling. By dividing the final equation into a kinetic coefficient [$k_C C_t K$ in Eq. (9-46)], a driving force [$p_{A_i} p_{B_i} - (1/K) p_{C_i}$], and an adsorption term $(1 + K_A p_{A_i} + K_B p_{B_i} + K_C K p_{A_i} p_{B_i})$ they were able to prepare tables from which the rate equation for a specific situation could be quickly assembled.

Such equations as (9-42), (9-45), and (9-46) will have value if they can be used to predict the rate over a wide range of conditions and hence be suitable for use in reactor design. To be used as working expressions, the various constants (kinetic and equilibrium)[1] must be given numerical values. It has not proved possible to obtain K values from adsorption measurements which can be used with confidence in rate equations. Hence all the constants must be determined from experimental kinetic data. This means, for example, that $k_C C_t$, K_A, K_B, and K_C in Eq. (9-46) would be obtained from rate measurements. Since four-constant equations offer considerable flexibility, it is frequently possible to fit experimental data with equations based upon several different mechanisms and assumptions regarding the step which is controlling. This situation makes it hazardous to propose a specific mechanism for the reaction and difficult to evaluate the several assumptions used in developing the rate equations.

The quantitative interpretation of kinetic data in terms of the theoretical equations is discussed in Sec. 9-9 with an illustrative example. However, before proceeding to the evaluation of constants in rate equations, it is helpful to consider some of the implications of Eqs. (9-42), (9-45), and (9-46) from a qualitative point of view.

The adsorption terms in the denominator are all different. For surface-rate controlling, adsorption equilibrium groups ($K p_i$) are included for each component, and the entire term is squared because reaction is between adsorbed A and adsorbed B. For adsorption of A controlling, no group for the adsorption of A is present, and the entire term is to the first power. For desorption controlling, no group for C is in the adsorption term. These differences result in separate and distinct relationships between the pressure and the rate and provide another method for studying the mechanism and controlling step of a reaction.[2] This qualitative analysis of the effect of pressure tends to overcome the disadvantage of

---

[1] Equations (9-42), (9-45), and (9-46) were developed for constant-temperature conditions. Hence the various specific rates k and equilibrium constants K are termed constants. They are, in theory, constant with respect to pressure and conversion changes, but not temperature variations.

[2] It is necessary to postulate both a controlling step and a mechanism (for the surface reaction) before a unique rate equation can be developed.

the equations due to the large number of unknown constants. Temperature is not so useful a variable as pressure in this qualitative study of mechanism, because all the constants are strong functions of temperature and many of the same ones are part of each equation. The primary value of temperature is to determine the energies of activation for the adsorption and surface processes. Measurements at different conversion levels can be used to study mechanism, but in general it is difficult to draw any conclusions from qualitative trends. Quantitative treatment of conversion vs. rate data is illustrated in Example 9-4. The importance of total pressure as a variable to study mechanism is shown in Example 9-3.

Example 9-3. A solid-catalyzed gaseous reaction has the form

$$A + B \rightarrow C$$

Sketch curves of the initial rate (rate at zero conversion) vs. the total pressure for the following cases:

1. The mechanism is the reaction between adsorbed A and adsorbed B molecules on the catalyst. The controlling step is the surface reaction.
2. Same mechanism as (1), but the adsorption of A is controlling.
3. Same mechanism as (1), but the desorption of C is controlling. Assume that the over-all equilibrium constant is large with respect to the adsorption equilibrium constants.
4. The mechanism is a reaction between adsorbed A and B in the gas phase. The controlling step is the surface reaction.

In each instance suppose that the initial reactants A and B are present in an equimolal mixture. Also, suppose that diffusional resistances are negligible.

Solution. At zero conversion $p_C = 0$, and for an equimolal mixture

$$p_A = p_B = \tfrac{1}{2} p_t$$

For the first three cases Eqs. (9-42), (9-45), and (9-46) are the appropriate rate equations. At initial conditions Eq. (9-42) simplifies to

$$r_0 = k_s C_t K_A K_B \frac{\tfrac{1}{4} p_t^2}{[1 + \tfrac{1}{2}(K_A + K_B)p_t]^2}$$

By combining constants this expression may be written

$$r_0 = \frac{a p_t^2}{(1 + b p_t)^2} \tag{A}$$

In a similar manner Eq. (9-45) for the adsorption of A controlling may be reduced to the form

$$r_0 = k_A C_t \frac{\tfrac{1}{2} p_t}{1 + \tfrac{1}{2} K_B p_t} = \frac{a'p}{1 + b'p} \tag{B}$$

Equation (9-46) for the case where desorption of C is controlling may be written

$$r_0 = k_C C_t K \frac{\frac{1}{4}p_t^2}{1 + \frac{1}{2}(K_A + K_B)p_t + \frac{1}{4}K_C K p_t^2}$$

If the equilibrium constant K is large with respect to K_A, K_B, and K_C, only the last term in the denominator is important and the result is

$$r_0 = \frac{k_C C_t}{K_C} = a'' \qquad (C)$$

Equation (A) for surface-reaction controlling represents a case where the initial rate will be proportional to the square of the pressure at low pressures and will approach a constant value at high pressures. This type of relationship is

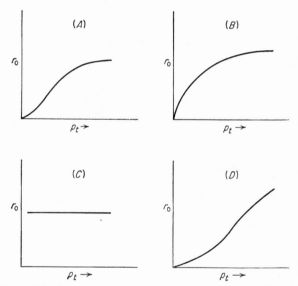

Fig. 9-1. Initial rate vs. total pressure; reaction $A + B \rightarrow C$.

shown in Fig. 9-1A. The case for adsorption controlling is shown in Fig. 9-1B and for desorption controlling in Fig. 9-1C. If the equilibrium constant were not very large in this latter case, the initial rate equation would be as shown in Fig. 9-1A, rather than the horizontal line of Fig. 9-1C.

For the fourth case the rate equation can be obtained from Eq. (9-20), which is based upon a surface reaction between adsorbed A and B in the gas phase. Combining this with Eqs. (9-17) and (9-35) for the equilibrium values for C_A and C_C gives

$$r = k_s C_v \left(K_A p_{A_i} p_{B_i} - \frac{K_C}{K_s} p_{c_i} \right)$$

Since there is no adsorption of B in this instance, Eq. (9-37) for C_v becomes

$$C_v = \frac{C_t}{1 + K_A p_{A_i} + K_C p_{C_i}}$$

The relationship between the equilibrium constants [Eq. (9-41)] is

$$K = \frac{K_A K_s}{K_C}$$

Substituting these two expressions into the rate equation yields

$$r = k_s K_A C_t \frac{p_{A_i} p_{B_i} - (1/K) p_{C_i}}{1 + K_A p_{A_i} + K_C p_{C_i}} \tag{D}$$

Equation (D) is the appropriate expression for the surface-rate controlling, with no adsorption of B. At initial conditions it reduces to the form

$$r = k_s K_A C_t \frac{\frac{1}{4} p_t^2}{1 + \frac{1}{2} K_A p_t} = \frac{a''' p_t^2}{1 + b''' p_t} \tag{E}$$

A schematic diagram of Eq. (E) would indicate the rate proportional to p_t at high pressures and is so shown in Fig. 9-1D.

Suppose that experimental rate data for the reaction $A + B \rightarrow C$ were obtained over a wide range of total pressures, all at the same temperature. It is evident that comparison of a plot of the observed results with curves such as shown in Fig. 9-1 would be of considerable value in determining the mechanism of the reaction. However, it is sometimes difficult in practice to cover a wide enough range of pressures to observe all the changes in shape of the curves shown in Fig. 9-1.

9-9. Quantitative Interpretation of Kinetic Data. *Differential- vs. Integral-reactor Data.* The problem of obtaining a satisfactory rate equation from kinetic data taken in a flow reactor was considered in Sec. 6-1. The same considerations are involved for catalytic reactions as were considered there for homogeneous systems. However, if the theoretical developments outlined in Secs. 9-4 to 9-7 are used, the resulting rate equations are rather complicated and involve several constants. For interpretation in this way it is preferable to obtain kinetic data in a differential reactor. Then the experimental rates are directly available for use in evaluating the constants in the equations.

It is also possible, in principle, to use integral-reactor data to obtain a rate equation. As described in Chap. 6, the data on a plot of conversion vs. W/F can be differentiated graphically to obtain the rate, or an alternate procedure is to integrate the assumed rate equation and compare the result with the experimental conversion data.[1] Either or

[1] Because of the complexity of the rate equation, graphical rather than analytical integration is usually necessary.

these procedures is subject to error.   In the first, graphical differentiation of the data is inaccurate.   In the second, it is difficult to make an accurate evaluation of a rate equation by working with its less sensitive, integrated result.[1]   Hence the integral-reactor approach is not recommended for studying the mechanism of a catalytic reaction.

When a conventional first- or second-order rate equation is employed to interpret kinetic data, it is much easier to apply the integral method. The rate expression is usually simple enough to integrate analytically. Since severe assumptions are already made in using a simple rate equation, the additional errors in treating the integral-reactor data may not be important.   This procedure does not give much information about the mechanism, but it is frequently employed as a simple method of obtaining a working rate equation for a catalytic reaction system.   Since a noncatalytic type of rate expression is used, the computations involved are the same as used in Chap. 6 for interpreting integral-reactor data (for example, Examples 6-2 and 6-3).

Interpretation of Differential-reactor Data.   If experimental rate data are available, the next steps in determining the most plausible rate equation are (1) assume various mechanisms, (2) develop rate equations corresponding to these mechanisms and for different controlling processes in the over-all reaction, (3) evaluate the constants in the several equations, and finally (4) choose the particular combinations of mechanism and controlling process which give the best agreement with the experimental data.   Other information about the reaction unrelated to the differential rate data may provide valuable help in the first step.   Also, qualitative examination of the effects of pressure on the rate (Sec. 9-8) may be useful in choosing likely mechanisms and controlling steps.

In evaluating the constants (step 3) a more methodical procedure is necessary than has been used in noncatalytic reactions.   There only one constant (the specific-reaction rate) was involved, and the k value usually could be determined precisely by arithmetic averaging of single values or visual adjustment of a curve to plotted data.   However, when there are several constants in the rate equation, a systematic procedure is necessary to obtain the most probable (and hence most accurate) values. Hougen and Watson[2] have shown how the concept of a least-mean-square

---

[1] L. N. Johanson and K. M. Watson, *Natl. Petroleum News, Tech. Secs.*, August and September, 1946, have applied this method in the conversion of xylene to toluene.   By taking data with the proper parameters constant, and with some assumptions, it was possible to integrate the rate equation analytically and thus avoid the tedious graphical integrations that are normally associated with this procedure for analyzing integral data.

[2] O. A. Hougen and K. M. Watson, "Chemical Process Principles," vol. III, Kinetics and Catalysis, p. 938, John Wiley & Sons, Inc., New York, 1949.

deviation can be applied to this problem.[1] Their procedure is illustrated in the following example:

Example 9-4. Olson and Schuler[2] determined reaction rates for the oxidation of sulfur dioxide, using a packed bed of cylindrical alumina pellets containing platinum. A differential reactor was employed, and the partial pressures as measured from bulk-stream compositions were corrected to interface values by taking diffusional resistances into account (see Example 9-1). The total pressure was about 790 mm.

From previous studies[3] and the qualitative nature of the rate data a likely mechanism appeared to be a controlling surface reaction between adsorbed atomic oxygen and unadsorbed sulfur dioxide. In order to determine all the constants in the rate equation for this mechanism, it is necessary to vary each partial pressure independently in the experimental work. Thus measuring the rate of reaction at different total pressures, but at constant composition, is not sufficient to determine all the adsorption equilibrium constants. Similarly, if the data are obtained at constant composition of initial reactants, but varying conversions, the partial pressures of the individual components do not vary independently. However, in these cases it is possible to verify the validity of the rate equation, even though values of the separate adsorption equilibrium constants cannot be ascertained. Olson and Schuler studied the effect of conversion alone and obtained the data of Table 9-3 at 480°C.

TABLE 9-3

Rate of reaction, g moles/(hr)(g of catalyst)	Partial pressure (at surface), atm		
	SO_3	SO_2	O_2
0.02	0.0428	0.0255	0.186
0.04	0.0331	0.0352	0.190
0.06	0.0272	0.0409	0.193
0.08	0.0236	0.0443	0.195
0.10	0.0214	0.0464	0.196
0.12	0.0201	0.0476	0.197

Test the proposed mechanism by (1) evaluating the constants in the rate equation and (2) comparing experimental rates of reaction with values computed from the equation.

Solution. To develop an expression for the rate of reaction, the method of obtaining adsorbed atomic oxygen must be postulated. If it is supposed that molecular oxygen is first adsorbed on a pair of vacant centers and that this product then dissociates into two adsorbed atoms, the process may be written

---

[1] Of course, for homogeneous reactions the least-mean-square method of obtaining the specific-reaction rate is the preferred approach.

[2] *Loc. cit.*

[3] O. Uyehara and K. M. Watson, *Ind. Eng. Chem.*, **35**:541 (1943).

$$O_2 + 2s \rightarrow \begin{matrix} O\text{---}O \\ | \quad | \\ s \quad s \end{matrix} \rightarrow 2O\cdot s$$

It is assumed that the surface reaction is controlling. Hence the adsorption of oxygen must be at equilibrium. Then the concentration of adsorbed atomic oxygen is given by the equilibrium equation

$$K_0 = \frac{C_0^2}{p_{O_2}C_v^2}$$

adsorption constant for O₂

in which C_0 represents the concentration of adsorbed atomic oxygen and C_v that of pairs of vacant centers. Solving this expression for C_0 yields

$$C_0 = K_0^{\frac{1}{2}}p_{O_2}^{\frac{1}{2}}C_v \tag{A}$$

The surface-reaction step is represented by the expressions

$$SO_2 + O\cdot s \rightarrow SO_3 \cdot s$$

$$r = k\left(p_{SO_2}\cdot C_0 - \frac{1}{K_s}C_{SO_3}\right) \quad \textit{surface rate equation} \tag{B}$$

The concentration of SO_3 adsorbed on the catalyst is given by the conventional equilibrium expression

$$C_{SO_3} = K_{SO_3}p_{SO_3}C_v \quad \textit{adsorption constant for SO₃} \tag{C}$$

r = k (p_{SO₂}C₀ − ⅟_K (C_{SO₃}))
r = 0

Substituting the values of C_0 and C_{SO_3} in Eq. (B) gives

$$r = k\left(K_0^{\frac{1}{2}}p_{SO_2}p_{O_2}^{\frac{1}{2}} - \frac{K_{SO_3}}{K_s}p_{SO_3}\right)C_v \tag{D}$$

The total concentration of centers is the following summation:

$$C_t = C_v + K_0^{\frac{1}{2}}p_{O_2}^{\frac{1}{2}}C_v + K_{SO_2}p_{SO_3}C_v + K_{N_2}p_{N_2}C_v \tag{E}$$

The last term is included to take into account the possibility of N_2 being adsorbed on the catalyst.

Eliminating C_v from Eq. (D) by introducing Eq. (E) and noting that $K_0^{\frac{1}{2}}K_s/K_{SO_3} = K$, Eq. (D) becomes

$$r = \frac{kC_tK_0^{\frac{1}{2}}\left(p_{SO_2}p_{O_2}^{\frac{1}{2}} - \frac{1}{K}p_{SO_3}\right)}{1 + K_0^{\frac{1}{2}}p_{O_2}^{\frac{1}{2}} + K_{SO_3}p_{SO_3} + K_{N_2}p_{N_2}} \tag{F}$$

Because the partial pressures of sulfur dioxide and sulfur trioxide are both small, the value of p_{N_2} will not vary significantly with conversion. Hence $K_{N_2}p_{N_2}$ may be regarded as a constant in Eq. (F). Since conversion was the only variable causing the composition to change, p_{O_2} and p_{SO_3} and p_{SO_2} are not independent but all related to the initial constant composition and the conversion. Hence, p_{O_2} in the denominator of Eq. (F) can be expressed in terms of conversion, or, more conveniently, in terms of p_{so_3}. Doing this, Eq. (F) may be simplified to read

$$r = \frac{kC_t K_0^{\frac{1}{2}}\left(p_{o_2}^{\frac{1}{2}}p_{so_2} - \dfrac{1}{K}\,p_{so_3}\right)}{A' + B'p_{so_3}}$$

Combining the constants and rearranging lead to the form

$$A + Bp_{i,so_2} = \frac{p_{i,so_2}p_{i,c_2}^{\frac{1}{2}} - (1/K)p_{i,so_3}}{r} = R \qquad (G)$$

The fact that conversion was the only variable resulted in the reduction in constants to two, A and B, and means that individual adsorption equilibrium constants cannot be determined. The i subscript is introduced in Eq. (G) to emphasize that partial pressures at the catalyst surface must be employed.

From the over-all equilibrium constant K and the data for the partial pressures and rates the right-hand side of Eq. (G) (designated as R) can be evaluated for each rate. The equilibrium constant decreases with temperature, the reaction being exothermic. However, it is still about 73 at 480°C, as estimated from the expression

$$\ln K = \frac{22,200}{RT} - 9.10$$

Table 9-4 shows the value of R computed from the data, using $K = 73$.

TABLE 9-4

Rate, g moles/(hr)(g of cat)	p_{i,so_3}, atm	R	Rp_{i,so_3}	$p_{i,so_3}^2 \times 10^4$
0.02	0.0428	0.521	0.0223	18.3
0.04	0.0331	0.372	0.0123	11.0
0.06	0.0272	0.294	0.0081	7.40
0.08	0.0236	0.241	0.00569	5.57
0.10	0.0214	0.203	0.00433	4.58
0.12	0.0201	0.174	0.00349	4.03
	0.168	1.805	0.0562	50.8

The most probable values of the constants are those corresponding to a least-mean-square fit of the data[1] to the straight line

$$y = bx + a \qquad (H)$$

Comparing Eq. (G) with (H),

$$y = R$$
$$x = p_{i,so_3}$$
$$a = A$$
$$b = B$$

[1] With only six data points the least-mean-square procedure is of doubtful value. It is more significant when 10 or more points are available.

The values of a and b are given by the two expressions[1]

$$b = \frac{\Sigma yx - \dfrac{(\Sigma x)(\Sigma y)}{n}}{\Sigma(x)^2 - (\Sigma x)^2/n} \tag{I}$$

$$a = \frac{\Sigma y - b\Sigma x}{n} \tag{J}$$

where n = number of measurements.

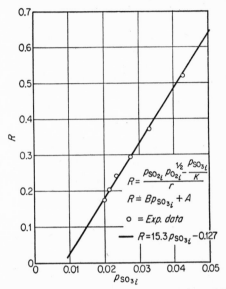

Fig. 9-2. Correlation of rate-data; oxidation of SO_2.

Equations (I) and (J) may be applied to the present case. Thus $yx = Rp_{i,so_3}$, etc. The necessary values and summations are given in the last four columns of Table 9-4. Solving for the constants,

$$b = B = \frac{0.0562 - (0.168 \times 1.805)/6}{0.00508 - 0.168^2/6} = 15.3$$

$$a = A = \frac{1.805 - 15.3 \times 0.168}{6} = -0.127$$

Using these values of the constants, Eq. (G) may be written

$$R = 15.3p_{i,so_3} - 0.127 \tag{K}$$

[1] These equations are obtained by (1) writing an expression for the sum of the squares of the deviations of the data points from the line of Eq. (H), (2) differentiating this equation with respect to both a and b, (3) setting the differentiated equations equal to zero to apply the minimum-deviation restriction, and (4) solving the two equations for the values of a and b.

Figure 9-2 is a plot of the experimental data and Eq. (K). Equation (K) can be used to compute values of the rate of reaction at any set of partial pressures by first calculating R and then using the definition of R,

$$R = \frac{p_{i,so_2}p_{i,o_2}{}^{\frac{1}{2}} - \dfrac{1}{K}\, p_{i,so_3}}{r}$$

to compute r. Thus for the first set of data, at $p_{i,so_3} = 0.0428$ atm,

$$R = 15.3 \times 0.0428 - 0.127 = 0.525$$

Then
$$0.525 = \frac{(0.0255)(0.1864)^{\frac{1}{2}} - \frac{1}{73} \times 0.0428}{r}$$

Solving for the rate,

$$r = 0.020 \text{ g moles/(hr)(g of catalyst)}$$

The results for the other points are as shown in Table 9-5.

TABLE 9-5

p_{i,so_3}	R	r (calc.)	r (exp.)
0.0428	0.525	0.020	0.020
0.0331	0.377	0.039	0.040
0.0272	0.287	0.061	0.060
0.0236	0.232	0.083	0.080
0.0214	0.199	0.102	0.100
0.0201	0.179	0.117	0.120

9-10. HRU Concept. In the design of continuous-absorption and -extraction equipment the height of a transfer unit (HTU) has sometimes been used rather than mass-transfer coefficients and rate equations. This concept can be applied also to the diffusion of reactants to the surface of a catalyst particle in a tubular-flow type of reactor. The definition of HTU is given by the equation

$$\text{HTU} = \frac{Z}{\int dp_{g_A}/(p_g - p_i)_A} = \frac{Z}{\text{NTU}} \qquad (9\text{-}47)$$

where Z = total height of catalytic reactor

p_{g_A} = partial pressure of component A in gas phase

p_{i_A} = partial pressure at surface of catalyst particle

The numerator in the integral is proportional to the amount of gas that must be transferred (since number of moles is proportional to dp), and the denominator is the driving force causing the transfer. Hence the integral as a whole is a measure of the difficulty of the transfer job and is called the number of transfer units (NTU).

Hurt[1] has extended this concept to gas-solid catalytic reactors by introducing two additional quantities.

1. Height of a catalytic unit (HCU)

$$\text{HCU} = \frac{Z}{\int \frac{dp_{gA}}{(p_i - p_g^*)_A}} \tag{9-48}$$

2. Height of a reactor unit (HRU)

$$\text{HRU} = \frac{Z}{\int \frac{dp_{gA}}{(p_g - p_g^*)_A}} \tag{9-49}$$

The symbol p_g^* represents the value of p_g in equilibrium with the products of the reaction.

Writing Eqs. (9-47) and (9-48) in differential form and solving for the pressure differences give

$$(p_g - p_i)_A = \text{HTU} \frac{dp_g}{dZ}$$

$$(p_i - p_g^*)_A = \text{HCU} \frac{dp_g}{dZ}$$

Adding these two expressions yields

$$(p_g - p_g^*)_A = (\text{HTU} + \text{HCU}) \frac{dp_g}{dZ}$$

Comparing this with the differential form of Eq. (9-49) shows that

$$\text{HRU} = \text{HTU} + \text{HCU} \tag{9-50}$$

It is apparent from Eq. (9-47) that the HTU depends entirely upon the rate of diffusion of reactant A to the catalyst surface and not at all on the surface processes. Hence HTU may be regarded as a measure of the resistance due to diffusion of component A, or step 1 in the list of resistances mentioned in Sec. 9-1. If HCU is independent of diffusional resistances for the products (step 5) and truly represents the resistances of the surface processes (steps 2, 3, and 4), Eq. (9-50) provides a simple way to separate the effects of diffusion from the rest of the resistances. The method of application is to apply Eq. (9-49) to experimental rate data and so determine HRU values. Then from independent diffusion data such as represented by Eqs. (9-7) and (9-8), HTU quantities can be obtained. Subtraction in Eq. (9-50) allows the resistances due to the surface processes, HCU values, to be determined. This is exactly analogous to computing $p_g - p_i$, subtracting to obtain p_i, as in Example 9-1, and then using these quantities to study the kinetics of the surface processes as done in Example 9-4.

[1] *Loc. cit.*

For Equation (9-50) to be useful, the surface processes must be first-order; otherwise the linear driving force in Eq. (9-48) cannot represent the kinetics of the surface steps. Even then a complication exists because HCU includes the diffusional resistance of the products formed. This is because the equilibrium value, $p_{g_A}^*$, is related to the partial pressures of the products in the gas phase, not at the interface. For example, if the reaction is $A \rightarrow C$ and the equilibrium constant for the homogeneous reaction is K, $p_{g_A}^*$ is given by the equation

$$p_{g_A}^* = \frac{K}{p_{g_C}} \tag{9-51}$$

To include the diffusional resistance of product C, p_{c_i} should be used in Eq. (9-51). However, this would yield a value of $p_{i_A}^*$ instead of $p_{g_A}^*$. Hence, in addition to the first-order restriction, another assumption is necessary if Eq. (9-50) is to give a real separation between diffusional and surface resistances. One possibility is for the reverse-reaction rate to be negligible. Then $p_{i_A}^*$ and $p_{g_A}^*$ would both be small with respect to p_{i_A}, and either could be used in Eq. (9-48).

Because of these assumptions Eq. (9-50) has not proved so useful as the procedure outlined in Sec. (9-1) for a careful separation of diffusional effects from the surface resistances. However, where only an approximate kinetic treatment is desirable and a first-order irreversible equation can be used for the surface processes, the HRU approach for tubular flow reactors is simple to apply and gives results which are easy to visualize physically.

As in the kinetic equations developed in Secs. 9-4 to 9-7, a constant temperature is implied. The values of HCU like the specific-reaction-rate constants, k, are strong functions of temperature. The HTU like the diffusion coefficients, k_g, changes slowly with temperature.

Example 9-5. The reaction $A \rightarrow C$ is to be carried out in a packed-bed catalytic reactor. Assuming that the reaction is irreversible and the surface processes (steps 2, 3, and 4) can be represented by a first-order rate equation, develop the relationship between $k_g a$ and HTU and between HCU and the specific-reaction rate k_s.

Solution. The relation between the HTU and $k_g a$ does not involve the kinetics of the reaction. It is concerned with diffusion to and from the catalyst surface.

The rate of mass transfer was defined in terms of $k_g a$ by Eq. (9-4) in Sec. 9-2. If this expression is written for a differential element dZ of a packed-bed reactor, it becomes

$$dN_A = k_g a(p_g - p_i)_A \rho_B A_c \, dZ \tag{A}$$

where A_c = cross-sectional area of reactor
ρ_B = density of packed catalyst

The number of moles of A transferred per unit time in the element can be expressed also in terms of the change in the partial pressure of A. If the mass velocity in the reactor is G, and the molecular weight of the reaction mixture is M, the molal-flow rate is G/M. For the simple isomerization reaction chosen, M is constant throughout the reactor. If the total pressure p_t is also constant,

$$dN_A = \frac{A_c G}{M} \frac{dp_{g_A}}{p_t} \tag{B}$$

Equating Eqs. (A) and (B) and rearranging,

$$\frac{dp_{g_A}}{(p_g - p_i)_A} = \frac{k_g a \rho_B M p_t}{G} dZ \tag{C}$$

Equation (9-47) may be written in the following differential form:

$$\mathrm{HTU} = \frac{dZ}{dp_{g_A}/(p_g - p_i)_A}$$

Comparison of this with Eq. (C) gives the relationship between HTU and $k_g a$.

$$\mathrm{HTU} = \frac{G}{k_g a \rho_B M p_t} \tag{D}$$

The relation between HCU and k_s can be obtained in an analogous fashion by comparing the equation for the rate of reaction on the surface, in terms of k_s, with Eq. (9-48). The amount of A reacting per unit time in the element of reactor dZ may be written

$$dN_A = r \rho_B A_c \, dZ = k_s p_{i_A} \rho_B A_c \, dZ \tag{E}$$

where k_s is the rate constant in units containing moles reacting per unit mass of catalyst.

Equating Eqs. (B) and (E),

$$\frac{dp_{g_A}}{p_{i_A}} = \frac{k_s M p_t \rho_B}{G} dZ \tag{F}$$

Writing the definition of the HCU [Eq. (9-48)] in differential form, it becomes

$$\mathrm{HCU} = \frac{dZ}{dp_{g_A}/(p_i - p_g^*)_A}$$

Taking $p_g^* = 0$ for the irreversible case and comparing with Eq. (F) give

$$\mathrm{HCU} = \frac{G}{k_s \rho_B M p_t} \tag{G}[1]$$

[1] In comparing Eqs. (D) and (G) it is helpful to recall that k_s and k_g are on a different basis. The specific-reaction rate k_s is based on a unit mass of catalyst, while the mass-transfer coefficient k_g is per unit external area of the catalyst particle. That explains why the latter needs to be multiplied by a, the external area per unit mass.

It has been mentioned that, if the reaction were reversible, the rate would involve p_i^*. Under these conditions a simple relationship like Eq. (G) is no possible. However, Hurt[1] has extended the concept to include pseudo-first order reactions, i.e., reactions whose rate can be expressed by a first-order equation multiplied by a correction factor.

Example 9-6. To illustrate the interpretation of experimental rate measurements in terms of HRU, the data of Olson and coworkers[1] for the oxidation of sulfur dioxide on a platinum catalyst ($\frac{1}{8}$- by $\frac{1}{8}$-in. cylindrical particles) may be used.

At a temperature of 400°C and a superficial gas mass velocity of 350 lb/(hr)(sq ft) the data for one run are as follows:

1. Moles SO_2 entering preconverter/hr   = 4.074
2. Total moles (SO_2 plus air)   = 62.45
3. Mass of catalyst in reactor, g   = 10.5
4. Total pressure, atm   = 1.04
5. Height of catalyst bed, ft   = 0.0313
6. Conversion of SO_2 to SO_3 entering reactor, x_1 =   0.5937
7. Conversion of SO_2 to SO_3 leaving reactor, x_2 =   0.6063

At 400°C the equilibrium constant for the reaction

$$SO_2 + \tfrac{1}{2}O_2 \rightarrow SO_3$$

is about 620. Hence the equilibrium value for the partial pressure of SO_2, p_g^*, is negligible (about 0.0003 atm).

The Schmidt group $(\mu/\rho D)^{\frac{2}{3}}$ for SO_2 diffusing into air is about 1.18 at 400°C.

From this information estimate the HRU and HTU for the oxidation of SO_2 at the reactor operating conditions.

Solution. The HTU can be determined without reference to the rate data. The modified Reynolds number is

$$\mathrm{Re} = \frac{d_p G}{\mu} = \frac{1}{8 \times 12} \frac{350}{0.077} = 47$$

where 0.077 lb/(hr)(ft) is the viscosity of air at 400°C.

Hurt[1] has published data on mass transfer in packed beds as a function of the Reynolds and Schmidt groups. From his correlations for a $\frac{1}{8}$-in. particle at Re = 47,

$$\frac{\mathrm{HTU}}{(\mu/\rho D)^{\frac{2}{3}}} = 0.35 \text{ in.}$$

Hence
$$\mathrm{HTU} = 0.35 \times 1.18$$
$$= 0.41 \text{ in., or } 0.035 \text{ ft}$$

The over-all reactor-unit height, HRU, can be obtained by integrating Eq. (9-49). This equation will be applied to SO_2, noting that $p_g^* = 0$. Integrating leads to the result

$$\mathrm{HRU} = \frac{Z}{\ln (p_{g_1}/p_{g_2})} \tag{A}$$

[1] *Loc. cit.*

where p_{g_2} and p_{g_1} are the partial pressures of SO_2 in the exit and inlet streams to the reactor. These partial pressures can be evaluated from the given conversion information in the following manner:

$$p_{g_1} = p_t y_1 = 1.04 \frac{\text{moles } SO_2 \text{ entering}}{\text{total moles entering}}$$

$$\text{Moles } SO_2 \text{ entering reactor} = 4.074(1 - x_1)$$
$$= 4.074(1 - 0.5937) \text{ moles/hr}$$
$$\text{Total moles entering reactor} = 62.45 - \tfrac{1}{2} \times 4.074 \times x_1$$
$$= 62.45 - 1.21 = 61.24 \text{ moles/hr}$$
$$p_{g_1} = 1.04 \frac{4.074(1 - 0.5937)}{61.24}$$
$$= 0.0281 \text{ atm}$$

In a similar way

$$p_{g_2} = 1.04 \frac{4.074(1 - 0.6063)}{62.45 - \tfrac{1}{2} \times 4.07 \times 0.6063} = 0.0273$$

Substituting these results in Eq. (A),

$$\text{HRU} = \frac{-0.0313}{\ln (0.0273/0.0281)} = 0.99 \text{ ft}$$

It is not correct in this case to use Eq. (9-50) and obtain HCU by subtracting 0.035 ft from the HRU value (0.99 ft). This is because the rate data do not follow a first-order expression. However, it is safe to state that the values for HRU and HTU show that external diffusion is not important at these operating conditions. This was demonstrated in another way in Example 9-1. There at a conversion level of 0.6, corresponding to the present situation, the pressure drop $p_g - p_i$ for SO_3 was shown to be very small with respect to p_i.

9-11. Internal Diffusion in Porous Catalysts.

If the interior surface of porous catalysts were as effective as the outer, it would not be necessary to consider the problem of diffusion into the pores. Stating this in another way, if the rate of diffusion in the pores were always large in comparison with the rate of the surface processes, porous catalysts would be equivalent to those with the same amount of surface spread out in a flat sheet. Particularly for fast surface process (a very active catalyst) and small pore diameters, diffusion rates are not relatively large. Practical results of this situation are of considerable importance. For example, in such cases it may be necessary to use a smaller catalyst particle than would be indicated from other considerations (i.e., pressure drop, initial cost, etc.). Measurements at low temperature, where the diffusion rates would be more likely to be large, may give an erroneous impression of the effect of temperature on the observed rate. This is not because low-temperature measurements would suggest an incorrect activation energy, but because the apparent activation energy would decrease at higher temperatures. Thus at higher temperatures internal diffusion is more significant than at lower ones, because the surface processes increase exponentially with temperature, while diffusion rates are not greatly affected. Observed rates of reaction at high temperatures are more of a measure of the diffusion resistances than at low temperatures. Finally, the form of the rate equation itself may be influenced by internal diffusion. The rate of catalytic hydrogenation of ethylene has been found under certain conditions to be independent of the ethylene partial pressure and first-order with respect to hydrogen.[1] This is presumably due to the ease of adsorption of ethylene on the catalyst. Regardless of its concentration in the gas phase, there is a large and constant fraction of the catalyst surface covered with ethylene. However, if the catalyst is employed in large-diameter small-pore-size particles, there would be a point in the interior of the pores where the ethylene partial pressure would be very nearly zero. At this location the rate would no longer be independent of the ethylene partial pressure.

The conclusions to be drawn from these observations are these: (1) The measured rate of reaction on a porous catalyst will include the resistance of internal diffusion. (2) The factors which increase the importance of diffusion are an active catalyst surface, a large particle size, and small pore diameter. (3) When these factors singly, or in combination, result in significant diffusion resistances, the activation energy, form of the rate equation (order of reaction), and other kinetic factors become dependent upon pore size and particle size.

The quantitative treatment of internal diffusion is complicated because of (1) the nonuniform nature of the pores in a catalyst particle and (2) the mathematical problem in integrating the equations which combine the effects of surface reaction and diffusion. These problems will be simplified by using an approximate geometrical model[2] of a catalyst particle and the Thiele[3] development for a first-order reaction. The difficulty in treating internal diffusion, for reactions other than first-order, raises an important point in the method of analysis of experimental rate data. It would be unwise to carry out a careful interpretation by the Langmuir–Hougen and Watson approach (Secs. 9-4 to 9-7) unless the resistance to internal diffusion in the pores has been shown to be negligible. By using the Thiele approach based upon a first-order rate equation it is possible quickly to ascertain the significance of diffusion in pores. Hence a logical approach to analyzing kinetic data on porous catalysts is as follows:

[1] R. Wynkoop and R. H. Wilhelm, *Chem. Eng. Progr.*, **46**:300 (1950).

[2] Proposed by A. Wheeler, "Advances in Catalysis," vol. III, pp. 250–326, Academic Press, Inc., New York, 1950; and in Emmett (ed.), *op. cit.*, vol. II, chap. 2, pp. 105–165.

[3] E. W. Thiele, *Ind. Eng. Chem.*, **31**:916 (1939).

1. Estimate an approximate first-order rate constant.

2. Use this constant to approximate the importance of pore diffusion (the method is described in the following paragraphs).

3. If the kinetic data truly reflect the kinetics of the surface steps and not internal diffusion, then a more careful kinetic analysis, perhaps by the Langmuir–Hougen and Watson approach, is warranted.

To carry out the evaluation in (2), it is necessary to consider the Wheeler[1] model of a catalyst pellet, the nature of diffusion rates in pores, and the mathematical solution of Thiele[2] for diffusion and reaction in pores.

Simplified Model of Porous Catalyst Particle. In Chap. 8 the surface area per gram, S_g, and the pore volume per gram, V_g, were found to be important characteristics of porous materials and also quantities which could be measured by sound experimental methods. To treat diffusion and reaction in pores, the needed properties are the average pore radius $\bar{r}$, the number of pores per particle, n, and their mean length $\bar{L}$. Accordingly the simplified model of the particle should express $\bar{r}$, n, and $\bar{L}$ in terms of S_g and V_g. Actually the pores in a real particle would be neither of constant radius nor straight but would follow a tortuous path, interconnect with other pores, and have a continually changing shape and size. In the model it is assumed that the n pores are straight cylinders of radius $\bar{r}$ and that they run from the surface of the particle into the center, a distance $\bar{L}$.

The void fraction of a catalyst particle has been designated in Chap. 8 as δ_p. If the void fraction of the external surface, i.e., the area of the pore mouths divided by the total external area S_x, is also δ_p, the number of pore mouths per particle will be

$$n = \frac{S_x \delta_p}{\pi \bar{r}^2 (2)^{\frac{1}{2}}} \tag{9-52}$$

The $(2)^{\frac{1}{2}}$ factor enters because the pore mouths, on the average, will meet the surface at an angle of 45°. The area of one pore mouth then will not be $\pi \bar{r}^2$, but, instead, the area of an ellipse whose plane makes an angle of 45° with the cylinder.

If the n pores in the model particle are to have the required surface and volume, two equations may be written,

$$\text{Pore volume/particle} = m_p V_g = n(\pi \bar{r}^2 \bar{L}) = \frac{S_x \delta_p \bar{L}}{(2)^{\frac{1}{2}}} \tag{9-53}$$

$$\text{Pore surface/particle} = m_p S_g = n(2\pi \bar{r} \bar{L}) \tag{9-54}$$

where m_p is the mass of a catalyst particle.

[1] A. Wheeler, "Advances in Catalysis," vol. III, pp. 250–326, Academic Press, Inc., New York, 1950.
[2] *Loc. cit.*

This development is the same as in Sec. 8-7, and the ratio of Eqs. (9-53) and (9-54) gives Eq. (8-23) for the mean pore radius,

$$\bar{r} = \frac{2V_g}{S_g} \tag{8-23}$$

The need for evaluating n is to obtain the mean pore length. Solving Eq. (9-53) for $\bar{L}$,

$$\bar{L} = \frac{m_p V_g}{S_x \delta_p} \sqrt{2} \tag{9-55}$$

Equation (9-55) can be simplified somewhat by introducing the volume of a single particle V_p. This quantity is easily measurable (for example, by mercury displacement) and is related to V_g by the expression

$$V_p \delta_p = m_p V_g$$

Hence Eq. (9-55) may be written

$$\bar{L} = \frac{V_p \sqrt{2}}{S_x} \tag{9-56}$$

Diffusion Rates in Pores. Two kinds of diffusion in pores are possible. If the mean free path of the diffusing molecule is small with respect to the pore radius, the collisions between molecules control diffusion and the usual molecular diffusivity is applicable. The pore size is unimportant, but the diffusivity is inversely proportional to the pressure.

If the pore size is small in comparison with the mean free path, collisions with the pore wall control the process. The diffusivity for this Knudsen diffusion is given by the equation

$$D_k = \frac{2r}{3} \sqrt{\frac{8k_B T}{\pi m}} \tag{9-57}$$

or

$$D_k = 9.7 \times 10^3 r \sqrt{\frac{T}{M}} \qquad \text{cm}^2/\text{sec}$$

where r = pore radius
    m = mass of diffusing molecule

Pressure has no effect on this diffusivity.

For most conditions of operation of catalytic reactors the pore diffusion is of the Knudsen kind. Only at high pressures and large pore radii does the process occur by molecular diffusion. For example, at atmospheric pressure for nearly all porous materials useful as catalysts, Knudsen diffusion controls. At 20 atm the pore radii should be below 20 A for Knudsen diffusion to predominate.

It would be most satisfactory to treat the problem of diffusion and reaction in porous catalysts by using direct measurements of diffusivities.

Ideally diffusion rates would be measured for each particular catalyst particle. Actually such information is seldom available, although data are beginning to appear in the literature.[1]

Diffusion and Reaction in Pores: Thiele Development. With Eqs. (8-23) and (9-56) available for replacing the actual catalyst particle with n pores of length $\bar{L}$ and radius $\bar{r}$, it is necessary to consider diffusion and reaction in only a single pore. Figure 9-3 shows such a pore with a plane of symmetry at the center. This plane corresponds to the center of the catalyst particle, where the concentration gradient is zero. The concentration at the outer surface of the particle is C_{A_0}, while at any distance x, measured from the outer surface, it is C_A. The reaction is assumed to be unimolecular with first-order kinetics and may be represented by the equation

$$A \to B$$

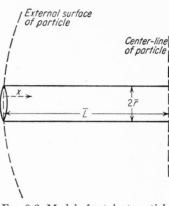

FIG. 9-3. Model of catalyst particle with mean pore of length $\bar{L}$ and radius $\bar{r}$.

At steady-state conditions a mass balance on an element of pore dx will be

(Rate of diffusion into element) − (rate of diffusion out of element)
$$- \text{(rate of reaction)} = 0$$

Expressing this mathematically,

$$- D \frac{dC_A}{dx} \pi \bar{r}^2 - (-D)\left(\frac{dC_A}{dx} + \frac{d^2 C_A}{dx^2}\, dx\right)\pi \bar{r}^2 - k_1'' C_A 2\pi \bar{r}\, dx = 0$$

where D = correct diffusivity, evaluated as explained in the foregoing paragraphs
k_1'' = first-order rate constant
The double-prime designation serves to emphasize that k_1'' is based upon a unit of surface area rather than the usual basis of a unit mass of catalyst. The expression may be simplified to the form

$$\frac{d^2 C_A}{dx^2} = \frac{2k_1''}{\bar{r} D}\, C_A \qquad (9\text{-}58)$$

With the boundary conditions

$$C_A = C_{A_0} \qquad \text{at } x = 0$$
$$\frac{dC_A}{dx} = 0 \qquad \text{at } x = \bar{L}$$

[1] J. Hoogschagen, *Ind. Eng. Chem.*, **47**:906 (1955).

the solution of this linear differential equation is

$$C_A = C_{A_0} \frac{\cosh h\,(1 - x/\bar{L})}{\cosh h} \tag{9-59}$$

in which the Thiele modulus h is defined as follows:

$$h = \bar{L}\sqrt{\frac{2k_1''}{\bar{r}D}} \tag{9-60}$$

The rate of conversion of A in the pore will be the rate of diffusion into the pore mouth.

$$r_{\text{pore}} = -D\left(\frac{dC_A}{dx}\right)_{x=0} \pi\bar{r}^2$$

Differentiating Eq. (9-59), evaluating the derivative at $x = 0$, and substituting in the expression for the rate give

$$r_{\text{pore}} = \frac{\pi\bar{r}^2 D C_{A_0}}{\bar{L}}\, h\,\tanh h \tag{9-61}$$

If there had been no resistance to diffusion in the pore, i.e., if the concentration were C_{A_0} all along the pore length, the rate per pore would have been

$$(r_{\text{pore}})_{\text{eff}} = k_1'' C_{A_0} 2\pi\bar{r}\bar{L} \tag{9-62}$$

The ratio of the actual rate to the hypothetical one, corresponding to a fully effective internal surface, is

$$\left(\frac{r}{r_{\text{eff}}}\right)_{\text{pore}} = \frac{\bar{r}D}{2k_1''\bar{L}^2}\, h\,\tanh h$$

According to Eq. (9-60) the coefficient in the preceding expression is $1/h^2$. Hence the ratio of the rates may be written

$$\left(\frac{r}{r_{\text{eff}}}\right)_{\text{pore}} = \frac{\tanh h}{h} = E \tag{9-63}$$

Thiele called this ratio the effectiveness factor, and it is shown as a function of h in Fig. 9-4. Combining Eq. (9-63) with (9-62) gives the final expression for the actual rate per pore.

$$r_{\text{pore}} = k_1'' C_{A_0} 2\pi\bar{r}\bar{L}E \tag{9-64}$$

In practice, the measured rate of reaction is not per pore but per mass of catalyst in the reactor. Hence the rate equation would be more usefule if it were on this latter basis. Equation (9-64) may be so converted by multiplying by the number of pores per particle, n, and the number of particles per unit mass, $1/m_p$. Using Eq. (9-52) for n,

$$r = r_{\text{pore}} \frac{S_x \delta_p}{\pi \bar{r}^2 \sqrt{2}} \frac{1}{m_p}$$

$$= k_1'' C_{A_0} \frac{\sqrt{2}\, \bar{L} S_x \delta_p}{\bar{r} m_p} E \qquad (9\text{-}65)$$

From the model of the catalyst particle [Eqs. (8-23) and (9-55)] the values of $\bar{L}$ and $\bar{r}$ can be substituted in Eq. (9-65). A considerable simplification occurs, leaving the result

$$r = k_1'' S_g C_{A_0} E \qquad (9\text{-}66)$$

Since the rate per unit mass for the case of no diffusion resistance is simply $k_1'' S_g C_{A_0}$, Eq. (9-63) for the ratio of the rates per pore is also true if the rates are per unit mass. That is,

$$\frac{r}{r_{\text{eff}}} = E \qquad (9\text{-}67)$$

The true specific-reaction rate per unit mass of catalyst is $k_1 = k_1'' S_g$. Also, the product $k_1 E$ may be looked upon as an experimental specific-reaction rate for the porous particle, since it is the quantity that may be

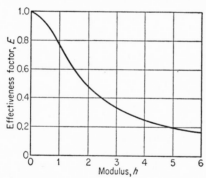

FIG. 9-4. Effectiveness factor for first-order reactions.

obtained directly from experimental measurements of the rate r.   Hence Eq. (9-66) may be written

$$r = k_1 E C_{A_0} = (k_1)_{\text{exp}} C_{A_0} \qquad (9\text{-}68)$$

From the second and third members of this equation the effectiveness factor can be expressed in terms of two specific-reaction rates,

$$E = \frac{(k_1)_{\text{exp}}}{k_1} \qquad (9\text{-}69)$$

Equation (9-68) and Fig. 9-4 provide the means to estimate the importance of internal diffusion.   They permit carrying out the second step in the procedure for studying kinetic data on porous catalysts, as listed at

$$E = \frac{\dfrac{K_{C\,EXP}}{S_g\ coarse}}{\dfrac{K_c\ EXP}{S_g\ FiNE}}$$

the beginning of this section.   The method of applying the equations and Fig. 9-4 is described and illustrated in the following paragraphs.

Applications of Effectiveness Factor.   Equation (9-67) or (9-69) suggests an experimental method for determining the effectiveness of the internal surface of a given porous catalyst.   Experimental rate data are first obtained when the catalyst is broken into particles small enough for the interior surface to be fully effective (no diffusion resistance).   This may be accomplished by using smaller and smaller sizes until the rate no longer changes.   The result establishes r_{eff} or k_1.   Then the rate is measured for the particular particle size of interest.   The ratio of these rates determines E for the particle.   This method requires measuring the rate of reaction for at least two sizes of catalyst.

Another approach may be used which requires rate measurements only for the particular catalyst particle.   According to Eq. (9-68) such a measurement of r gives a relationship between E and k_1.   Another equation relating E and k_1 is available from Fig. 9-4.   This is

$$E = \frac{\tanh h}{h}$$

In terms of the properties of the catalyst the modulus may be written

$$h = \bar{L} \sqrt{\frac{2k_1''}{\bar{r}D}} = \frac{2V_p}{S_x} \sqrt{\frac{k_1'' S_g}{2V_g D}} = \frac{2V_p}{S_x} \sqrt{\frac{k_1}{2V_g D}} \qquad (9\text{-}70)$$

Equations (9-68) and (9-70) and Fig. 9-4 provide three relationships between the three unknowns E, k_1, and h.   To use this method, the diffusivity D and the properties of the catalyst, V_p, S_x, V_g, and S_g, need to be known.   One method of solution is as follows: (1) Assume a value for the effectiveness factor.   (2) Read the modulus h from Fig. 9-4.   (3) Calculate the true first-order rate constant k_1 from Eq. (9-70).   (4) Using this value of k_1 and the experimental r, compute E from Eq. (9-68). If it agrees with the assumed value, the first assumption was correct. If the experimental data are available as rate constants instead of the rate itself, Eq. (9-69) is used to check the assumed effectiveness factor.

In using either method for estimating the effectiveness factor the assumption has been made of a first-order rate on the surface.   However, changes in the form of the rate equation have a small effect on the effectiveness-factor plot.   Hence the methods presented here are satisfactory for obtaining an approximate value of E.[†]   This is all that is

[1] A. Wheeler, in Emmett (ed.), *op. cit.*, vol. II, chap. 2, has developed a solution that does not involve trial-and-error calculations.

[†] This does not mean that the actual reaction rate on the surface is first-order; in most cases it will not be.   It does mean that the first-order assumption is satisfactory for effectiveness-factor calculations.

necessary in order to carry out step 2 in the analysis of kinetic data on porous catalysts. If the effectiveness factor is close to unity, the kinetic interpretation of the rate data can be continued by the methods outlined in Chap. 8. If E is considerably less than unity, the catalyst should be broken into smaller particle sizes and new rate data obtained before attempting mechanism studies.

Prior to illustrating the methods with examples some general trends are worthwhile to note. For h values larger than 2, tanh $h = 1.0$, and E becomes $1/h$. Then Eq. (9-66) for the rate may be written

$$ r = \frac{k_1'' S_g C_{A_0}}{h} = \frac{k_1'' C_{A_0} S_g S_x}{V_p} \sqrt{\frac{V_g D}{k_1'' S_g}} \qquad (9\text{-}71) $$

The ratio of the external surface S_x to the total volume V_p of a particle is inversely proportional to the size of the particle. Hence for h greater than 2, that is, for an active catalyst with a small pore radius, the rate is inversely proportional to the particle size. Also, it is noted from Eq. (9-71) that the rate is proportional to the square root of the rate constant k_1''. This means that measurements of the effect of temperature for such a catalyst particle would show only one-half the true activation energy.

Example 9-7. Wheeler[1] has made a study of the data of Prater, Weisz, and Lago[2] for the cracking of isopropyl benzene ($C_6H_5—C_3H_7$) on several sizes of silica-alumina catalysts. The observed rate data at 420°C interpreted in terms of a first-order equation gave values of the specific-reaction rate of 6.5 cc/(g)(sec) for particles 0.0112 cm in diameter and 1.30 cc/(g)(sec) for 0.35 cm particles.[3]

Assuming that all the surface is effective in the smaller particles, estimate the effectiveness factor for the 0.35-cm catalyst.

Solution. Since the 0.0112-cm particle is assumed to have an effectiveness factor of 1.0, $k_1 = 6.5$ cc/(g)(sec). Then from Eq. (9-69)

$$ E = \frac{1.30}{6.50} = 0.20 $$

[handwritten margin note: R probably means $\frac{R}{S_g}$ instead of R.]

Example 9-8. Estimate the effectiveness factor by the second method, not using the rate data for the 0.0112-cm particle. The surface area is 349 sq m/g, and V_g may be taken equal to 0.35 cc/g.

Solution. The solution now requires the application of the second method based upon Eq. (9-70).

On the basis of Example 9-7, it will be assumed, for the first trial, that $E = 0.20$. From Fig. 9-4 $h = 5$. The mean pore radius can be evaluated from the surface

[1] A. Wheeler, in Emmett (ed.), *op. cit.*, vol. II, chap. 2, p. 146.

[2] C. D. Prater, P. B. Weisz, and R. M. Lago, Paper 84, presented at Kansas City, American Chemical Society meeting, Division of Physics and Inorganic Chemistry, March, 1954.

[3] These k values apply in the equation $r = k_1 C$.

area and pore volume per gram.   From Eq. (8-23)

$$r = \frac{2V_g}{S_g} = \frac{2 \times 0.35}{349 \times 10^4}$$

$$= 20 \times 10^{-8} \text{ cm}$$

For this small pore size, and at atmospheric pressure, the diffusion will be of the Knudsen type.   Then from Eq. (9-57)

$$D_k = 9.7 \times 10^3 (20 \times 10^{-8}) \sqrt{\frac{273 + 420}{120}}$$

$$= 4.6 \times 10^{-3} \text{ sq cm/sec}$$

The values of V_p and S_x required in Eq. (9-70) are not available for the granular particles.   However, their ratio can be well approximated by considering the shape to be spherical.   Then

$$\frac{V_p}{S_x} = \frac{\frac{1}{6}\pi d_p^3}{\pi d_p^2} = \frac{d_p}{6}$$

$$= \frac{0.35}{6} \text{ cm}$$

Substituting these values in Eq. (9-70),

$$h = 5.0 = \frac{2 \times 0.35}{6} \sqrt{\frac{k_1}{2 \times 0.35(4.6 \times 10^{-3})}} = 2.04(k_1)^{\frac{1}{2}}$$

or $k_1 = 6.0 \text{ cc/(g)(sec)}$

Now to check the assumed value of E, use the experimental rate constant $(k_1)_{\text{exp}}$ and Eq. (9-68),

$$E = \frac{(k_{1\text{exp}})}{k_1} = \frac{1.30}{6.0} = 0.22$$

Since this is in good agreement with the assumed value of 0.20, further trial calculations are not necessary.   In this case using the second method, based upon estimating a value of the diffusivity, gave a result in good agreement with that based upon rate data alone (Example 9-7).

NOMENCLATURE

A_c Cross-sectional area of reactor
a External area of catalyst particles per unit mass
C Bulk concentration
C_i Concentration at surface of catalyst, moles/unit volume
C_v Molal concentration of vacant centers on catalyst surface, moles/g of catalyst
$C_A, C_B,$ etc.   Molal concentration of adsorbed A, B, etc., on surface, moles/g of catalyst

C_t Total concentration of active centers, moles/g of catalyst

D Diffusivity

D_k Knudsen diffusivity

d_p Diameter of catalyst particle

E Effectiveness factor for porous catalysts

G Superficial mass velocity

HCU Height of a catalyst unit

HRU Height of a reactor unit

HTU Height of a transfer unit

h Thiele modulus $[h = \bar{L}\sqrt{2k_1''/\bar{r}D} = (2V_p/S_x)\sqrt{k_1/2V_gD}]$

K_A Adsorption equilibrium constant for component A

K_s Equilibrium constant for surface reaction

K Equilibrium constant for homogeneous reaction

k_g Gas-phase mass-transfer coefficient, g moles/(hr)(atm) (sq cm of external area)

k_L Liquid-phase mass-transfer coefficient, g moles/(hr) (moles/liter) (sq cm of external area of particle)

k Specific-reaction rate (subscripts A, B, C refer to components A, B, C and apply to adsorption or desorption processes)

k_s Reaction-rate constant on surface of catalyst

k_1 First-order specific-reaction-rate constant for reaction occurring on the surface of pores, based upon unit mass of catalyst

$(k_1)_{exp}$ Experimentally determined first-order rate constant for porous catalyst [this value includes effect of internal diffusion; see Eq. (9-68)]

k_1'' First-order specific-reaction-rate constant for surface reaction in porous catalyst, based upon unit surface area (thus $k_1''S_g = k_1$)

j Dimensionless function of Reynolds number

$\bar{L}$ Mean pore length in model of actual catalyst particle, cm

M Molecular weight

M_m Mean molecular weight

m_p Mass of single catalyst particle

n Number of pores of length $\bar{L}$ in model of particle

p_g Partial pressure in gas phase

p_i Partial pressure at catalyst-gas interface

p_g^* Partial pressure of a given component when the reaction mixture is at equilibrium

p_t Total pressure

r Rate of reaction, moles/(time)(mass of catalyst)(at steady-state conditions in catalytic flow reactors r also equals rate of adsorption and rate of desorption)

r_{eff} Rate of reaction in a porous catalyst when there is no internal diffusion resistance, that is, r when $E = 1.0$

r_{pore} Rate of reaction per pore, moles/(unit time)(pore of catalyst particle)

$\bar{r}$ Mean pore radius in model of catalyst particle

S Total number of active centers/unit surface of catalyst

S_g Surface area of porous catalyst/g

S_x External area of a single particle of catalyst

V_g Pore volume/g of porous catalyst

V_p Total volume of a single catalyst particle

x Conversion; fraction of a reactant converted (also used to denote distance along the axis of a pore in treatment of effectiveness factors)

Z Depth of catalyst bed in a reactor
δ Void fraction of a bed of catalyst particles
δ_p Void fraction within a single porous particle
ρ Density of reaction mixture
ρ_B Density of packed catalyst bed
μ Viscosity of reaction mixture

PROBLEMS

1. To illustrate the effect of mass velocity on the external diffusion in the oxidation of sulfur dioxide, SO_2, with a platinum catalyst, consider the data of Table 9-6, all at

TABLE 9-6

Mass velocity, lb/(hr)(sq ft)	Partial pressures, p_g, atm			Rate of reaction, g moles SO_2/(hr)(g of catalyst)
	SO_2	SO_3	O_2	
514	0.0601	0.00668	0.201	0.1346
350	0.0599	0.00666	0.201	0.1278
245	0.0603	0.00668	0.201	0.1215
147	0.0603	0.00670	0.201	0.0956

480°C. The reactor consisted of a fixed bed of $\frac{1}{8}$- by $\frac{1}{8}$-in. cylindrical pellets. The pressure was 790 mm. The external area of catalyst particles was 5.12 sq ft/lb, and the platinum did not penetrate into the interior of the alumina particles.

Calculate the pressure drop between the bulk-gas phase and the surface of the catalyst for SO_2, at each mass velocity. What conclusions may be stated with regard to the importance of external diffusion?

2. A gas-solid catalytic reaction of the type

$$A + B \rightarrow C$$

is believed to occur by a molecule of B in the gas phase reacting with a molecule of A adsorbed on the catalyst surface.

Preliminary experimental studies indicate that both external and internal diffusional resistances are negligible. Also, the equilibrium constant for the homogeneous reaction $K = (p_C/p_A p_B)_g$ is very large.

The rate of reaction per gram of catalyst is measured at varying total pressures but constant composition of reactants. The results show a linear relationship between r and p_t all the way down to pressures approaching zero.

What conclusions may be drawn from these data concerning the controlling steps in the reaction?

3. Two gas-solid catalytic reactions, A and B, are studied experimentally in fixed-bed reactors. Rates of reaction per unit mass of catalyst, at constant composition and total pressure, indicate the variations with mass velocity and temperature shown in Fig. 9-5. The interior pore surface in each case is fully effective.

What do the results in Fig. 9-5 suggest about the two reactions?

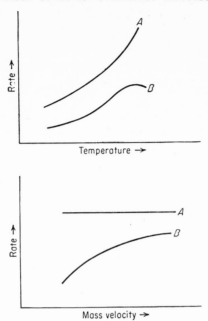

FIG. 9-5. Rate vs. temperature and mass velocity (Prob. 3).

4. In a study of the kinetics of two different gas-solid catalytic reactions, it is found that all diffusional resistances are negligible. Also, both are irreversible.

As an aid in establishing the mechanism of the reactions, the rate is measured at a constant composition over a wide range of temperature.

For the first case, reaction A, the rate increases exponentially over the complete temperature range. For the second reaction, B, the rate first increases and then decreases as the temperature continues to rise.

What does this information mean with regard to the controlling step in each of the reactions?

5. An isomerization reaction has the simple form

$$A \to B$$

a. Assuming operating conditions and the condition of the catalyst are such that the external- and internal-diffusion steps have negligible pressure gradients, propose rate equations for the following cases:

1. The adsorption of A on the catalyst is controlling.
2. The surface interaction between adsorbed A and an adjacent vacant center is controlling.
3. The desorption of B from the surface is controlling.

In all cases the mechanism is: adsorption of A, reaction on the surface to form adsorbed B, and desorption of B into the gas phase.

b. Sketch the rate of reaction (per unit mass of catalyst) vs. total pressure in each of the above three cases. Also, for comparison, include a sketch of the rate of the homogeneous reaction, assuming it is first-order.

2: $A + S \to A \cdot S$ ADSORPTION
(a) $A \cdot S + S \to A^* a (A \cdot S) \cdot S \to$ REACTION (?)
$(A \cdot S) \cdot S \to B \cdot S + S$ · REACTION
$B \cdot S \to B + S$ DESORPTION

6. Potter and Baron[1] studied the reaction

$$CO + Cl_2 \rightarrow COCl_2$$

at atmospheric pressure, using an activated carbon catalyst. Preliminary studies showed that the rate of reaction did not depend upon the mass velocity of gases through the reactor. *Diffusion negligible*

Analysis of the rate data indicated that the reaction occurred by adsorption of Cl_2 and CO on the catalyst and surface reaction between the adsorption compounds. It appeared that the surface reaction, rather than the adsorption or desorption steps, was controlling the over-all reaction rate. Furthermore, preliminary adsorption measurements indicated that chlorine and phosgene were readily adsorbed on the catalyst, while carbon monoxide was not. Hence the adsorption equilibrium constant of carbon monoxide, although not zero, was considered negligible with respect to those for Cl_2 and $COCl_2$.

a. On the basis of this information, develop by the Langmuir–Hougen and Watson method an expression for the rate of reaction in terms of the bulk partial pressures in the gas phase. The reaction is irreversible.

b. Determine the best values for the adsorption equilibrium constants for Cl_2 and $COCl_2$, and the product $C_t k_s K_{co}$, at 30.6°C, from the experimental data of Table 9-7.

TABLE 9-7

Rate of reaction, g moles/(hr)(g of catalyst)	Partial pressure, atm		
	CO	Cl_2	$COCl_2$
0.00414	0.406	0.352	0.226
0.00440	0.396	0.363	0.231
0.00241	0.310	0.320	0.356
0.00245	0.287	0.333	0.376
0.00157	0.253	0.218	0.522
0.00390	0.610	0.113	0.231
0.00200	0.179	0.608	0.206

Temperature = 30.6°C; catalyst size = 6- to 8-mesh.

C_t = total concentration of active centers, moles/g of catalyst

k_s = specific-reaction rate for surface reaction

K_{co} = adsorption equilibrium constant for CO

In the analysis, assume that the 6- to 8-mesh catalyst particles are small enough so that the pore surface was fully effective.

7. Potter and Baron also made rate measurements at other temperatures, and their results at 42.7, 57.5, and 64.0°C are as shown in Table 9-8. Assume that the adsorption equilibrium constants and the rate constant k_s follow an equation of the form $y = ae^{-b/RT}$, where a and b are constants and y is K_{Cl_2}, K_{COCl_2}, or $C_t k_s K_{co}$. Then determine values of a and b for each case.

[1] C. Potter and S. Baron, *Chem. Eng. Progr.*, **47**:473 (1951).

TABLE 9-8

Temp, °C	Rate of reaction, g moles/(hr)(g of catalyst) $r \times 10^3$	Partial pressure, atm		
		CO	Cl_2	$COCl_2$
42.7	5.07	0.206	0.578	0.219
42.7	11.20	0.569	0.194	0.226
42.7	1.61	0.128	0.128	0.845
42.7	9.34	0.397	0.370	0.209
42.7	8.76	0.394	0.373	0.213
52.5	14.70	0.380	0.386	0.234
52.5	15.80	0.410	0.380	0.210
52.5	6.15	0.139	0.742	0.118
52.5	6.30	0.218	0.122	0.660
64.0	26.40	0.412	0.372	0.216
64.0	26.40	0.392	0.374	0.234
64.0	16.10	0.185	0.697	0.118
64.0	9.40	0.264	0.131	0.605

8. Wheeler has summarized the work on internal diffusion for catalytic cracking of gas-oil.[1] At 500°C the rate data for fixed-bed operation, using relatively large ($\frac{1}{8}$-in.) catalyst particles, and that for fluidized-bed reactors (very small particle size) are about the same. This suggests that the effectiveness factor for the large particles is high. Confirm this by estimating E from the following data on the $\frac{1}{8}$-in. catalyst:

$$\bar{r} = 30 \text{ A}$$
$$d_p = 0.31 \text{ cm}$$
$$V_g = 0.35 \text{ cc/g of catalyst}$$

At atmospheric pressure with 30-A pores the diffusion will be of the Knudsen type. The rate data, interpreted in terms of a first-order rate equation, indicate at atmospheric pressure $k_{1exp} = 0.25$ cc/(sec)(g of catalyst).

9. Blue and coworkers[2] have studied the dehydrogenation of butane at atmospheric pressure, using a chromia-alumina catalyst at 530°C. For a catalyst size of $d_p = 0.32$ cm the experimental data suggest a first-order rate constant of about 0.94 cc/(sec) (g of catalyst). The pore radius is given as 110 A. Assuming Knudsen diffusion at this low pressure and estimating V_g as 0.35 cc/g, predict an effectiveness factor for the catalyst.

[1] A. Wheeler, "Advances in Catalysis," vol. III, pp. 250-326, Academic Press, Inc., New York, 1950.

[2] R. W. Blue, V. C. F. Holm, R. B. Reiger, E. Fast, and L. Heckelsberg, *Ind. Eng. Chem.* **44**:2710 (1952).

CHAPTER 10

HEAT AND MASS TRANSFER IN REACTORS

10-1. Introduction. Heat transfer is an important feature of practical reactor design for two reasons: (1) Most commercially important reactions must be carried out at temperatures other than atmospheric; this requires that the reaction environment be either cooled or heated by transfer of energy with the surroundings. (2) Commercial reactions frequently have a significant heat of reaction so that it is necessary to transfer energy to or from the reaction system in order to maintain the temperature within the required limits.

In many cases it is permissible, because of good mixing, to assume that the temperature is uniform within the reactor. Under these conditions the heat transfer to the surroundings can be evaluated from a knowledge of the over-all heat-transfer coefficient between the surroundings at a temperature t_s and the reaction mixture at t. For a batch reactor the heat transfer dQ_s in an element of time $d\theta$ is given by the expression

$$dQ_s = UA_B(t - t_s)\,d\theta \qquad (10\text{-}1)$$

where A_B is the heat-transfer area.

Equation (10-1) is a transient expression, since the temperature t and the heat-transfer rate will vary with time. This equation has been used in Sec. 5-2 as part of the energy balance in batch reactors.

In the special case where the reaction temperature is constant the rate of heat transfer is constant, $dQ/d\theta = Q'_s$, and Eq. (10-1) may be written in the integrated form

$$\frac{dQ_s}{d\theta} = Q'_s = UA_B(t - t_s) \qquad (10\text{-}2)$$

A semibatch reactor operated so that the reaction temperature remains constant (Example 7-3) is a practical illustration of this special case.

For a tubular flow reactor the operation is normally steady-state; i.e., time is not a variable, but the rate of heat transfer varies because the temperature t changes as the mixture flows along the tube. Hence the heat-transfer equation must again be written in a differential form. The rate of heat transfer in a length of reactor dz, corresponding to a heat-transfer area dA, is

$$dQ'_s = U(t - t_s) \, dA \tag{10-3}$$

Equations (10-1) to (10-3) have been used in Chaps. 5 to 7 to compute how the temperature changes with time in a batch reactor and with reactor length in a tubular flow reactor. However, no attempt was made to evaluate the coefficient of heat transfer U. Instead arbitrary values were chosen to illustrate the calculations. It is the objective of Secs. 10-2 and 10-3 of the present chapter to analyze the available data on heat-transfer rates to batch and flow reactors from the point of view of the type of equipment used. Before proceeding with this problem it is desirable to consider the limitations of Eqs. (10-1) and (10-3).

In some instances, particularly tubular reactors containing a bed of solid catalyst particles, it is not justified to assume a uniform reaction temperature across the tube. Under these circumstances the rate of heat transfer and the variation in temperature within the reaction mixture must be studied. Equations (10-1) and (10-3) are not applicable, and the problem of reactor design becomes complex.

Such conditions of nonuniform temperature may be encountered in batch and semibatch reactors when the degree of mixing is poor, as with a poorly designed agitation device. At present there is insufficient information on the relationship between the agitator design and the nonuniformity of temperatures to be able to handle this problem in an adequate way analytically.

A similar situation exists in the case of homogeneous tubular flow reactors. Under certain conditions it may be that a significant amount of mixing will occur in the direction of flow owing to turbulent diffusion. This in turn will affect the temperature distribution along the reactor length, making Eq. (10-3) incorrect. In this instance the ideal situation is based upon no mixing, while in the batch reaction the ideal case is for perfect mixing. Again, for lack of suitable diffusion data, the problem of longitudinal diffusion in a flow reactor cannot be treated analytically. However, work has begun on this problem,[1] and it may become possible to modify Eq. (10-3) to include this intermediate case.

In summary, for batch reactors only the case of perfect mixing, where no variations in temperature exist in the reactor, can be handled at present. For flow reactors only the case of no longitudinal mixing can be treated. Fortunately, these requirements are close to fulfillment in many cases, i.e., in batch reactors with efficient mixing and in flow cases with long reactors operated at moderate or high fluid velocities. The fixed-bed catalytic flow reactor is a case where the degree of radial mix-

---

[1] H. Kramers, G. M. Baars, and W. H. Knoll, *Chem. Eng. Sci.*, **2**:35 (1953).

ing may be significant.   This last case forms an important objective of the present chapter and is considered in Sec. 10-4.

While the question of nonuniformity in the reaction mixture has been discussed from the point of view of temperature and heat transfer, the same conclusions apply to mass transfer.   Thus in a well-agitated batch reactor both the temperature and concentration will be uniform throughout the vessel.   In the case of poor mixing, both concentration and temperature gradients will exist, except for the unusual case of a negligible heat of reaction and negligible heat exchange with the surroundings, in which instance the temperature will be uniform.   Hence the design of batch reactors will be based upon the existence of perfect mixing, that of flow reactors upon the existence of no mixing in the direction of flow. Only for fixed-bed catalytic reactors will mass-transfer rates be taken into account and then only for diffusion in the radial direction.

10-2. Heat Transfer in Batch Reactors.   The experimental and theoretical investigation of heat-transfer coefficients in kettles has lagged behind the development of similar coefficients for more usual heat-transfer equipment, i.e., shell and tube and double-pipe exchangers. However, a few recent investigations have provided at least a basis for estimating the heat-transfer rates in kettles or tanks.

Energy can be transferred from the reaction mixture by jacketing the kettle and passing a cold, or evaporating, fluid through the jacket or by submerging in the kettle mixture a coil through which the cold fluid is circulated.   In cases where temperature control is particularly important a coil may be used since this arrangement supplies energy more uniformly throughout the fluid.   Sometimes both a jacket and coil are used to increase the rate of energy transfer.   As might be expected, the heat-transfer coefficients are different in the two types.   However, in any case the over-all coefficient U may be related to the individual film resistances in series by the usual additive relationship

$$\frac{1}{U} = \frac{1}{h_k} + \frac{L}{k}\frac{A_k}{A_m} + \frac{1}{h_i}\frac{A_k}{A_i} + r_s \tag{10-4}$$

where U = over-all coefficient based upon kettle-side surface
h_k = film coefficient on kettle side
h_i = film coefficient on jacket side (or on inside of coil if a submerged coil is used)
r_s = scale or dirt resistance, based upon kettle-side surface
k = thermal conductivity of kettle wall or submerged-coil wall
L = thickness of metal wall
A_k = heat-transfer area on kettle side
A_i = heat-transfer area on jacket side (or inside area of submerged coil)
A_m = logarithmic mean of A_k and A_i

Kettle-side Coefficient. For well-agitated kettles Chilton, Drew, and Jebens[1] have correlated a considerable number of data for both jacket and coil heat-transfer coefficients. Their results may be represented by the following dimensionless equations.

For jacket heat transfer

$$\frac{h_k d}{k}\left(\frac{\mu_s}{\mu}\right)^{0.14} = 0.36\left(\frac{P^2 N \rho}{\mu}\right)^{\frac{2}{3}}\left(\frac{c\mu}{k}\right)^{\frac{1}{3}} \tag{10-5}$$

For coil heat transfer

$$\frac{h_k d}{k}\left(\frac{\mu_s}{\mu}\right)^{0.14} = 0.87\left(\frac{P^2 N \rho}{\mu}\right)^{\frac{2}{3}}\left(\frac{c\mu}{k}\right)^{\frac{1}{3}} \tag{10-6}$$

where d = diameter of kettle, for both equations

h_k = kettle-side film coefficient at inside kettle surface in Eq. (10-5) and at outside surface of coil for Eq. (10-6)

μ_s = viscosity of kettle mixture at temperature of kettle or coil surface

μ = viscosity at bulk temperature of kettle mixture

P = length of paddle agitator

N = agitator shaft speed, revolutions per hour

ρ = density of kettle mixture at bulk temperature

c = specific heat of kettle fluid at bulk temperature

k = thermal conductivity of kettle mixture at bulk temperature

These correlations were based upon data taken in a 1-ft-diameter kettle, using a flat paddle 0.6 ft long and 0.1 ft in thickness. However, Pratt[2] studied both circular and square kettles up to 2 ft in diameter and obtained results very close to Eqs. (10-5) and (10-6). His data included variations in coil-tube diameter, the gap between coil turns, diameter of the coil, height of the coil, width of the stirrer, and arrangements of the single paddle. Cummings and West[3] obtained data in a larger kettle (100 gal capacity) equipped with a turbine-type impeller. With this more intense agitation a coefficient of 1.01 in Eq. (10-6), instead of 0.87, was obtained.

Jacket-side Coefficients. Specific data for water-film coefficients on the jacket side of a sufonation-reaction kettle were determined by Brown and coworkers.[4] However, general correlations have not been developed because of lack of information. It may be permissible in certain cases to predict the magnitude of the coefficient from other correlations, particularly when the jacket-side resistance is not a large part of the overall value. For example, in a steam-jacketed vessel the conventional

[1] T. H. Chilton, T. B. Drew, and R. H. Jebens, *Ind. Eng. Chem.*, **36**:510 (1944).

[2] N. H. Pratt, *Trans. Inst. Chem. Engrs.* (*London*), **25**:163 (1947).

[3] G. H. Cummings and A. S. West, *Ind. Eng. Chem.*, **42**:2303 (1950).

[4] R. W. Brown, M. A. Scott, and C. Toyne, *Trans. Inst. Chem. Engrs.* (*London*), **25**:181 (1947).

correlation for condensing on vertical surfaces is a satisfactory method of approach.

In unusual instances where the jacket-side resistance is a major factor in determining the over-all heat-transfer coefficient, no entirely satisfactory procedure is available. Two methods of approach are possible. One is to estimate the jacket-side coefficient from existing correlations for other mechanical arrangements, such as flow in annular spaces. The second is to forgo the division of the resistances into specific parts and estimate U from available information on over-all coefficients. Tables of such data are given by McAdams.[1]

Coil-side Coefficients. The heat-transfer coefficient inside a coiled tube is increased over that for a straight tube because of the turbulence induced by the turning of the coil. By comparing data for the two cases McAdams[1] has suggested that the straight-tube coefficient be multiplied by $1 + 3.5\, d_t/d_c$ to obtain the value for the coil arrangement. d_t/d_c is the ratio of the inside diameter of the tube to the diameter of the coil. This procedure is probably as precise as any now available.

Example 10-1. In Example 7-3 a reactor design was considered in which the rate of heat transfer, rather than the rate of reaction, determined the reactor size. Under such circumstances a careful estimate of the heat-transfer coefficient for the equipment is of considerable importance.

Suppose the reactor is a 4- by 6-ft vessel and is equipped with a paddle-type agitator, operating at 100 rph. The paddle length is to be 3 ft.

Assume that the properties of the reaction solution are the same as those of water and that the reaction temperature is 100°C.

The system is cooled by a coil consisting of 1-in.-OD (16-gauge) steel tubing wound in a 3-ft-diameter coil. The water flow rate in the coil is 670 lb/hr at 25°C.

Predict the over-all coefficient of heat transfer between reaction mixture and cooling water, if the scale resistance is estimated to be 0.002.

Solution. The kettle-side coefficient of the coil can be estimated from Eq. (10-6).

At 100°C

$$d_t = 0.87 \text{ in.}$$

$$\frac{c\mu}{k} = 1.7$$

$$\rho = \frac{1}{0.01670}$$
$$= 59.9 \text{ lb/cu ft}$$
$$k = 0.412 \text{ Btu/(hr)(ft)(°F)}$$
$$\mu = 0.690 \text{ lb/(hr)(ft)}$$

$$\frac{h_k \times 4}{0.412} = 0.87 \left(\frac{3^2 \times 100 \times 59.9}{0.690} \right)^{\frac{2}{3}} (1.7)^{\frac{1}{3}} = (0.87)(78{,}100)^{\frac{2}{3}}(1.14)$$

[1] W. H. McAdams, "Heat Transmission," 2d ed., pp. 249–250, McGraw-Hill Book Company, Inc., New York, 1942.

The correction factor $(\mu_s/\mu)^{0.14}$ is negligible in this case because of the low viscosity of water.

$$h_k = 186$$

The coil-side coefficient can be estimated from the expression

$$\frac{h_i d_t}{k} = 0.023 \left(\frac{d_t G}{\mu}\right)^{0.8} \left(\frac{c\mu}{k}\right)^{0.4} \left(1 + 3.5\frac{d_t}{d_c}\right)$$

$$\frac{d_t}{d_c} = \frac{0.87}{12 \times 3} = 0.024$$

At 25°C

$$\frac{c\mu}{k} = 5.1$$

$$\rho = \frac{1}{0.01608} = 62.2$$

$$k = 0.387 \text{ Btu/(hr)(ft)(°F)}$$
$$\mu = 2.01 \text{ lb/(hr)(ft)}$$
$$G = \frac{670 \times 12^2}{0.7854 \times 0.87^2}$$
$$= 163,000 \text{ lb/(sq ft) (hr)}$$

$$\frac{h_i(0.87/12)}{0.387} = 0.023 \left(\frac{0.87 \times 163,000}{12 \times 2.01}\right)^{0.8} (5.1)^{0.4}(1 + 3.5 \times 0.024)$$

$$h_i = \frac{0.387 \times 12}{0.87}(0.023)(5,850)^{0.8}(1.97)(1.084) = 250$$

Then the over-all coefficient from Eq. (10-4) is

$$\frac{1}{U} = \frac{1}{186} + \frac{0.065}{12 \times 26}\frac{1}{0.935} + \frac{1 \times 1.0}{250 \times 0.87} + 0.002$$
$$U = 82 \text{ Btu/(hr)(sq ft)(°F)}$$

10-3. Heat and Mass Transfer in Homogeneous Flow Reactors. The heat-transfer rates in well-agitated tank-type reactors, operated continuously, can be estimated from the information given in Sec. 10-2.

For tubular-type flow reactors the well-developed correlations[1] for turbulent flow can be used to estimate the heat exchange with the surroundings. It may be noted that even in turbulent flow the temperature across the diameter of the tubular reactor is not entirely uniform. A rigorous approach to the design of such a reactor would take into account radial variations in temperature. In practice this has not been done because (1) there are insufficient data on heat-transfer rates in the radial direction in turbulent flow in tubes; and (2) the error made in assuming a uniform temperature is probably small, particularly at high Reynolds numbers. In any event the heat-transfer rate at the wall of the reactor is correctly given by use of the dimensionless correlations for the heat-

[1] For example, see *ibid.*, p. 154.

transfer coefficient, h_i, and a temperature difference based upon the bulk mean temperature of the reaction mixture. In other words, the heat exchange with the surroundings can be computed from the equation:

$$dQ'_s = h_i (t - t_i) \, dA_i \qquad (10\text{-}7)$$

where t = bulk mean temperature of reaction mixture
    t_i = inside temperature of tube wall

If the inside-surface temperature t_i is not known, as is usually the case in commercial reactors, an over-all coefficient must be developed before the heat-transfer rate can be obtained. For example, if the reactor is jacketed and the heat-transfer coefficient between the jacket fluid and the outside wall of the reactor tube is h_0, the over-all coefficient U is given by an expression analogous to Eq. (10-4) for kettle-type equipment,

$$\frac{1}{U} = \frac{1}{h_i} + \frac{L}{k} \frac{A_i}{A_m} + \frac{1}{h_o} \frac{A_i}{A_o} + r_s \qquad (10\text{-}8)$$

In this expression U is based upon the inside surface of the reactor tube.

In Sec. 6-3 the importance of heat transfer in tubular-reactor design was illustrated in Example 6-5. There the inside-wall temperature was known so that it was not necessary to calculate an over-all heat-transfer coefficient. Example 10-2 that follows considers the case where the wall temperature is unknown and Eq. (10-8) is applicable.

Example 10-2. Suppose that in Example 6-5 the glycol in the reactor jacket was boiling at the constant temperature of 210°C.† Estimate the over-all heat-transfer coefficient U based upon the inside surface. The tube-wall thickness is 0.125 in. [$k = 26$ Btu/(hr)(ft)(°F)].

Solution. The inside-film coefficient is 5.0. If it is supposed that this includes any scale resistance r_s on the inside, application of Eq. (10-8) will require, in addition, only the evaluation of the boiling outside coefficient h_o, the resistance of the metal wall, and the outside scale resistance. This second term is

$$\frac{L}{k} \frac{A_i}{A_m} = \frac{0.125/12}{26} \frac{d_i}{d_m} = \frac{0.125}{12 \times 26} \frac{2.0}{(2.0 + 2.25)/2}$$
$$= 0.00377$$

The outside coefficient for boiling glycol on a vertical tube is difficult to estimate because a general correlation of data for various liquids remains to be discovered. This is so, even for the case of vertical or horizontal tubes submerged in a pool of liquid. Boiling in the jacket of tubes may be somewhat different owing to the flow patterns developed. The coefficient is a function of the temperature difference and reaches a maximum value as Δt is increased to a critical point. McAdams has discussed this problem and summarized available data for various

† This is a more realistic condition than a constant inside temperature of 200°C, for t_i would change along the tube length as the heat-transfer rate changed.

liquids.[1] A method of estimating the maximum, or peak, heat-transfer rate (per unit area) and critical Δt is also presented. Using these correlations leads to the following results:

$$\left(\frac{q}{A}\right)_{max} = 440,000 \text{ Btu}/(\text{hr})(\text{sq ft})$$

$$(\Delta t)_{crit} = 75°F$$

These values are simply approximations, and about all that can be said is that the actual flux and Δt would be less. Fortunately, the inside coefficient will be very much more important than the boiling value, so that an approximation of the latter quantity is not serious.

It is estimated that the actual value in the reactor will still be in the nucleate boiling range and about half of the maximum. If Δt is 70 per cent of the critical value, the boiling coefficient would be

$$\frac{q}{A} = h_o \, \Delta t$$

$$h_o = \frac{440,000 \times 0.5}{75 \times 0.7}$$

$$= 4200 \text{ Btu}/(\text{hr})(\text{sq ft})(°F)$$

Now, using Eq. (10-8), the over-all coefficient between the boiling glycol in the jacket and the reaction mixture inside the tube will be given by the expression

$$\frac{1}{U} = \frac{1}{5.0} + 0.00377 + \frac{1}{4,200} \frac{2.0}{2.25} + r_{s_0}$$

where r_{s_0} represents the scale resistance on the boiling-glycol side. If it is estimated to be 0.001,

$$\frac{1}{U} = 0.20 + 0.00377 + 0.00019 + 0.001$$

$$U = 4.9 \text{ Btu}/(\text{hr})(\text{sq ft})(°F)$$

It is evident that accurate estimation of the boiling coefficient and the scale resistance is not necessary in determining the over-all U in this instance. The latter value is determined by the poor heat-transfer properties of the gaseous reaction mixture inside the tube. If, instead of boiling glycol, a liquid such as Dowtherm was passed through the jacket, the outside coefficient would be of the order of 100 rather than 4200 Btu/(hr)(sq ft)(°F). This would have a larger effect on the value of U, but still the gas side h_i would predominate. For example, if $h_o = 100$,

$$\frac{1}{U} = 0.20 + 0.00377 + \frac{1}{100} \frac{2.0}{2.25} + 0.001$$

$$U = 4.7 \text{ Btu}/(\text{hr})(\text{sq ft})(°F)$$

[1] W. H. McAdams, "Heat Transmission," 3d ed., p. 368, McGraw-Hill Book Company, Inc., New York, 1954.

10-4. Heat Transfer Radially in Packed-bed Reactors. In the consideration of homogeneous reactors only the effect of heat exchange with the surroundings has been studied. Mass and energy transfer within a cross section of the reaction mixture has been assumed rapid enough to result in uniform concentration and temperature. However, in a packed-bed reactor heat and mass transfer *within* the bed frequently must be taken into account. First, if the reactor is jacketed for heating or cooling, there may be significant temperature variations in the radial direction across the diameter of the reactor tube. Second, in some fixed-bed reactors there may be appreciable differences in temperature and concentration between the fluid and solid particles. For example, in the case of noncatalytic reactions between a flowing gas and a solid reactant in the form of particles in the bed, mass-transfer rates between gas and solid particle may be the controlling factor in determining the rate of reaction. The first situation, radial heat and mass transfer, is considered in the present section, and the second in Sec. 10-6.

In homogeneous tubular reactors the assumption has been made that the temperature is uniform in a cross section perpendicular to the direction of flow. Along the axis just the opposite assumption was made, namely, that the rate of heat transfer from one element of fluid to the next was negligible with respect to the rate of energy evolution due to the reaction. By these assumptions it was not necessary to consider the rate of heat transfer within the fluid itself, but only at the reactor wall. That is, all the resistance to heat transfer inside the tube is assumed to be at the inside surface and can be handled adequately by an inside-film coefficient as in Examples 6-5 and 10-2. The temperature profile would consist of a flat central portion extending to very near the wall, where a sharp decrease to the wall-surface temperature occurs. A somewhat analogous situation exists for *mass* transfer in homogeneous reactors. The composition is assumed to be uniform in a radial direction and not influenced by mass transfer in the axial direction.[1] As in heat transfer, these assumptions were frequently made, even in doubtful cases, because of the lack of experimental data.

This simplified scheme of analysis is often unsatisfactory for fixed-bed catalytic reactors. Here the reaction mixture, gas or liquid, is passed through a fixed bed of solid particles acting as a catalyst for the reaction. A small tube diameter and large flow rate favor the establishment of a

---

[1] It may be noted that the important type of mass transfer involved here is a convective or eddy type, not the molecular process determined by the molecular diffusivity. The molecular process is too slow to be important under most conditions. Indeed, this is the chief reason the mass-transfer rate in the axial direction can be neglected. The eddy process is masked by the mass flow in the axial direction, and the molecular process is too slow to be important.

uniform temperature and concentration profile across the diameter of the reactor. However, to provide residence time, the fluid velocities are low. This means that there will be insufficient turbulence to approach complete mixing in the radial direction. Accordingly, the assumption of a uniform temperature or composition is not warranted where the particle size is small or tube size large. Fortunately data on mass- and heat-transfer rates radially in packed beds are available. Hence a reaction-design procedure (Chap. 11) can be developed for such cases, taking into account radial variations.

The purpose of the present section is twofold: (1) To present heat-transfer rates at the wall of the fixed-bed reactor. These are useful when the simplified procedure of assuming that the temperature is uniform up to the wall can be made. (2) To summarize heat- and mass-transfer data within the bed of solid catalyst particles. These data are necessary when radial temperature variations must be taken into account by the more rigorous approach.

Wall Heat-transfer Coefficients. The presence of the solid particles increases the heat-transfer coefficient [defined by Eq. (10-7)] in a packed bed several times over that in an empty tube at the same gas flow rate. In the earliest experimental investigation[1] of the subject the results were reported as ratios of the coefficient in the packed bed to that in the empty pipe. Later studies[2-5] agreed with the work of Colburn. It was found that this ratio of heat-transfer coefficients varied with the ratio d_p/d_t (diameter of the particle divided by that of the tube), reaching a maximum value at about $d_p/d_t = 0.15$. Colburn's results are summarized in Table 10-1.

TABLE 10-1. RATIO OF HEAT-TRANSFER COEFFICIENTS IN PACKED (h_p) AND EMPTY (h_i) TUBE

d_p/d_t	0.05	0.10	0.15	0.20	0.25	0.30
h_p/h_i	5.5	7.0	7.8	7.5	7.0	6.6

Presumably the large increase in heat-transfer coefficient over that in an empty pipe is due to the mixing, or turbulence, caused by the presence of the solid particles. This turbulence tends to prevent the build-up of a slow-moving layer of fluid next to the wall and also increases the radial transfer of heat within the fluid in the tube. Up to a point, decreasing

[1] A. P. Colburn, *Ind. Eng. Chem.*, **28**:910 (1931); *Trans. AIChE*, **26**:166 (1931).
[2] Emanuel Singer and R. H. Wilhelm, *Chem. Eng. Progr.*, **46**:343 (1950).
[3] M. Leva, *Ind. Eng. Chem.*, **39**:857 (1947).
[4] M. Leva and M. Grummer, *Ind. Eng. Chem.*, **40**:415 (1948).
[5] M. Leva, M. Weintraub, M. Grummer, and E. L. Clark, *Ind. Eng. Chem.*, **40**:747 (1948).

the particle size increases the importance of these factors, and the heat-transfer coefficient continues to increase. However, the maximum at a certain d_p/d_t ratio suggests that another factor is involved. This is concerned with the size of the radial eddies in the fluid in the bed. As the particle size continues to decrease, the size of the eddies decreases and the distance over which each mixing process occurs is decreased. Also, there is a larger number of more or less stagnant films, between the fluid and the solid particles, which the heat must cross in reaching the wall. The maximum in the heat-transfer coefficient would represent the point where this second factor counterbalances favorable effects of the mixing process obtained with the smaller particles.

Leva and Wilhelm and coworkers[1] have correlated fixed-bed heat-transfer coefficients for air over a wide range of variables. They can be used to predict the heat-transfer rate by Eq. (10-7) when the variation in temperature within the bed itself is neglected. Leva's expressions are as follows:

$$\frac{h_p d_t}{k} = 0.813 \left(\frac{d_p G}{\mu}\right)^{0.9} e^{-6 d_p/d_t} \qquad \text{heating} \qquad (10\text{-}9)$$

$$\frac{h_p d_t}{k} = 3.50 \left(\frac{d_p G}{\mu}\right)^{0.7} e^{-4.6 d_p/d_t} \qquad \text{cooling} \qquad (10\text{-}10)$$

Heat Transfer within a Packed Bed (the Effective Thermal Conductivity). In a bed of solid particles through which a fluid is passing, heat can be transferred in the radial direction by a number of mechanisms. Nevertheless, it has been customary to consider that the bed of particles and the gas may be replaced by a hypothetical solid in which conduction is the only mechanism for heat transfer. The thermal conductivity of this solid has been termed the effective thermal conductivity, k_e. With this scheme the temperature t of any point in the bed may be related to k_e and the position parameters, r and z, by one of the following differential equations (which are derived in Example 10-3):

$$-G c_p \frac{\partial t}{\partial z} + k_e \left(\frac{1}{r}\frac{\partial t}{\partial r} + \frac{\partial^2 t}{\partial r^2}\right) = 0 \qquad (10\text{-}11)$$

$$-G c_p \frac{\partial t}{\partial z} + k_e \left(\frac{1}{r}\frac{\partial t}{\partial r} + \frac{\partial^2 t}{\partial r^2}\right) + \frac{\partial k_e}{\partial r}\frac{\partial t}{\partial r} = 0 \qquad (10\text{-}12)$$

If k_e is known at any point in the bed, these equations can be integrated (usually a numerical integration is required) to give the temperature at any point. Such information can be used to design a packed-bed reactor when radial gradients must be taken into account.

Owing to the many heat-transfer mechanisms in the gas-solid bed,

[1] See footnotes 2 to 5 on page 289.

k_e is not an ordinary thermal conductivity, but a property of the bed that depends upon a large number of variables such as gas flow rate, particle diameter, porosity, true thermal conductivity of the gas and of the solid phases, and temperature level. For this reason the most logical method of correlating k_e data (and developing methods of prediction) is to divide k_e into separate contributions, each of which corresponds to a mechanism of heat transfer. This scheme has evolved from a very simple division,[1] through several extensions[2-6] to the most recent developments.[7,8] Before going into the details of the correlations and theoretical developments for the effective thermal conductivity, let us gain some experience with the term by deriving Eqs. (10-11) and (10-12) in Example 10-3, and by computing a single value of k_e from experimental data, Examples 10-4 and 10-5.

Example 10-3. Derive Eqs. (10-11) and (10-12).
Solution. The rate of radial heat transfer per unit area in the bed is

$$Q' = -k_e \frac{\partial t}{\partial r}$$

where t is the temperature of the gas. If an energy balance is written on an element of volume $2\pi r\, dr\, dz$ of the bed, it will include the following terms:

ENERGY INTO ELEMENT

1. Radially: $-k_e(2\pi r\, dz)\left(\dfrac{\partial t}{\partial r}\right)_r$

2. Axially:[9,10] $Gc(2\pi r\, dr)t_z$

---

[1] T. E. W. Schumann and V. Voss, *Fuel*, **13**:249 (1934).

[2] G. Damköler, "Der Chemie Ingenieur," Euken Jacob 3, pt I, p. 44, Akademische Verlagsgesellschaft m.b.H., Leipzig, 1937.

[3] R. H. Wilhelm, W. C. Johnson, R. Wynkoop, and D. W. Collier, *Chem. Eng. Progr.*, **44**:105 (1948).

[4] D. G. Bunnell, H. B. Irvin, R. W. Olson, and J. M. Smith, *Ind. Eng. Chem.*, **41**: 1977 (1949).

[5] H. B. Irvin, R. W. Olson, and J. M. Smith, *Chem. Eng. Prog.*, **47**:287 (1951).

[6] H. Vershoor and G. C. A. Schuit, *Appl. Sci. Research*, **42**(A.2): 97 (1950).

[7] Singer and Wilhelm, *loc. cit.*

[8] W. B. Argo and J. M. Smith, *Chem. Eng. Progr.*, **49**:443 (1953).

[9] No term is included here for heat flow by other mechanisms than mass movement of the gas. Temperature measurements indicate that under most conditions the temperature gradient in the radial direction is many times that in the axial direction. Hence, except at very low flow rates and small radial temperature gradients, the heat flow in the axial direction, other than by mass movement of the gas, can be safely neglected.

[10] From this point on, the subscript p is not used with the specific heat, since c will always refer to the constant-pressure value.

ENERGY OUT

1. Radially: $-k_e 2\pi (r + dr)\, dz \left(\dfrac{\partial t}{\partial r}\right)_{r+dr}$

2. Axially:[1] $Gc(2\pi r\, dr)t_{z+dz}$

No terms have been included for heat transfer between gas and solid. For this to be true, the average temperature of the solid particle and that of the gas at the same position in the bed must be the same. Bunnell et al.,[1] in experimental temperature measurements in a packed bed with air flow, found no significant differences between the gas and solid temperature. However, where reaction is occurring with an evolution of heat, the temperature of the solid catalyst will be greater than that of the gas. Hall and Smith[2] in the oxidation of sulfur dioxide found differences up to 10 to 15°C. Under reaction conditions, then, it is not rigorous to write the heat balance in terms of one temperature. Instead, two energy balances should be developed, one for the gas and one for the solid. These involve heat-transfer terms between solid and gas phases. However, in practice such a procedure leads to equations too difficult to handle conveniently so that the assumption of identical average temperatures of gas and sol.d particle is made.

A final assumption for the simple form of the heat balance is that the effective thermal conductivity and the specific heat c_p do not vary in the bed. Then the terms as shown are correct and may be combined by equating the heat in and heat out to give[3]

$$-Gc(2\pi r\, dr)\,\frac{\partial t}{\partial z}\,dz + k_e\left(2\pi\, dr\, dz\,\frac{\partial t}{\partial r} + 2\pi r\, dz\,\frac{\partial^2 t}{\partial r^2}\,dr\right) = 0$$

or $$-Gc\,\frac{\partial t}{\partial z} + k_e\left(\frac{1}{r}\,\frac{\partial t}{\partial r} + \frac{\partial^2 t}{\partial r^2}\right) = 0$$

which is Eq. (10-11).

If c is assumed constant, but not k_e, then the term for the energy out of the element in the radial direction becomes

$$-k_{e,r+dr}2\pi (r + dr)\left(\frac{\partial t}{\partial r}\right)_{r+dr} dz$$

Neglecting second-order differentials, this becomes, on expansion,

$$-2\pi r\, dz\, k_e\left(\frac{\partial t}{\partial r}\right)_r - 2\pi r\, dz\, dr\left(k_e\,\frac{\partial^2 t}{\partial r^2} + \frac{1}{r}\,k_e\,\frac{\partial t}{\partial r} + \frac{\partial k_e}{\partial r}\,\frac{\partial t}{\partial r}\right)$$

---

[1] *Loc. cit.*

[2] R. E. Hall and J. M. Smith, *Chem. Eng. Progr.*, **45**:459 (1949).

[3] It may be pointed out that

$$\left(\frac{\partial t}{\partial r}\right)_{r+dr} = \left(\frac{\partial t}{\partial r}\right)_r + \left(\frac{\partial^2 t}{\partial r^2}\right) dr$$

and $$t_{z+dz} = t_z + \left(\frac{\partial t}{\partial z}\right)_z dz$$

Now equating the energy into and out of the element as before,

$$-Gc(2\pi r\ dr)\frac{\partial t}{\partial z}\ dz + 2\pi r\ dz\ dr\left(k_e\frac{\partial^2 t}{\partial r^2} + \frac{1}{r}k_e\frac{\partial t}{\partial r} + \frac{\partial k_e}{\partial r}\frac{\partial t}{\partial r}\right) = 0$$

or
$$-Gc\frac{\partial t}{\partial z} + k_e\left(\frac{\partial^2 t}{\partial r^2} + \frac{1}{r}\frac{\partial t}{\partial r}\right) + \frac{\partial k_e}{\partial r}\frac{\partial t}{\partial r} = 0$$

This is Eq. (10-12)

It should be noted that both Eqs. (10-11) and (10-12) apply at steady-state conditions; i.e., there is no accumulation of energy in the solid particles within the bed.

These expressions relating k_e and t can be used (1) to obtain k_e from experimental temperature measurements (Example 10-4) or (2) to compute temperatures within the bed from known values of the effective thermal conductivity (Example 10-7).

Experimental Determination of Effective Thermal Conductivity. The first application of Eqs. (10-11) and (10-12) has been used by a number of investigators to obtain effective thermal conductivities from experimental data and then correlate the results in terms of the pertinent variables. Two methods have been used in this connection. In the first, Eq. (10-11) has been integrated and put in terms of the mean temperatures entering and leaving the bed. Then from measured values of these two quantities an average over-all k_e could be computed. The investigations of Hougen and Piret,[1] Vershoor and Schuit,[2] and Singer and Wilhelm[2] are of this type.

The second method involves actual measurement of temperatures across the diameter of the bed and has been used by another group of investigators[3-6] to establish what are called point values of the effective thermal conductivity. The first studies of Bunnell et al.[2] assumed that k_e did not vary with radial position and hence involved use of Eq. (10-11). However, the results indicated that k_e was not constant so that it is necessary to use the more elaborate Eq. (10-12) in order to obtain valid values of k_e at different radial positions.[7] This correct procedure was

[1] J. O. Hougen and E. L. Piret, *Chem. Eng. Progr.*, **47**:295 (1951).

[2] *Loc. cit.*

[3] C. A. Coberly and W. R. Marshall, *Chem. Eng. Progr.*, **47**:141 (1951).

[4] J. R. Felix and W. K. Neill, Preprints Heat Transfer Symposium, p. 125, American Institute of Chemical Engineers, annual meeting, Atlantic City, December, 1951.

[5] Irvin, Olson, and Smith, *loc. cit.*

[6] R. W. Schuler, V. P. Stallings, and J. M. Smith, *Chem. Eng. Progr., Symposium Ser.* 4, **48**:19 (1952).

[7] It should be noted that the k_e values computed from Eq. (10-11) do not represent true results even though they show variations with radial position. This is because Eq. (10-11) itself is derived on the supposition that k_e is constant. Nevertheless the values of k_e so computed show the correct trend of the variation of k_e with r/r_0. These approximate results are more appropriate to use in computing temperatures in a packed bed than a single constant value. This point is illustrated in Example 10-7.

employed by Schuler *et al.*[1] The approximate method based upon Eq. (10-11) is illustrated in Example 10-4 and the corrected approach in Example 10-5.

Example 10-4. Using Eq. (10-11), calculate the effective thermal conductivity as a function of radial position at a packed-bed depth of 0.354 ft from the experimental temperature data given in Table 10-2. This information was determined for air flowing at a superficial mass velocity of 350 lb/(hr)(sq ft) in a standard 2-in. pipe packed with $\frac{1}{8}$- by $\frac{1}{8}$-in. cylindrical alumina pellets. The

TABLE 10-2

Radial position, $\frac{r}{r_0}$	Packed-bed depth, ft				
	0.030	0.0625	0.137	0.354	0.473
	Temperature, °C				
0	400	398	392	347.5	325
0.1	400	397.5	391	346	323
0.2	400	396.5	389.5	341.5	318
0.3	399.5	395	386	333	310.5
0.4	398	392	381	319.5	301
0.5	396	387	374	303.5	289
0.6	390.5	378	363	287.5	274.5
0.7	381	365	347	271	258.5
0.8	364	345.5	323.5	252	239.5
0.9	333	312	285	228.5	217

TABLE 10-3

Radial position, $\frac{r}{r_0}$	$-\dfrac{\partial t}{\partial z}$, °C/ft	$\dfrac{-\partial t}{\partial r}$, °C/ft	$\dfrac{-\partial^2 t}{\partial r^2}$, °C/sq ft	$\dfrac{k_e}{cG}$	$\dfrac{k_e}{cG}$ (by integration)
0.0	210	0	18,000		
0.1	214	344	42,500	0.0026	
0.2	216	730	50,200	0.0023	0.0022
0.3	223	1220	56,300	0.0022	
0.4	200	1650	35,800	0.0024	0.0023
0.5	192	1850	13,100	0.0034	
0.6	152	1920	7,880	0.0034	0.0027
0.7	137	2040	27,500	0.0022	
0.8	125	2410	47,600	0.0015	0.0012
0.9	112	2840	52,800	0.0012	

Bed depth = 0.354 ft.

[1] *Loc. cit.*

air entered the bed at a center temperature of 400°C, and the tube was jacketed with boiling ethylene glycol.   Data were obtained at a number of bed depths. This is required in order to evaluate the temperature gradient in the axial direction, $\partial t/\partial z$.

Solution.   To determine k_e from Eq. (10-11), the partial derivatives must be evaluated from slopes of temperature vs. r and z plots.   Figure 10-1 shows the temperature data given in Table 10-2 plotted against bed depth z, for four radial positions.   Since $\partial t/\partial z$ values are required at a bed depth of 0.354 ft, slopes of curves in Fig. 10-1 should be taken at this z value.   The results so obtained are

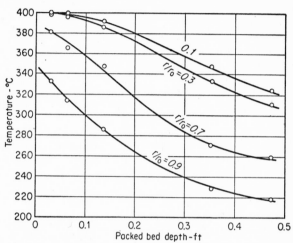

FIG. 10-1. Temperatures in a packed bed with air flow.

shown in the second column of Table 10-3, along with analogous values for the radial positions not shown in the figure.

From a graph of temperature vs. radial position at a bed depth of 0.354 ft, the slopes at each radial position were determined.   This procedure gave values of $\partial t/\partial(r/r_0)$.   Since $dr = r_0\, d(r/r_0)$, where r_0 is the radius of the tube, the required values of $\partial t/\partial r$ are given by the relationship

$$\frac{\partial t}{\partial r} = \frac{1}{r_0}\frac{\partial t}{\partial r/r_0} = \frac{12}{1.03}\frac{\partial t}{\partial(r/r_0)} = \frac{1}{0.0859}\frac{\partial t}{\partial(r/r_0)}$$

The numerical results for $\partial t/\partial r$ are given in the third column of Table 10-3.

The second derivatives can be obtained by plotting $\partial t/\partial r$ vs. r/r_0.   Slopes of this curve are equal to $\dfrac{\partial}{\partial r/r_0}\left(\dfrac{\partial t}{\partial r}\right)$.   The values of $\dfrac{\partial^2 t}{\partial r^2}$ can be found by dividing the slope by r_0.   Thus

$$\frac{\partial^2 t}{\partial r^2} = \frac{1}{r_0}\frac{\partial}{\partial r/r_0}\left(\frac{\partial t}{\partial r}\right)$$

The fourth column of Table 10-3 gives these second derivatives.

Solving Eq. (10-11) for k_e/cG yields

$$\frac{k_e}{cG} = \frac{\partial t/\partial z}{(1/r)(\partial t/\partial r) + \partial^2 t/\partial r^2}$$

At a radial position of 0.1, $r = 0.0859 \times 0.1 = 0.00859$ ft, and the partial derivatives are given in Table 10-3. Substitution in the preceding equation gives for k_e/cG

$$\frac{k_e}{cG} = \frac{-214}{(1/0.00859) \times -344 - 42,500}$$
$$= 0.0026 \text{ ft}$$

In a similar way the results at other radial positions can be computed. All the results are shown in the fifth column of Table 10-3.[1]

The effective thermal conductivity itself is obtained by multiplying the group k_e/cG by the specific heat and mass velocity. At a radial position of 0.1, $c = 0.252$; so

$$k_e = 0.0026 \times 0.252 \times 350$$
$$= 0.23 \text{ Btu/(hr)(ft)(°F)}$$

The precision of such calculations is not high owing to the necessity for differentiating the data. This is particularly true in connection with $\partial^2 t/\partial r^2$ because two differentiations are required. An alternate, but more time-consuming, method of obtaining k_e/cG is by numerical integration of Eq. (10-11). In this procedure values of k_e/cG are assumed at each radial position, and the differential equation integrated to obtain the temperature. If the temperatures so computed do not agree with the measured values, a new assumption of k_e/cG is made, etc., until agreement is achieved. The numerical-integration procedure is described in the next part of this section and illustrated in Example 10-7. Values of k_e/cG obtained by this alternate method are shown in the last column of Table 10-3.

The dimensionless Peclet number for heat transfer is given by the expression

$$\text{Pe}_h = \frac{cd_pG}{k_e} = \frac{d_p}{k_e/cG} = \frac{0.125}{12 \times 0.0026} = 4.0 \qquad \text{for } r/r_0 = 0.1$$

The results shown as k_e and Pe are given in Table 10-4.

The primary reason for the variation in k_e across the diameter of the packed bed is that the velocity also varies. As will be seen later, two of

[1] Equation (10-11) becomes indeterminate at $r/r_0 = 0.0$ because both r and $\partial t/\partial r$ are zero. Differentiation to determine the value of an indeterminate form gives $\partial^2 t/\partial r^2$, so that

$$\frac{k_e}{cG} = \frac{\partial t/\partial z}{2 \, \partial^2 t/\partial r^2}$$

However, this equation is not accurate to use because of the importance of the graphically determined second derivative. For this reason values of k_e/cG are not shown at the center of the bed.

the most important contributions to k_e depend upon the degree of turbulence, and hence the velocity level, in the bed.

No data are available for the linear velocity distribution in packed beds under nonisothermal conditions. However, Schwartz[1] has determined such profiles for isothermal beds. Since the effect of temperature variations on the mass velocity is probably small, this isothermal information was used by Schuler *et al.* to compute k_e values according to Eq. (10-12). The details of the calculations involved are illustrated in Example 10-5.

TABLE 10-4

Radial position, $\dfrac{r}{r_0}$	k_e, Btu/(hr)(ft)(°F)	Pe_h
0.0		
0.1	0.23	4.0
0.2	0.20	4.5
0.3	0.19	4.7
0.4	0.21	4.3
0.5	0.30	3.1
0.6	0.30	3.1
0.7	0.19	4.7
0.8	0.13	7.0
0.9	0.10	8.7

Example 10-5. Estimate more accurate values of the effective thermal conductivity from the data in Example 10-4 by employing Eq. (10-12). The mass-velocity profile for $\frac{1}{8}$- by $\frac{1}{8}$-in. cylindrical pellets in a 2-in. pipe at a mean value of $G = 350$ lb/(hr)(sq ft) is shown in Table 10-5.

TABLE 10-5

Radial position, $\dfrac{r}{r_0}$	Mass velocity, G, lb/(hr)(sq ft)
0	292
0.1	312
0.2	338
0.3	368
0.4	400
0.5	430
0.6	453
0.7	464
0.8	427
0.9	270

[1] C. E. Schwartz and J. M. Smith, *Ind. Eng. Chem.*, **45**:1209 (1953).

Solution. If Eq. (10-12) is solved for k_e, there is obtained

$$k_e = \frac{cG\,\partial t/\partial z}{(1/r)(\partial t/\partial r) + \partial^2 t/\partial r^2} - \frac{\partial t/\partial r}{(1/r)(\partial t/\partial r) + \partial^2 t/\partial r^2}\frac{\partial k_e}{\partial r} \qquad (A)$$

or

$$k_e = A - B\frac{\partial k_e}{\partial r} \qquad (B)$$

where

$$A = \frac{dt/dz}{(1/r)(\partial t/\partial r) + \partial^2 t/\partial r^2}\,cG = \left(\frac{k_e}{cG_0}\right)_{unc} cG \qquad (C)^1$$

$$B = \frac{\partial t/\partial r}{(1/r)(\partial t/\partial r) + \partial^2 t/\partial r^2} \qquad (D)$$

At a fixed bed depth, where the only independent variable is r, Eq. (B) may be solved graphically for the value of k_e at each radial position. The quantities A and B are not constant but can be evaluated from the temperature data in Table 10-2. Actually, in Eq. (C) for A, the ratio is equal to the uncorrected value of k_e/cG_0 as determined in Example 10-4. Hence values of A can be obtained from the results in Table 10-3 by multiplying $(k_e/cG_0)_{unc}$ by the specific heat and the point value of G given in Table 10-5. Thus, at a radial position of 0.1,

$$A = \left(\frac{k_e}{cG_0}\right)_{unc} cG = 0.0026 \times 0.252 \times 312 = 0.204$$

From the data in Table 10-3 the value of B at $r/r_0 = 0.1$ is

$$B = \frac{-344}{(1/0.00859) \times -344 - 42{,}500} = 0.00419$$

The results for A and B at other radial positions at the same bed depth of 0.354 ft are given in Table 10-6.

TABLE 10-6

$\dfrac{r}{r_0}$	A [Eq. (C)]	B [Eq. (D)]	k_e	$\dfrac{k_e}{cG}$	Pe_h
0.0	0.21†	0	0.21	0.0029	3.6
0.1	0.204	0.00419	0.21	0.0027	3.9
0.2	0.199	0.00793	0.20	0.0024	4.4
0.3	0.159	0.0119	0.19	0.0021	5.0
0.4	0.243	0.0201	0.19	0.0019	5.5
0.5	0.264	0.0336	0.21	0.0019	5.5
0.6	0.385	0.0435	0.23	0.0020	5.2
0.7	0.259	0.0337	0.25	0.0021	4.9
0.8	0.160	0.0295	0.24	0.0022	4.6
0.9	0.0836	0.0320	0.20	0.0030	3.5

† This value was obtained by extrapolating the results at higher values of r/r_0 down to zero.

[1] G_0 refers to the bulk mean mass velocity in the bed, while G is the point value at any radial position.

Using the known values of A and B, Eq. (B) may be used to compute k_e by the following procedure: Starting at the center of the bed and applying Eq. (B),

$$k_{e_0} = A_0 - 0 = A_0 = 0.21$$

If $r/r_0 = 0.1$ is designated by subscript 1, $r/r_0 = 0.2$ by subscript 2, etc., the following difference equation may be written:

$$k_{e_1} = k_{e_0} + \left(\frac{\partial k_e}{\partial r}\right)_{av} \Delta r \qquad (E)$$

where $\Delta r = 0.1 r_0 = 0.00859$ ft and

$$\left(\frac{\partial k_e}{\partial r}\right)_{av} = \frac{1}{2}\left[\left(\frac{\partial k_e}{\partial r}\right)_0 + \left(\frac{\partial k_e}{\partial r}\right)_1\right] = \frac{1}{2}\left[0 + \left(\frac{\partial k_e}{\partial r}\right)_1\right] \qquad (F)$$

Applying Eq. (B) at $r/r_0 = 0.00859$,

$$k_{e_1} = A_1 - B_1\left(\frac{\partial k_e}{\partial r}\right)_1 \qquad (G)$$

Equations (E) to (G) may be solved simultaneously for k_1, $(\partial k_e/\partial r)_1$, and $(\partial k_e/\partial r)_{av}$. Illustrating with numerical values,

$$\left(\frac{\partial k_e}{\partial r}\right)_{av} = \frac{1}{2}\left(\frac{\partial k_e}{\partial r}\right)_1$$

and Eq. (E) becomes

$$k_1 = 0.21 + \frac{1}{2}\left(\frac{\partial k_e}{\partial r}\right)_1 \times 0.00859$$

Equation (G) is

$$k_1 = 0.204 - 0.00419\left(\frac{\partial k_e}{\partial r}\right)_1$$

Solving these two simultaneous equations,

$$\left(\frac{\partial k_e}{\partial r}\right)_1 = \frac{0.21 - 0.204}{-0.00430 - 0.00419} = -0.71$$

and
$$k_1 = 0.204 - 0.00419 \times -0.71 = 0.207$$

For the next increment the equations are

$$k_2 = k_1 + \left(\frac{\partial k_e}{\partial r}\right)_{av} \Delta r \qquad (E')$$

$$\left(\frac{\partial k_e}{\partial r}\right)_{av} = \frac{1}{2}\left[\left(\frac{\partial k_e}{\partial r}\right)_1 + \left(\frac{\partial k_e}{\partial r}\right)_2\right] \qquad (F')$$

and
$$k_{e_2} = A_2 - B_2\left(\frac{\partial k_e}{\partial r}\right)_2 \qquad (G')$$

Solving Eqs. (E') to (G') yields

$$\left(\frac{\partial k_e}{\partial r}\right)_2 = -0.37$$

$$k_{e_2} = 0.202$$

Continuing these computations gives k_e values at each radial position as shown in Table 10-6.

At $r/r_0 = 0$

$$\frac{k_e}{cG} = \frac{0.21}{0.252 \times 292} = 0.0029$$

and

$$\text{Pe}_h = \frac{d_p}{\dfrac{k_e}{cG}} = \frac{0.125}{12 \times 0.0029} = 3.6$$

Results at other radial positions are shown in the last columns of Table 10-6.

In comparing these corrected results for k_e and Pe_h with those obtained by the simplified procedure in Example 10-4, it is seen that the corrected values show much less variation with radial position. This is particularly noticeable near the wall, $r/r_0 = 0.9$. The uncorrected k_e decreases to 0.10 from 0.23 at the center, while the corrected value falls only to 0.20, indicating that an important factor in causing k_e to drop near the wall is the corresponding fall in mass velocity.

Prediction of the Effective Thermal Conductivity. By analyzing experimentally determined k_e values in the ways just described, various methods of predicting effective thermal conductivities have been developed.

One of the earliest proposals[1] was to divide the total value of k_e into two parts: (1) a static contribution corresponding to the conductivity of the bed when the fluid velocity was zero; (2) the increase in conductivity resulting when the fluid moved through the bed at a forced mass velocity G. Recently[2,3] the individual mechanisms by which heat is transferred radially have been examined and methods proposed for predicting the contribution of each. Basically these mechanisms are conduction, convection, and radiation. However, the two-phase nature of the bed means that some of these mechanisms operate in series as well as parallel. Also, there is opportunity for heat transfer between the solid particle and fluid stream. Qualitatively, it may be said that the transfer occurs by conduction through the solid phase, by conduction, convection, and radiation from the solid-fluid boundary, and by conduction, convection, and radiation in the fluid phase. The treatment of this combination of series and parallel processes is complicated. Also, the subject is still in a state of development. For these reasons no further discussion of the mathe-

---

[1] Schumann and Voss, *loc. cit.*

[2] Singer and Wilhelm, *loc. cit.*

[3] Argo and Smith, *loc. cit.*

matical approach to predicting the value of k_e is given here. However, the fundamental procedure proposed by Argo is described and illustrated in Appendix B as a continuation of this section.

Estimation of Temperatures in the Packed Bed. The problem of predicting the temperature at any point in the packed bed, knowing the effective thermal conductivities, is essentially the reverse of the procedure for determining k_e from experimental data. It is now necessary to integrate Eq. (10-11) or (10-12). Since the same type of equation is involved in the reactor-design problem (Chap. 11) and a numerical-integration procedure is required there, the integration of Eqs. (10-11) and (10-12) will also be carried out numerically.[1]

The numerical procedure is based upon replacing the differential equation with one involving finite differences. As such, the accuracy and amount of labor both increase as the size of the finite increment is decreased. If n and L represent the number of increments in the radial and axial directions, respectively, and Δr and Δz their magnitude,

$$r = n \, \Delta r \tag{10-37}$$
$$z = L \, \Delta z \tag{10-38}$$

If the cylindrical packed bed is divided into such increments, the temperature at any point can be represented by $t_{n,L}$, that is, the temperature at $r = n \, \Delta r$ and $z = L \, \Delta z$. Note that r is measured from the center of the bed and z from the bottom upward, corresponding to a vertical bed with the fluid entering the bottom and flowing upward.

The first difference Δt in the r direction can be written

$$\Delta_r t = t_{n+1,L} - t_{n,L} \tag{10-39}$$

Similarly the first difference Δt in the z direction may be written

$$\Delta_z t = t_{n,L+1} - t_{n,L} \tag{10-40}$$

The second difference in the r direction is

$$\Delta_r^2 t = (t_{n+1,L} - t_{n,L}) - (t_{n,L} - t_{n-1,L}) \tag{10-41}$$

With these definitions, the differential equation (10-11) may be replaced approximately with the following difference expression:

$$\frac{t_{n,L+1} - t_{n,L}}{\Delta z} = \frac{k_e}{cG} \left[\frac{1}{n \, \Delta r} \frac{t_{n+1,L} - t_{n,L}}{\Delta r} + \frac{t_{n+1,L} - t_{n,L} - (t_{n,L} - t_{n-1,L})}{\Delta r^2} \right]$$

or

$$t_{n,L+1} = t_{n,L} + \frac{\Delta z}{(\Delta r)^2} \frac{k_e}{cG} \left[\frac{1}{n} (t_{n+1,L} - t_{n,L}) + t_{n+1,L} - 2t_{n,L} + t_{n-1,L} \right] \tag{10-42}$$

[1] Note that it is possible to integrate Eq. (10-11) analytically, but not Eq. (10-12).

Equation (10-42) presents a method of computing the temperature a any point in the bed, provided the entrance-temperature distribution $t_{n,0}$, is known. The procedure is first to take $L = 0$ and compute t a the end of the first increment of z. This can be done at each radia position, $n = 1, 2, 3, \ldots$, from the chosen values of Δz and Δr and th known values of k_e, c, G, and $t_{n,0}$.

Some simplification in the formula can be obtained by restricting th choice of Δr and Δz so that

$$\frac{\Delta z}{(\Delta r)^2} \frac{k_e}{cG} = \frac{1}{2} \tag{10-43}$$

With this restriction Eq. (10-42) may be written

$$t_{n,L+1} = \frac{1}{2} \left[\frac{1}{n} (t_{n+1,L} - t_{n,L}) + t_{n+1,L} + t_{n-1,L} \right] \tag{10-44}$$

Equation (10-42) or (10-44) is satisfactory at every radial position except the center of the bed, $n = 0$. For this point a special formula can be developed by modifying the original differential equation. It i noted that in Eq. (10-11) the term $\frac{1}{r} \frac{\partial t}{\partial r}$ is indeterminate at the center i.e., both r and $\partial t/\partial r$ approach zero. If the numerator, $\partial t/\partial r$, and th denominator, r, of this fraction are differentiated separately, the result i $\partial^2 t/\partial r^2$. With this modification Eq. (10-11) may be written for the center of the pipe, as follows:

$$\frac{\partial t}{\partial z} = 2 \frac{k_e}{cG} \frac{\partial^2 t}{\partial r^2}$$

In difference form this becomes

$$t_{0,L+1} - t_{0,L} = 2 \frac{\Delta z}{(\Delta r)^2} \frac{k_e}{cG} [(t_{1,L} - t_{0,L}) - (t_{0,L} - t_{-1,L})]$$

By symmetry $t_{-1,L} = t_{1,L}$, so that

$$t_{0,L+1} = t_{0,L} + \frac{2 \Delta z}{(\Delta r)^2} \frac{k_e}{cG} (2t_{1,L} - 2t_{0,L}) \tag{10-45}$$

This expression can be used to evaluate the temperature at radia position $n = 0$, for all bed depths. If the fixed relationship between th size of Δr and Δz given by Eq. (10-43) is used, Eq. (10-45) becomes

$$t_{0,L+1} = 2t_{1,L} - t_{0,L} = t_{1,L} + (t_{1,L} - t_{0,L}) \tag{10-46}$$

The application of Eqs. (10-42) and (10-45) to the computation of temperatures within a packed bed is illustrated in Example 10-7. It may be noted that different values of k_e can be used for different radial positions in the numerical-solution procedure. This arbitrary procedure permits a closer approximation to the true temperature distribution in a bed, because, as has been already mentioned, k_e decreases rapidly near the wall of the tube. Of course, the varying values of k_e so employed are not true quantities. A better procedure is to use Eq. (10-12) as a starting point for the numerical calculations since it was derived on the basis of a variable k_e. This more rigorous approach, illustrated by Schuler,[1] is more tedious.

Example 10-7. In Example 10-4 temperature data were given for the flow of air through a bed packed with cylindrical pellets and jacketed with boiling glycol. Values of k_e/cG were computed from the temperature data at a bed depth of 0.354 ft.

Using the temperatures measured at $z = 0.03$ ft and the k_e/cG results from Example 10-4, compute the temperatures profile in the bed at 0.354 ft. Compare the results with the experimental data shown in Table 10-2. The wall temperature was approximately constant and equal to 200°C.

Solution. Since the effective-thermal-conductivity data are given at radial positions of 0.1, 0.2, etc., it is convenient to take Δr as 0.1 of the pipe radius. Hence for the 2-in. standard pipe $\Delta r = 0.1 r_0 = 0.1 \times 0.0859 = 0.00859$ ft.

Different values of k_e/cG are available for each radial position. They may be used to obtain a more accurate solution. If the fixed relation between Δz and Δr is employed, i.e., Eq. (10-43), varying values of Δz are found across the bed diameter. This results from the variation in k_e/cG and would lead to temperatures at uneven bed depths at the same values of L. For this reason, when variable thermal-conductivity data are employed, it is better to use the general temperature equations (10-42) and (10-45). When k_e/cG is a constant, the simplified forms [Eqs. (10-44) and (10-46)] are convenient.

The smaller the increment of bed depth, the more accurate the results, but the more lengthy the calculations to attain a given bed depth. In this case choose $\Delta z = 0.05$ ft. Then

$$\frac{\Delta z}{\Delta r^2} = \frac{0.05}{0.00859^2}$$
$$= 678 \text{ ft}^{-1}$$

If the calculations are started at $n = 1$, $L = 0$, Table 10-2 gives the temperature at $L = 0$ ($z = 0.03$ ft) as 400°C. At radial position 2, $t = 400$°C, and, at $n = 0$, $t = 400$°C. Also, from Table 10-3, at $n = 1$, $k_e/cG = 0.0026$ ft. These values[2] can be substituted in Eq. (10-42) to arrive at the temperature at $L = 1$, that is, $z = 0.03 + 0.05 = 0.08$ ft, and $n = 1$.

$$t_{1,1} = t_{1,0} + 678 \times 0.0026[\tfrac{1}{1}(t_{2,0} - t_{1,0}) + t_{2,0} - 2t_{1,0} + t_{0,0}]$$
$$= 400 + 1.76[(400 - 400) + 400 - 2 \times 400 + 400]$$
$$= 400\text{°C}$$

[1] Schuler, Stallings, and Smith, *loc. cit.*

[2] It is valid to express temperatures in degrees centigrade because the group $\dfrac{k_e}{cG}\dfrac{\Delta z}{(\Delta r)^2}$ is dimensionless.

Since the temperatures at $z = 0.03$ were all 400°C, the t at 0.08 ft and $n = 1$ is still 400°C. However, as the calculations are continued at larger radial positions different results will be obtained.

At $n = 2$

$$t_{2,1} = 400 + 678 \times 0.0023[\tfrac{1}{2}(399.5 - 400) + 399.5 - 2 \times 400 + 400]$$
$$= 400 + 1.55(-0.75) = 400 - 1.2$$
$$= 398.8°C.$$

At $n = 3$

$$t_{3,1} = 399.5 + 678 \times 0.0022[\tfrac{1}{3}(398 - 399.5) + 398 - 2 \times 399.5 + 400]$$
$$= 399.5 + 1.49 \times -1.5$$
$$= 397.3°C$$

Similar calculations at other radial positions give the results at $z = 0.08$ ft $(L = 1)$ shown in the second row of Table 10-8:

TABLE 10-8. TEMPERATURES IN PACKED BED

Temp, °C	Radial position, $\dfrac{r}{r_0} = n$										
	0	0.1	0.2	0.3	0.4	0.5	0.6	0.7	0.8	0.9	1.0
$t_{n,0}$ (exp., from Table 10-2)...............	400	400	400	399.5	398	396	390.5	381	364	333	200
$t_{n,1}$ (calculated)........	400	400	398.8	397.3	396.4	385.4	377.8	366.2	346	239	200
$t_{n,1}$ (smoothed, from Fig. 10-5)...............	400	399.8	399.2	397.3	393.5	387.6	379	366	346	290	200

The value at the center and $L = 1$ was obtained by substitution in Eq. (10-45). Actually the result is still 400°C since the temperatures $t_{1,0}$ and $t_{0,0}$ are 400°C. The temperature at radial position 0.9 and $L = 1$ was obtained in the usual fashion, using Eq. (10-42) and the wall temperature of 200°C.

Such calculations may yield erratic and inconsistent results, particularly at low bed depths. Therefore it is desirable to plot the computed values and draw a smooth curve as in Fig. 10-5. Then the smoothed results read from the curve should be used for the calculations at the next bed depth. The temperatures in the third row of Table 10-8 are such smoothed values.

The calculations may now be repeated for the second increment of bed depth, giving temperatures at $z = 0.03 + 2 \times 0.05 = 0.13$ ft. For example, to compute $t_{5,2}$, Eq. (10-42) becomes

$$t_{5,2} = t_{5,1} + 678 \times 0.0034[\tfrac{1}{5}(t_{6,1} - t_{5,1}) + t_{6,1} - 2t_{5,1} + t_{4,1}]$$
$$= 387.6 + 2.31[\tfrac{1}{5}(379 - 387.6) + 379 - 2 \times 387.6 + 393.5]$$
$$= 385.4 + 2.31 \times -4.4$$
$$= 375.3°C$$

The complete results at a bed depth of $z = 0.13$ ft are shown in Table 10-9. In the row following these computed temperatures are listed the experimental values at $z = 0.137$ ft as taken from Table 10-2.

TABLE 10-9. TEMPERATURES IN PACKED BED: COMPARISON AT LOW BED DEPTHS

Temp, °C	Radial position, $\frac{r}{r_0} = n$										
	0	0.1	0.2	0.3	0.4	0.5	0.6	0.7	0.8	0.9	1.0
$t_{n,2}$....................	400	398.1	395.7	392.5	387.6	375.3	364	351	302	254	200
t (exp., at $z = 0.137$ ft)....	392	391	389.5	386	381	374	363	347	323.5	285	200

To proceed with the sequence of steps, the calculated values of $t_{n,2}$ are themselves plotted, as shown in Fig. 10-5. Temperatures read from the dotted curve are then used to compute $t_{n,3}$. This procedure is repeated until the desired bed

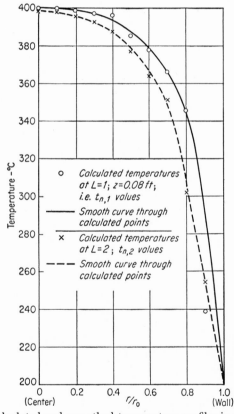

FIG. 10-5. Calculated and smoothed temperature profiles in a packed bed.

depth is reached. The results obtained at $L = 7$, or $z = 0.03 + 0.35 = 0.38$ ft, are given in Table 10-10. Also are tabulated the experimental temperatures at $z = 0.354$ ft taken from Table 8-2. It is seen that the two sets of temperatures are in reasonably good agreement.

TABLE 10-10. TEMPERATURES

Temp, °C	Radial position, $\dfrac{r}{r_0} = n$										
	0.0	0.1	0.2	0.3	0.4	0.5	0.6	0.7	0.8	0.9	1.0
$t_{n,7}$ (calc.), at $z = 0.38$ ft...	350	348	346	335	320	304	284	267	247	225	200
t (exp., at $z = 0.354$ ft)....	347.5	346	341.5	333	319.5	303.5	287.5	271	252	228.5	200

10-5. Mass Transfer within a Packed Bed. The process of radial mass transfer in packed beds is similar to that of heat transfer, but some differences exist. These arise because the diffusion rate through the solid particles is very small with respect to that in the surrounding gas phase. Thus all the mechanisms which are important in heat transfer are not significant in mass transfer. For example, the series mechanism involving both solid and gas phases, as proposed by Argo, would have a negligible contribution to the total effective diffusivity D_e (analogous to the effective thermal conductivity k_e). In fact the only significant contribution to D_e at reasonably high gas flow rates is the one based upon turbulent diffusion in the gas phase. At low velocities the molecular diffusivity may be important. Hence the summation expression for mass transfer, similar to Eq. (10-16) for heat transfer, is

$$D_e = D_{td} + D_c \qquad (10\text{-}47)$$

If the diffusivity is defined in terms of the concentration gradient by the expression

$$\text{Rate of mass transfer/unit area} = -\frac{D_e}{u}\frac{\partial(Cu)}{\partial r} \qquad (10\text{-}48)[1]$$

then the differential equation relating the concentration of a component to position in the bed is exactly analogous to Eq. (10-11) for temperature and may be written

$$-\frac{\partial(uC)}{\partial z} + \frac{D_e}{u}\left[\frac{1}{r}\frac{\partial(uC)}{\partial r} + \frac{\partial^2(uC)}{\partial r^2}\right] = 0 \qquad (10\text{-}49)$$

It is supposed in this equation that D_e/u does not vary with r, just as Eq. (10-11) is based upon k_e being constant.

Because of the mathematical similarity of these equations with those for heat transfer, the evaluation of the concentration distribution in a packed bed can be carried out by the same type of numerical procedure used in Example 10-7. However, in reactor-design problems, the concentration gradients are due to reaction and Eqs. (10-48) and (10-49)

---

[1] The diffusion equation is written in this form rather than in the usual way since the major contribution to D_e will normally be due to turbulent diffusion and this depends upon the velocity u.

do not include the effects of a chemical reaction.[1] Therefore the calculation of concentration profiles will be delayed until Chap. 11, where the effects of chemical reaction will be included.

We are concerned here with the available data for mass-transfer rates in terms of D_e or the more useful Peclet number $d_p u/D_e$. This information has already been discussed briefly in connection with the evaluation of the turbulent-diffusion contribution k_{td} to the effective thermal conductivity (Appendix B). Since the transport of heat and mass are by the same mechanism, it is reasonable to suppose that, for turbulent diffusion, the Peclet numbers based upon heat and mass transfer are identical, i.e.,

$$\text{Pe}_m = \frac{d_p u}{D_e} = \frac{d_p Gc}{k_{td}} = \frac{d_p u \rho c}{k_{td}}$$

or
$$k_{td} = \frac{d_p u \rho c}{\text{Pe}_m} \tag{10-50}$$

Hence Fig. 10-4 (Appendix B) can be used to estimate k_{td} for gases from Pe_m data.

In order to obtain a picture of the magnitude of the diffusion coefficients, consider a case where the mass-transfer Peclet number is 10 at a modified Reynolds number of 100. Suppose in addition that the packed bed consists of $\frac{1}{2}$-in. particles through which air is flowing at 100°C and 1 atmosphere pressure. [The viscosity of air at 100°C is 0.0508 lb/(hr)(ft), and its density is 0.059 lb/cu ft.]

$$\text{R}_e = 100 = \frac{d_p u \rho}{\mu}$$

or
$$d_p u = \frac{100}{\rho} \mu$$

From the Peclet number

$$\text{Pe}_m = 10 = \frac{d_p u}{D_e}$$

$$D_e = \frac{100\mu}{\rho} \times \frac{1}{10} = \frac{0.0508 \times 10}{0.059}$$

$$= 8.60 \text{ sq ft/hr}$$

It is noted that this value of D_e was computed independently of the nature of the diffusing gas. This is not rigorously true because D_e in Eq. (10-47) includes the molecular diffusivity D_c. Thus the value just computed should be D_{td} rather than D_e. However, if D_c is small, $D_{td} = D_e$, and the result is satisfactory. To check this point, assume carbon dioxide is the diffusing gas. Then the molecular diffusivity may

[1] These equations are applicable for nonreaction cases, for example, where a stream of a tracer gas is introduced into the packed bed at one point and it is desired to know the concentration of that gas at any point upstream in the bed. This is, in fact, a common experimental procedure used to measure D_e.

be estimated from the expression

$$D_c = 0.0069 \frac{T^{\frac{3}{2}}}{p_t(V_A^{\frac{1}{3}} + V_B^{\frac{1}{3}})^2} \sqrt{\frac{1}{M_A} + \frac{1}{M_B}} \qquad (10\text{-}51)$$

The molecular volumes, from Table 9-2, are

$$V_A \text{ (carbon dioxide)} = 34.0$$
$$V_B \text{ (air)} = 29.9$$

$$D_c = \frac{0.0069(212 + 460)^{\frac{3}{2}}}{1[(34.0)^{\frac{1}{3}} + (29.9)^{\frac{1}{3}}]^2} \sqrt{\frac{1}{44} + \frac{1}{28.9}}$$
$$= 0.71 \text{ sq ft/hr}$$

In this case D_c is less than 10 per cent of the value of D_{td} so that the assumption that $D_e = D_{td}$ is a good one.

10-6. Heat and Mass Transfer between Solid Particle and Fluid. In applying the theoretical method of predicting the radial-heat-transfer rate in packed-bed reactors (Appendix B) it was necessary to employ the heat-transfer coefficient between the fluid stream and the solid particle [Eq. (10-27) or (10-28)]. While such coefficients were only of indirect importance in determining radial-heat-transfer rates in packed beds, they are of major significance in evaluating the temperature difference between fluid and solid particle. As mentioned earlier, heat- and mass-transfer rates of this kind may control the design of reactors of the noncatalytic type where one reactant is a fluid passing over the second, held as particles of solid in a fixed bed. Metallurgical-reduction processes are examples.

Heat- and mass-transfer coefficients for this case have generally been measured for systems where no reaction occurs, so that the transfer rates constitute the entire resistance. It is frequently possible to obtain both mass- and heat-transfer coefficients in the same experiment by measuring concentration and temperatures. For example, Hougen and coworkers,[1,2] in developing Eqs. (10-27) and (10-28), evaporated water from saturated particles into air of known temperature and humidity passing through the bed. Other investigators have evaporated naphthalene from beds of pure naphthalene particles exposed to streams of air, carbon dioxide, and hydrogen.[3,4] Mass-transfer rates from solid particles to liquids passing through the bed have also been studied.[5-7] There are some differences in the results of the various investigations, probably due to differences in properties of the bed other than the usual ones of particle size, gas velocity, and tube diameter. Thus bed depth may have an effect on such

[1] O. A. Hougen, B. M. Gamson, and G. Thodos, *Trans. AIChE*, **39**:1 (1943).

[2] O. A. Hougen and C. R. Wilkie, *Trans. AIChE*, **41**:445 (1945).

[3] D. M. Hurt, *Ind. Eng. Chem.*, **35**:522 (1943).

[4] R. R. White and W. Resnick, *Chem. Eng. Progr.*, **45**:517 (1949).

[5] M. Hobson and G. Thodos, *Chem. Eng. Progr.*, **45**:517 (1949).

[6] L. K. McCume and R. H. Wilhelm, *Ind. Eng. Chem.*, **41**:1124 (1949).

[7] G. B. Gaffney and T. B. Drew, *Ind. Eng. Chem.*, **42**:1120 (1950).

transport properties. In application of transfer coefficients for evaluating heat- and mass-transfer rates between fluid and solid particle, it is best to use the data on the bed most nearly fitting the required specifications. The equations of Hougen and coworkers for heat transfer were given in Appendix B. The corresponding equations for mass transfer are as follows:

$$j_D = \frac{k_g p_m M_m}{G}\left(\frac{\mu}{\rho D_c}\right)^{\frac{2}{3}} = 0.989\left(\frac{d_p G}{\mu}\right)^{-0.41}\frac{d_p G}{\mu} > 350 \qquad (10\text{-}52)$$

$$j_D = \frac{k_g p_m M_m}{G}\left(\frac{\mu}{\rho D_c}\right)^{\frac{2}{3}} = 1.82\left(\frac{d_p G}{\mu}\right)^{-0.51}\frac{d_p G}{\mu} < 350 \qquad (10\text{-}53)$$

where D_c = molecular diffusivity of diffusing gas
M_m = mean molecular weight of nondiffusing fluid stream
G = mass velocity of fluid stream
p_m = mean partial pressure of nondiffusing stream, atm
k_g = mass-transfer coefficient, lb moles/(hr)(sq ft)(atm)

Ergun[1] has made an attempt to bring all data from different studies into a reasonable correlation by application of Reynolds analogy.

Example 10-8. Water vapor is being evaporated from saturated cellite particles in a packed bed through which air is flowing at a rate of 500 lb (hr)(sq ft of empty bed). The particles have an effective diameter of 0.25 in. If the average temperature is 70°F and the pressure 1 atm, estimate the coefficient of mass transfer between the air and the solid particles.

Solution. At 70°F the viscosity of air is about 0.0435 lb/(hr)(ft). The Reynolds number is

$$\frac{d_p G}{\mu} = \frac{0.25 \times 500}{12 \times 0.0435} = 240$$

so that Eq. (10-53) is applicable.

The diffusivity of water vapor in air may be computed from Eq. (10-51).

$$V_A \text{ (water vapor)} = 14.8$$
$$V_B \text{ (air)} = 29.9$$

$$D_c = 0.0069\,\frac{(460 + 70)^{\frac{3}{2}}}{1[(14.8)^{\frac{1}{3}} + (29.9)^{\frac{1}{3}}]^2}\left(\frac{1}{18} + \frac{1}{28.9}\right)^{\frac{1}{2}}$$

$$= 0.0069\,\frac{12,300}{30.8}\,0.30$$

$$= 0.83 \text{ sq ft/hr}$$

$$\rho = \frac{28.9}{359\,\dfrac{460 + 70}{492}}$$

$$= 0.0748 \text{ lb/cu ft}$$

The Schmidt number is

$$\frac{\mu}{\rho D_c} = \frac{0.0435}{0.0748 \times 0.83} = 0.70$$

[1] Sabri Ergun, *Chem. Eng. Progr.*, **48**:227 (1952).

The Schmidt number is

$$\frac{\mu}{\rho D_c} = \frac{0.0435}{0.0748 \times 0.83} = 0.70$$

From Eq. (10-53),

$$j_D = \frac{k_g M_m p_m}{G} (0.70)^{\frac{2}{3}} = (1.82)(240)^{-0.51} = 0.111 \text{ (dimensionless)}$$

$$k_g = \frac{0.111 G}{(0.70)^{\frac{2}{3}} M_m p_m} = \frac{(0.111)(500)}{(28.9)(1)(0.70)^{\frac{2}{3}}} = 2.4 \text{ lb moles/(hr)(sq ft)(atm)}$$

10-7. Fluidized-bed Reactors. The vertical fluidized-bed reactor differs from its fixed- or packed-bed counterpart in that the solid catalyst

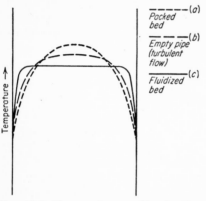

particles are much smaller (usually 1 to 200 microns) and are allowed to move in the fluid stream. As pointed out in Chap. 4, under *ideal* conditions these fluidized particles increase the transfer of heat to an extent that the temperature is essentially uniform throughout the reactor.

Under these circumstances it is not necessary to consider heat transfer within the bed. The transfer of heat to or from the reactor

FIG. 10-6. Temperature profiles (cooling conditions) in reactors.

can be considered by assuming that a finite heat-transfer coefficient exists at the wall and that the temperature across the bed is uniform. This situation is depicted in Fig. 10-6, where curve *c* applies to the fluidized-bed case. For comparison, curve *b* represents a homogeneous tubular reactor in *turbulent* flow where the temperature profile is not so flat as in the fluidized bed, but still more uniform than for the packed bed (case *a*).[1] In the latter circumstance the temperature changes within the bed may be severe and must be computed as outlined in Sec. 10-4.

Heat Transfer to the Wall. A number of investigations of heat-transfer coefficients at the wall in fluidized beds have been reported,[2-6] and all report considerably larger values for *h* than in an empty tube at the same fluid velocity. Presumably this is because of (1) the increase in mixing

[1] The comparison between the homogeneous tubular reactor and the packed-bed case depends upon the velocity level. It is possible for the temperature profile in the packed bed to be more uniform than in case (b).

[2] L. J. Jolley, *Fuel*, **28**(5):114 (1949).

[3] M. Leva, M. Weintraub, and M. Grummer, *Chem. Eng. Progr.*, **45**:563 (1949).

[4] O. Levenspiel and J. S. Walton, *Trans. Heat Transfer Fluid Mech. Inst.*, 1949.

[5] H. S. Mickley and C. A. Trilling, *Ind. Eng. Chem.*, **41**:1135 (1949).

[6] W. M. Dow and Max Jakob, *Chem. Eng. Progr.*, **47**:637 (1951).

lue to the solid particles, especially near the wall, where they tend to prevent the development of a slow-moving layer or film of gas and (2) he heat-carrying capacity of the particles themselves as they move between the center and the wall of the reactor.[1]

The various investigations show results which are not in complete agreement, perhaps owing to differences in flow patterns of the solid and gas phases in the bed. Because the solid particles are in motion, it is much more difficult to characterize the paths of solid and gas phases in a fluidized bed than in a fixed one. Several different types of behavior have been observed, depending upon the particle size and size range and the magnitude of the fluid velocity. At very low velocities the solid particles appear stationary, as in a fixed bed. As the velocity is increased, the bed of solids expands and each particle appears in rapid motion. However, the bed as a whole has a sharp upper boundary separating the solid particles from the gas and has the same appearance as the interface between the vapor phase and a boiling liquid. This region has been termed smooth fluidization. As the gas velocity is increased still further, large bubbles rise intermittently through the bed, carrying above them layers of solids. Visual observation shows slugs, or aggregates, of solid particles rising to the top of the bed and then falling back. This phenomenon has been called slug flow. It is evident that heat-transfer rates to the wall and also heat- and mass-transfer rates between gas and solid particle will vary depending upon the type of fluidization. Small variations in flow pattern may lead to significant differences in transfer rates and thus explain the lack of agreement in results of investigators.

The work of Dow and Jakob,[2] which includes an analysis of the earlier investigations, proposed the following empirical correlation of the heat-transfer coefficient at the inside wall under smooth fluidization conditions,

$$\frac{h_i d_t}{k_c} = 0.50 \left(\frac{d_t}{d_p}\right)^{0.17} \left(\frac{d_t}{L}\right)^{0.65} \left(\frac{d_t G}{\mu}\right)^{0.80} \left(\frac{\rho_s c_s}{\rho_g c_g}\right)^{0.25} \tag{10-54}$$

where h_i = heat-transfer coefficient at inside-wall surface
d_p = diameter of particle
d_t = diameter of tube
L = length of tube
μ, k_c = viscosity and thermal conductivity of gas, respectively
ρ_g = density of gas
ρ_s = density of solid particles
c_g = specific heat of gas
c_s = specific heat of solid particles

---

[1] The dominant pattern of the solid particles in a vertical fluidized bed is up the center section and back down near the wall.

[2] *Loc. cit.*

Example 10-9. Estimate the heat-transfer coefficient to the wall in a 6-in.-ID tube through which air is passed at a mass rate of 20 lb/hr at 100°F and 1 atm pressure, under each of the following bed conditions:

1. Solid particles [$c_s = 0.5$ Btu/(lb)(°F) and $\rho_s = 90$ lb/cu ft] of average diameter of 100 microns are fluidized in the tube. The tube length is 10 ft.
2. The tube is empty.
3. The tube is packed with $\frac{1}{2}$-in. spheres.

Solution. FLUIDIZED BED

$$d_t = \tfrac{6}{12} = 0.50 \text{ ft}$$
$$d_p = 100 \text{ microns}$$

which is

$$\frac{100 \times 10^{-4}}{2.54 \times 12} = 3.28 \times 10^{-4} \text{ ft}$$

$$\mu = 0.0448 \text{ lb/(hr)(ft)}$$
$$k_c = 0.0156 \text{ Btu/(hr)(ft)(°F)}$$

$$G = \frac{40}{(0.7854)(\tfrac{6}{12})^2}$$
$$= 204 \text{ lb/(hr)(sq ft)}$$

$$\frac{d_t}{d_p} = \frac{0.50}{0.000328} = 1{,}524$$

$$\frac{d_t}{L} = \frac{0.50}{10} = 0.05$$

$$\frac{d_t G}{\mu} = \frac{0.50 \times 204}{0.0448} = 2{,}280$$

$$\rho_g = \frac{28.9}{359 \dfrac{100 + 460}{492}}$$
$$= 0.0707 \text{ lb/cu ft}$$

$$\frac{\rho_s c_s}{\rho_g c_g} = \frac{90 \times 0.5}{0.0707 \times 0.24} = 265$$

Substituting these quantities in Eq. (10-54),

$$\frac{h_i d_t}{k_c} = (0.50)(1{,}524)^{0.17}(0.05)^{0.65}(2{,}280)^{0.80}(265)^{0.25}$$

$$\frac{h_i \times 0.50}{0.0156} = 486$$
$$h_i = 15.2 \text{ Btu/(hr)(sq ft)(°F)}$$

EMPTY PIPE. The flow is just inside the turbulent zone with a Reynolds number of 2,280. The coefficient for an empty pipe may be estimated from the expression

$$\frac{h_i d_t}{k_c} = 0.023(\text{Re})^{0.8}\left(\frac{c\mu}{k_c}\right)^{0.4}$$

$$\frac{c\mu}{k_c} = \frac{0.24 \times 0.0448}{0.0156} = 0.69$$

$$\frac{h_i d_t}{k_c} = (0.023)(2{,}280)^{0.8}(0.69)^{0.4} = 10.5$$

$$h_i = \frac{10.5 \times 0.0156}{0.50}$$

$$= 0.33 \text{ Btu/(hr)(sq ft)(°F)}$$

FIXED BED. With $\frac{1}{2}$-in. spherical packing

$$\frac{d_p}{d_t} = \frac{0.5}{6} = 0.083$$

From Table 10-1 the ratio of h_p/h_i is estimated to be 6.5. Hence the heat-transfer coefficient for the packed-bed case is

$$6.5 \times 0.33 = 2.1 \text{ Btu/(hr} \times \text{sq ft)(°F)}$$

For this particular case the coefficient in the fluidized bed is more than 7 times that in the packed pipe and 45 times that in an empty pipe.

Heat and Mass Transfer between Solid Particles and Fluid. Mass-transfer and heat-transfer rates between fluid and particle have been studied by the same methods as in fixed beds, but not to the same extent. Data for smooth fluidization of particles (14- to 48-mesh, B. & S. sieve size) in air were reported by Kettenring and Smith[1] in the following way:

$$\frac{h_c d_p}{k_c} = 0.0135 \left(\frac{d_p G}{\mu}\right)^{1.30} \qquad \text{for heat transfer} \qquad (10\text{-}55)$$

$$\frac{k_g p_m M_m}{G} = 0.00180 \left(\frac{d_p G}{\mu}\right)^{0.30} \qquad \text{for mass transfer} \qquad (10\text{-}56)$$

where k_g = mass-transfer coefficient, lb moles/(hr)(sq ft)(atm)
M_m = mean molecular weight of nondiffusing stream
p_m = mean partial pressure of non-diffusing stream

In the slugging region Resnick and White[2] measured mass-transfer coefficients by vaporizing naphthalene from fluidized particles into air, carbon dioxide, or hydrogen.

NOMENCLATURE

A Heat-transfer area
A_B Area for tank reactor
A_R Area for tubular reactor

[1] K. N. Kettenring and J. M. Smith, *Chem. Eng. Progr.*, **46**:139 (1950).
[2] W. Resnick and R. R. White, *Chem. Eng. Progr.*, **45**:377 (1949).

A_k Area on kettle, or inner, side of tank reactor

A_i Area on jacket, or outer, side of tank reactor, or on inside of tubing in a coil

C Concentration

c Specific heat

c_p or c Specific heat at constant pressure

c_s Specific heat for solid particle in a fluidized bed

c_g Specific heat for gas in a fluidized bed

D_e Effective diffusivity, based upon total void plus nonvoid area

D_c Molecular diffusivity

D_{td} Turbulent-diffusion contribution to effective diffusivity

d Inside diameter of kettle or tank

d_t Inside diameter of tube

d_c Diameter of coil of tubing

d_p Particle diameter in fixed or fluidized bed

G Mass velocity, lb/(hr)(sq ft of total tube area)

h Individual heat-transfer coefficient

h_k Kettle or tank side coefficient

h_i Inside coefficient in tubing

h_o Outside coefficient in tubing

h_c Convection coefficient from particle to fluid

j Dimensionless function of Reynolds number for correlating heat- and mass-transfer coefficients

k_g Mass-transfer coefficient, lb moles/(hr)(sq ft) (atm)

k_c Molecular thermal conductivity

k_e Effective thermal conductivity, per unit of void plus nonvoid area

$k_c, k_{td}, k_{series}, k_r$ Separate contributions to effective thermal conductivity (see Appendix B) (prime denotes values based upon void or nonvoid area)

k_g Mass-transfer coefficient between particle and fluid, lb moles/(hr)(sq ft)(atm)

L Metal wall thickness of tube or kettle; also, number of longitudinal increments, Δz, in a packed bed

M Molecular weight

M_m Mean molecular weight of nondiffusing stream

N Speed, rpm, of rotating agitation device in kettle

n Number of radial increments, Δr, in a packed bed

P Paddle length on agitation device

Pe_m Peclet number for mass transfer, $(d_p u/D_e)$

Pe_h Peclet number for heat transfer in packed bed, $d_p c G/k_e$

Q_s Heat transfer to surroundings, Btu

Q' Heat-transfer rate, $dQ/d\theta$, Btu/hr

q Heat-transfer flux, Btu/(hr)(sq ft)

r Radial distance, measured from center

r/r_0 Radial position (r_0 = radius of tube)

t Temperature

t_s Surroundings temperature

u Superficial velocity, i.e., based upon *total* cross-sectional area of tube

z Reactor length

δ Void fraction

θ Time, in batch reactor

ρ Density

μ Viscosity

Subscripts

n, L Number of radial increments Δr and longitudinal increments Δz
g, s Gas and solid phases in fluidized bed

PROBLEMS

1. Recently Oldshue and Gretton[1] have investigated heat-transfer coefficients for the outside surface of helical coils in vessels equipped with baffles. In comparison with the equation for unbaffled vessels [Eq. (10-6)] their correlation for $\mu/\mu_s = 1.0$ is as follows:

$$\frac{h_k d_o}{k} = 0.17 \left(\frac{P^2 N \rho}{\mu}\right)^{\frac{2}{3}} \left(\frac{c\mu}{k}\right)^{0.37} \left(\frac{P}{d}\right)^{0.1} \left(\frac{d_o}{d}\right)^{0.5}$$

where d = inside diameter of kettle or tank
   P = diameter of paddle or impeller
   d_o = outside diameter of tube
   h_k = coefficient on outside, or kettle side, of coil
Compare the heat-transfer coefficient for unbaffled and baffled tanks at the following operating conditions:

d = 4 ft
P = 3 ft
d_o = 1 in. (1-in.-OD tubing is used to construct the coil)
N = 60 rpm

Fluid in tanks, water at 70°F
2. A kettle equipped with baffles is to be heated with a helical coil, 1-in.-OD 16-gauge steel tubes, with a diameter of 2 ft. The tank is 3 ft in diameter. The fluid in the tank has the following properties:

c_p = 0.7 Btu/(lb)(°F)
ρ = 0.9 g/cc

	Temp, °F			
	70	100	150	200
μ, centipoises................	3.0	2.7	2.0	1.0
k, Btu/(hr)(ft)(°F)..........	0.3	0.34	0.4	0.5

The 2-ft. paddle rotates at a speed of 100 rpm.
Calculate the heat-transfer coefficient for the outside surface of the coil at each of the four temperatures.
3. Estimate the time required to heat a 1,200-lb batch of fluid from 70 to 200°F under the conditions of Prob. 2. The coil will be heated by steam condensing in the tubes at 220°F.
4. It is necessary to design equipment to heat 1,000 lb/hr of air from 70 to 200°F, using condensing steam. It has been decided to use an exchanger consisting of ten 2-in.-ID tubes in parallel with steam condensing at 220°F on the outside of the tubes.

[1] J. Y. Oldshue and A. T. Gretton, *Chem. Eng. Progr.*, **50**:615 (1954).

To improve the heat-transfer rate the tubes will be packed with alumina spheres of the optimum (for heat transfer) size. What length of tubes will be required?

5. Begley[1] has reported temperature data taken in a bed, consisting of $\frac{1}{4}$- by $\frac{1}{4}$-in. alumina pellets packed in a 2-in. pipe (actual ID = 2.06 in.), through which heated air was passed. The tube was jacketed with boiling glycol to maintain the tube wall at about 197°C.

For a superficial mass velocity of air equal to 300 lb/(hr)(sq ft) the experimental temperatures at various radial positions and bed depths are as shown in Table 10-11

TABLE 10-11

Radial position, $\dfrac{r}{r_0}$	Packed-bed depth, ft				
	0.076	0.171	0.255	0.365	0.495
0.0	378.7	354.7	327.8	299.0	279.3
0.1	377.2	353.7	327.0	298.0	278.9
0.2	374.6	349.9	324.1	294.7	277.0
0.3	369.5	343.9	319.7	289.2	273.2
0.4	360.3	336.3	313.8	282.1	267.6
0.5	347.7	327.4	306.4	274.0	260.8
0.6	331.9	316.1	298.2	265.0	252.7
0.7	313.2	300.7	287.9	254.8	243.8
0.8	291.0	282.8	273.1	242.2	234.5
0.9	256.5	257.9	244.2	224.8	224.6

The mass velocity profile at an average value of 300 lb/(hr)(sq ft) for $\frac{1}{4}$- by $\frac{1}{4}$-in. cylindrical packing is given in Table 10-12.

TABLE 10-12

Radial position, $\dfrac{r}{r_0}$	Superficial mass velocity, lb/(hr)(sq ft)
0	247
0.1	254
0.2	262
0.3	282
0.4	307
0.5	349
0.6	400
0.7	476
0.8	382
0.9	234

a. Employing the simpler equation (10-11), estimate k_e/cG at different radial positions and a bed depth of 0.365 ft.

b. Assuming that the given velocity profile on a mass basis is also applicable under nonisothermal conditions, estimate more realistic values of k_e and Pe_h at a bed depth of 0.365 ft, using Eq. (10-12).

[1] J. W. Begley, M. S. thesis, Purdue University, February. 1951.

By comparison with the results of Example 10-5 what is the effect of packing size on the effective thermal conductivity?

6. Instead of allowing k_e to vary radially, suppose that the higher resistance to heat transfer near the tube wall in a packed bed is taken into account by a wall heat-transfer coefficient. In other words, suppose that a constant value of k_e applies over the entire tube, but right at the wall there is a further resistance corresponding to a heat-transfer coefficient h_w.

Estimate the "constant" k_e and the wall heat-transfer coefficient which would best fit the experimental data given in Table 10-11. In this case neglect the variations in velocity across the diameter of the packed bed. Instead assume that a constant value of 300 lb/(hr)(sq ft) applies.

Note that, at the boundary between the wall film (over which h_w operates) and the central core of the bed, the following relation must apply:

$$h_w(t_i - t_w) = - (k_e) \left(\frac{\partial t}{\partial r} \right)_i$$

where (k_e) = constant k_e for central core of bed

t_i = temperature at boundary between film and central core

$\left(\dfrac{\partial t}{\partial r} \right)_i$ = gradient in central core at boundary between core and wall film

7. Using the k_e/cG results of Prob. 5a, calculate by numerical integration the temperatures at a bed depth of 0.365 ft for comparison with the experimental data in Table 10-11.

The entrance-temperature distribution is as shown in Table 10-13.

TABLE 10-13

Radial position, $\dfrac{r}{r_0}$	Temperature at zero bed depth, ft
0.020	399.7
0.216	397.3
0.245	391.8
0.483	377.6
0.497	381.0
0.673	347.1
0.695	372.3
0.883	291.7
0.892	313.7
1.000	197

8. Calculate the bulk mean temperature entering the packed bed from the profile given in Prob. 7. Neglect variations in mass velocity across the tube diameter. Then estimate a wall heat-transfer coefficient from Leva's correlations [Eqs. (10-9) and (10-10)], and determine the bulk mean temperature at a bed depth of 0.495 ft. Compare this result with the bulk mean temperature computed from the experimental data given in Table 10-11.

9. Estimate average values of the effective diffusivity for the entire bed for the conditions of Prob. 5. Neglect the contribution of the molecular diffusivity, D_c, to the effective value. Use method outlined in Appendix B ($\delta = 0.40$, $\epsilon = 0.9$).

Assuming that, for turbulent diffusion, the Peclet numbers for mass and heat transfer are the same, calculate mean values of Pe_h for the entire bed. Compare these with the point results determined in Prob. 5.

CHAPTER 11

DESIGN OF GAS-SOLID CATALYTIC REACTORS

In the gas-solid catalytic classification of reaction systems the reactants initially and products finally are in the gas phase. The problem of
combining the rates of the individual physical and chemical steps, including those on the solid surface, into this over-all gas-phase result was considered in Chap. 9. The methods of predicting the heat and mass transfer
which may take place in such reactors were the objective of Chap. 10.
The purpose here is to apply the rate equations and transport data to
the problem of designing the gas-solid catalytic reactor. In doing this
it is well to remember that the gas-phase reaction mixture with a solid
catalyst is but one of many types of heterogeneous systems, albeit an
important one. Frequently lack of rate data for the physical mass-
transfer steps prevents a quantitative treatment for other cases. For
example, there is little information on the rate of mass transfer between
the liquid and solid phase in slurries or between the two liquid phases in
liquid-liquid systems. This limits the application of design procedures
for heterogeneous reactions carried out in tank reactors with solid, or
immiscible liquid, catalysts or reactants. In such cases the methods
presented in Chap. 9 for combining physical and chemical steps are applicable, but the data are not available for estimating the importance of
the diffusion processes. In the event diffusion is unimportant, the design
follows the same procedure as for the homogeneous batch and tank flow
reactors considered in Chap. 5.

Noncatalytic reactions between gases and solids are similar in most
respects to the gas-solid catalytic type. The same sequence of steps in
the over-all reaction occurs as that described in Chap. 9 for the catalytic
case. Also, the design procedures outlined in the present chapter are
similar. The differences that may arise are due primarily to using up
the solid reactant. Whereas in the catalytic case the solid phase remains
unchanged, in the noncatalytic instance the solid reactant will be gradu-
ally replaced by another solid phase or a liquid or gaseous product. Most
of the practical applications in the noncatalytic category have been in
combustion or high-temperature metallurgical processes (reduction of
ores). At these high temperatures diffusional resistances regulating mass

318

transfer between the gas and solid phases are seldom negligible. Also, the high-temperature kinetics of the reactions on the solid surfaces are often complicated and poorly understood. For these reasons design methods have not advanced so rapidly as for gas-solid catalytic reactions.

Sometimes the quantitative design of gas-solid catalytic systems is difficult because of the complex geometry of the reactor. For example, reactors may be equipped with internal cooling coils to provide for better temperature control. In such cases it may not be possible to evaluate the temperature and concentration gradients in the reactor because of insufficient heat- and mass-transfer data. Similarly the catalyst may be arranged in such a form that available transport data are not applicable. In this text the developments in Chaps. 9 and 10 will be applied in detail to the fixed-bed reactor. In this case, which is perhaps the most widely used industrially, the solid catalyst particles are held in a fixed position in a cylindrical tube and the reaction mixture passed through them. Because of its importance the fixed-bed reactor has been the object of considerable investigation, and adequate data are frequently available for carrying out the design procedures.

Fluidized-bed reactors are increasing in importance, particularly for large-scale operations. The design of these reactors will also be considered, although in less detail. The exact treatment is complicated also by insufficient knowledge of mixing rates and, in general, inadequate understanding of the fluid dynamics of fluidized systems.

Before proceeding with the design procedures, it is worthwhile to consider some practical aspects of the construction and operation of these reactors.

CONSTRUCTION AND OPERATION

11-1. Fixed-bed Reactors. Fixed-bed reactors normally consist of one or more tubes packed with catalyst particles and operated in a vertical position. The catalyst particles may be of a variety of sizes and shapes: granular, pelleted, cylinders, spheres, etc. In some instances, particularly with metallic catalysts such as platinum, single particles are not used, but instead wires of the metal are made into screens. Multiple layers of these screens constitute the catalyst bed. Such screen or gauze catalysts are used in the commercial processes for the oxidation of ammonia and the oxidation of acetaldehyde to acetic acid.

Because of the necessity of removing or adding heat it may not be possible to use a single large-diameter tube packed with catalyst. Rather, the reactor must be built up of a number of tubes encased in a single body, such as is illustrated in Fig. 11-1. The energy exchange with the surroundings is obtained by circulating, or perhaps boiling, a fluid in the space between the tubes. For example, in the Downs[1] reactor for the oxidation of naphthalene to phthalic anhydride the cooling space is filled with boiling mercury, and the temperature is controlled by the pressure on the mercury. Since the heat evolved in the oxidation is large, each catalyst tube must be small (tubes of about 1.0 in. diameter are generally used) in order to prevent high temperatures within the reaction mixture

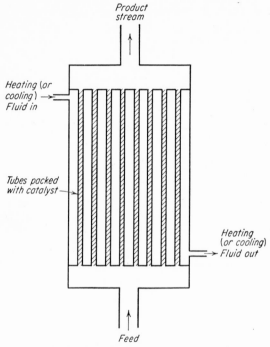

FIG. 11-1. Multitube reactor, fixed-bed.

and the resultant complete oxidation to carbon dioxide. The problem of deciding how large the tube diameter can be, and thus how many tubes are necessary to achieve a given production, forms an important problem in the design of such reactors.

A disadvantage of this method of cooling is that the rate of heat transfer to the fluid surrounding the tubes is about the same all along the tube length. Yet the major share of the reaction usually takes place near the entrance to the tube. For example, in an exothermic reaction the rate will be relatively large at the entrance to the reactor tube owing to the high concentrations of reactants. It will become even higher as the reaction mixture moves a short distance into the tube. This is because the

---

[1] U.S. Patent 1,604,739 (1926); *Ind. Eng. Chem.*, **32**:1294 (1940).

heat liberated by the high rate of reaction is greater than that which can be transferred to the cooling fluid. Hence the temperature of the reaction mixture will rise, resulting in an increase in the rate of reaction. This continues as the mixture moves up the tube until the disappearance of reactants has a larger effect on the rate than the increase in temperature. Further along the tube the rate will decrease. The smaller amount of heat can now be removed through the wall with the result that the temperature decreases. This situation leads to a maximum in

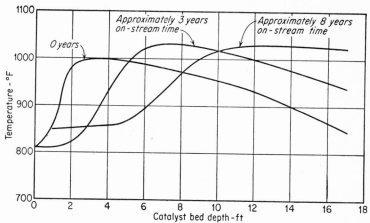

FIG. 11-2. Variation in temperature profile with on-stream time in fixed-bed ammonia-synthesis reactor. [*Reproduced with permission from Chem. Eng. Progr.*, **49**:393 (1954).]

the curve of temperature vs. reactor-tube length. Such a case is shown in Fig. 11-2 for a TVA ammonia-synthesis reactor.[1] The basic reason for the "hot spot," or maximum temperature, a short way in the tube is that the heat transfer to the cooling fluid is almost the same along the entire length, while the heat evolved due to reaction is much greater near the entrance of the catalyst bed. Such a maximum temperature would occur only for an exothermic reaction with cooling through the reactor-tube wall. Endothermic reactions and different types of cooling systems would lead to different-shaped temperature profiles.

As mentioned in Chap. 4, other means of cooling may be employed besides circulating a fluid around the catalyst tube. Dividing the reactor into parts with intercoolers between each part (see Fig. 11-3) is a commonly used procedure. The Jaeger converter[2] for the oxidation of sulfur dioxide is of this type. Another scheme which has worked satisfactorily for reactions of moderate heat of reaction, such as the dehydrogenation

[1] A. V. Slack, H. Y. Allgood, and H. E. Maune, *Chem. Eng. Progr.*, **49**:393 (1953).
[2] A. Rogers, "Manual of Industrial Chemistry," vol. 1, pp. 275, 320, D. Van Nostrand Company, Inc., New York, 1942.

of butene, is to add a large quantity of an inert component to the reaction mixture.

The particular scheme employed for cooling (or heating) the fixed-bed reactor depends upon a number of factors: cost of construction, cost of operation, maintenance, and special features of the reaction such as the magnitude of ΔH.

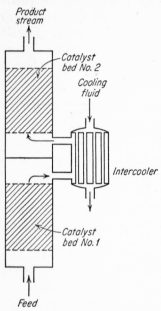

Product stream

Catalyst bed No. 2

Cooling fluid

Intercooler

Catalyst bed No. 1

Feed

FIG. 11-3. Divided reactor with intercooler between catalyst beds.

For example, the heat of reaction of the naphthalene oxidation is so high that small, externally cooled tubes provide about the only way to prevent excessive temperatures in fixed-bed-type equipment. In the sulfur dioxide oxidation the much smaller heat of reaction permits the use of less expensive large-diameter, adiabatic catalyst bins in series, with external intercoolers for removing the heat evolved. In the dehydrogenation of butene the heat of reaction is also fairly low so that small-diameter catalyst tubes need not be used. Here the use of external heat exchangers (the reaction is endothermic, and energy must be supplied to maintain the temperature) is possible, and a satisfactory system could be designed by alternating adiabatic reaction sections with heat exchangers. However, in this case there were several auxiliary advantages to be gained by adding a hot inert material (steam) to supply the energy. Thus the blanketing effect of the steam molecules reduced the polymerization of the butadiene product.

Also, the steam lowered the partial pressure of the hydrocarbons and, in so doing, improved the equilibrium yield of the reaction system.

It may be observed that all the operating devices mentioned for energy exchange have the objective of preventing excessive temperatures or maintaining a required temperature level; i.e., they are attempts to achieve isothermal operation of the reactor. The need for such an approach to isothermal operation stems from many reasons. One is illustrated in the naphthalene oxidation process. There it is necessary to control the temperature to prevent the oxidation from becoming complete, that is, producing carbon dioxide and water, instead of phthalic anhydride. This is a common situation in partial oxidation reactions. The air oxidation of ethylene is another illustration.

Another frequent reason for avoiding excessive temperatures is to prevent lowering of the catalyst activity. Changes in structure of the solid catalyst particles as the temperature is increased may reduce the activity of the catalyst for the desired reaction. The selectivity of the catalyst may be adversely affected: i.e., the activity for undesirable side reactions may increase. The life of the catalyst may also be affected by operating at higher than normal temperatures. For example, the iron oxide catalyst for the ammonia-synthesis reaction shows a more rapid decrease in activity with time if the synthesis unit is operated above the normal temperature range of 400 to 550°C.

The reason for limiting the temperature in the sulfur dioxide oxidation is based upon two factors: excessive temperatures decrease the catalyst activity as just mentioned; also, the equilibrium yield is adversely affected by raising the temperature. This last point is the important one in explaining the need to maintain the temperature level in the dehydrogenation of butene.

Still other factors such as physical properties of the equipment may require limiting the temperature level. For example, in reactors operated at very high temperatures, particularly under pressure, it may be necessary to cool the reactor-tube wall to prevent shortening the life of the tube itself.

The problem of regeneration of the catalyst to restore activity may be a serious one in the fixed-bed reactor. In a great many instances the catalyst is too valuable to discard. If the catalyst activity decreases with time, frequent regeneration may be necessary. Even when the cost is so low that regeneration is not required, shutting down the process and starting up again after new catalyst has been added is an expensive procedure. If this is necessary at frequent intervals, the entire process may become uneconomical. The exact economic limit on the time required between shutdowns depends upon the particular process, but in general if the activity cannot be maintained over a period of several months, the cost of shutdowns is likely to be prohibitive. Of course, regeneration in place is a possible way out of this difficulty. This requires one or more additional reactors, if continuous operation is to be maintained, and hence increases the initial cost of the installation. The most successful fixed-bed reactor systems are those where the catalyst activity is sustained for long periods without regeneration.

The fixed-bed reactor requires a minimum of auxiliary equipment and is particularly suitable for small commercial units where the investment of large sums for instrumentation, catalyst handling, and the like, would be uneconomical.

In order to prolong the time between regenerations and shutdowns, the reactor tube may be made longer than required. For example, suppose a length of 3 ft is necessary to approach the equilibrium conversion with fresh catalyst of high activity. The reactor may be built with tubes 10 ft long.   Initially the desired conversion will be obtained in the first 3 ft.   As the catalyst activity falls off, the section of the bed in which the reaction is mainly accomplished will move up the bed until finally all 10 ft are deactivated.   This technique can be used only with certain types of reactions but has been successfully employed in the ammonia synthesis to prolong time between shutdown periods. ·

11-2. Fluidized-bed Reactors.   Fluidized beds are particularly suitable when frequent catalyst regeneration is required or for reactions with

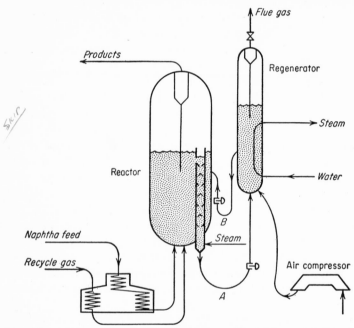

FIG. 11-4. Flow diagram for fluid hydroformer.   Illustration of fluidized reactor-regenerator combination.   (*Reproduced by permission of Esso Standard Oil Company, Baton Rouge, La.*)

a very high heat effect.   Frequently the reactors are vessels of large diameter (10 to 30 ft is not unusual for catalytic cracking units in the petroleum industry), partially filled with solid catalyst particles in a fluidized state as described in Chap. 4.   A typical system is shown in Fig. 11-4.   The movable catalyst permits continuous regeneration in place.   Thus, in Fig. 11-4, part of the catalyst is continuously withdrawn from the reactor in line A and flows into the regenerator.   The regenerator shown in the figure is another fluidized bed from which reactivated catalyst is returned to the reactor through line B.   Actually it is not necessary to carry out the regeneration in a fluidized bed, as catalyst could be withdrawn through line A continuously, and reactivated catalyst returned through line B, with the regeneration accomplished by any procedure.   However, the process is most economical if both reaction and regeneration are carried out in fluidized beds with the integral setup illus-trated by Fig. 11-4.

An important feature of the fluidized-bed reactor is that it operates at a nearly constant temperature and, hence, is easy to control.   There is no possibility of hot spots developing, as in the case of the fixed-bed unit.   The fluidized bed does not possess the flexibility of the fixed bed for adding or removing heat.   A diluent can be added to control the tem-perature level, but this may not be desirable for other reasons (requires separation after the reactor, lowers the rate of reaction, increases the size of the equipment).   A heat-transfer fluid can be circulated through a jacket around the reactor, but if the reactor is large in diameter, the energy exchange by this method is limited.

Another factor involved in the fluidized bed is the small size and den-sity of catalyst particle necessary to maintain proper fluidization.   Thus it would not be practical to oxidize acetaldehyde to acetic acid with a silver catalyst, using a fluidized bed.   On the other hand the small parti-cle size provides a much larger external surface per unit mass of catalyst than a fixed-bed unit.   This results in a higher rate of reaction for a nonporous catalyst.   It also will increase the rate for a porous catalyst, if the resistance to diffusion in the pores is significant.

From a practical viewpoint catalyst loss due to carry-over with the gas stream from the reactor and regenerator may be an important prob-lem.   Attrition of particles decreases their size to a point where they are no longer fluidized but move with the gas stream.   It has been customary to recover most of these catalyst fines by cyclone separators, sometimes followed by electrical precipitation equipment, placed in the effluent lines from reactor and regenerator.

Erosion of lines and vessels due to the scraping action of the sharp, solid particles has caused concern in the fluidized cracking process.   Ero-sion has been particularly severe in the small-diameter transfer lines, where the particle velocity is high.   Discussion of these questions and others relating to the commercial operation of fluidized catalytic crack-ing plants has been described in the literature.[1,2]

DESIGN OF FIXED-BED REACTORS

11-3. Outline of the Problem.   Commercial applications of fixed-bed reactors include the oxidation of SO_2, the synthesis of NH_3, and many hydrocarbon transformation processes.   The reactant gases usually enter the catalyst bed at a uniform temperature and composition, but as they

[1] E. V. Murphree, C. L. Brown, E. J. Goba, C. E. Hohnig, H. Z. Martin, and C. W. Tyson, *Trans. AIChE*, **41**:19 (1945).

[2] A. L. Conn, W. F. Meeham, and R. V. Shankland, *Chem. Eng. Progr.*, **46**:176 (1950).

pass through the bed, changes in composition take place, and these may be accompanied by variations in temperature and pressure. Furthermore, the composition and temperature may also vary in the radial direction across the diameter of the reactor tube.

The difficulty in the design calculations is directly dependent upon the number of these variations that need be taken into account. In isothermal reactors in which the pressure drop is small enough to be neglected, the only important variable is concentration in the longitudinal direction. The rate of reaction will decrease as the gases pass through the catalyst bed, but this decrease is dependent only upon the concentration change. The integration of the design equations given in Chap. 4 is relatively simple under such circumstances.

The next possibility in increasing degree of complexity occurs when the temperature is still constant throughout the bed, but the pressure drop is significant compared with the total pressure. If the reaction mixture is gaseous, the rate will vary in passing through the bed owing to both pressure and concentration changes.

A more important case from a practical viewpoint is the adiabatic reactor. As mentioned before, it is difficult to achieve isothermal operation, because most reactions have a significant heat effect. In adiabatic operation heat transfer to the reactor wall can be neglected, and the temperature will change only in the longitudinal direction. The rate will vary in passing through the bed because of (1) concentration changes, (2) temperature changes, and (3) pressure changes, if the pressure drop is significant.

The most difficult alternative occurs when heat transfer through the reactor wall must be taken into account. This type of reactor operation arises when it is necessary to supply or remove heat through the wall, but the rate of energy transfer is not sufficient to approach isothermal operation. It is a frequent occurrence in fixed-bed reactors, because the fluid velocities must be low enough to allow for the required space velocity or contact time. This, in turn, results in insufficient turbulence and mixing to obtain uniform concentration and temperature profiles. Under these conditions the concentration and temperature will change in both the radial and the longitudinal direction. Then the rate will also vary in both the longitudinal and the radial direction, and the integration of the design equation becomes a numerical, stepwise procedure. A general treatment of this type of reactor involves an incremental calculation across the diameter of the reactor tube for a small longitudinal increment, and the repetition of this process for each successive longitudinal increment. There are approximate procedures for avoiding or limiting the stepwise calculations in the radial direction, and these will be considered (Examples 11-2 and 11-3) prior to the general treatment.

11-4. Isothermal and Adiabatic Operation.   The design calculations for the isothermal and adiabatic cases are basically the same as those illustrated in Chap. 6 for homogeneous reactions in tubular flow reactors. The rate equation for the catalytic case may be of a different form, and it has been suggested that a design equation [Eq. (4-11)] based upon catalyst mass rather than reaction volume be used.   Otherwise the design computations are the same as for the homogeneous case.   For example, in Example 6-4, the homogeneous isothermal dehydrogenation of benzene was considered.   The same reactions can be carried out catalytically, and the design calculations would have been identical, except that (1) the catalyst mass W would be substituted for the reactor volume V_R and (2) the rate equation would be different.

Because of these similarities only adiabatic operation will be examined (Example 11-1).   Then attention will be devoted to the non-adiabatic case, where radial gradients are important, and design procedures not considered heretofore may be required.

Example 11-1.   Wenner and Dybdal[1] have studied experimentally the catalytic dehydrogenation of ethyl benzene and found that with a certain catalyst the rate could be represented by the stoichiometry of the following reaction:

$$C_6H_5C_2H_5 \rightarrow C_6H_5CH{=}CH_2 + H_2$$

This means that the rate equation may be written,

$$r_c = k \left(p_E - \frac{1}{K} p_S p_H \right)$$

where p_E = partial pressure of ethyl benzene
p_S = partial pressure of styrene
p_H = partial pressure of hydrogen
The specific-reaction rate and equilibrium constants are

$$\log k = -\frac{4{,}770}{T} + 4.10$$

where k = lb moles styrene produced/(hr)(atm)(lb of catalyst)
T = °K

t, °C	K
400	1.7 × 10⁻³
500	2.5 × 10⁻²
600	2.3 × 10⁻¹
700	1.4

It is desired to estimate the volume of reactor necessary to produce 15 tons of styrene per day, using vertical tubes, 4 ft in diameter, and packed with catalyst pellets.   Wenner and Dybdal have considered this problem, taking into account

[1] R. R. Wenner and F. C. Dybdal, *Chem. Eng. Progr.*, **44**:275 (1948).

the side reactions producing benzene and toluene. However, to simplify the calculations in this introductory example, suppose (1) that the sole reaction is the dehydrogenation to styrene and (2) that there is no heat exchange between the reactor and the surroundings.

Assume that under normal operation the exit conversion will be 45 per cent. However, also prepare graphs of conversion and temperature vs. catalyst bed depth, up to equilibrium conditions.

Additional data are as follows:

1. Feed rate per reactor tube

$$\text{Ethyl benzene} = 13.5 \text{ lb moles/hr}$$
$$\text{Steam} = 270 \text{ lb moles/hr}$$

2. Temperature of mixed feed entering reactor = 625°C
3. Bulk density of catalyst as packed = 90 lb/cu ft
4. Average pressure in reactor tubes = 1.2 atm
5. Heat of reaction ΔH = 60,000 Btu/lb mole
6. Surroundings temperature = 70°F

Solution. The reaction is endothermic so that heat must be supplied to maintain the temperature. This is to be done by adding a large quantity of steam to the feed, providing a reservoir of energy in its heat capacity. An alternate approach of transferring heat from the surroundings is utilized for the same system in Example 11-2.

In the present problem the operation is adiabatic, and the energy balance takes the simple form

$$F y_0 \, dx(-\Delta H) = \Sigma m_i c_{p_i} \, dT \tag{A}$$

If x refers to the conversion of ethyl benzene, then $F y_0 = 13.5$ lb moles/hr. Since there is a large excess of steam, it will be satisfactory to use for c_p a value of 0.52. Actually, the specific heat will vary with both temperature and pressure, and allowance could be made for these variations, but the errors involved are small. Then the heat capacity of the reaction mixture will be

$$\Sigma m_i c_{p_i} = (270 \times 18 + 13.5 \times 106)0.52$$
$$= 3,270 \text{ Btu/°F}$$

Substituting numerical values in Eq. (A),

$$13.5 \, dx \times -60,000 = 3,270 \, dT$$
$$-dT = 248 \, dx$$
or
$$T - 1,616 = -248x \tag{B}$$

where T is in degrees Rankine and 1616°R is the entering temperature of the feed.

The design equation in terms of the density of the bulk catalyst and catalyst bed depth is

$$F y_0 \, dx = r_c \rho_B A_c \, dz$$
or
$$dz = \frac{F y_0}{r_c \rho_B A_c} \, dx = \frac{13.5 \, dx}{(90)(0.7854)(16)r} = \frac{0.0119}{r} \, dx \tag{C}$$

The partial pressures can be expressed in terms of the conversion in the following way:

At any conversion x

$$\text{Moles steam} = 20$$
$$\text{Moles ethyl benzene} = 1 - x$$
$$\text{Moles styrene} = x$$
$$\text{Moles hydrogen} = x$$
$$\text{Total} = 21 + x$$

$$p_E = \frac{1 - x}{21 + x} \times 1.2$$

$$p_S = p_H = \frac{x}{21 + x} \times 1.2$$

Then the rate equation becomes

$$r_c = \frac{1.2}{21 + x} k \left[(1 - x) - \frac{1.2}{K} \frac{x^2}{21 + x} \right]$$

or, using the expression for k determined by Wenner and Dybdal,

$$r_c = \frac{1.2}{21 + x} \times 12{,}600 e^{-19{,}800/T} \left[(1 - x) - \frac{1.2}{K} \frac{x^2}{21 + x} \right]^\dagger \qquad (D)$$

Substituting this value of r_c in Eq. (C) gives an expression for the catalyst bed depth in terms of the conversion and temperature,

$$dz = \frac{21 + x}{1{,}270{,}000} e^{19{,}800/T} \left[(1 - x) - \frac{1.2}{K} \frac{x^2}{21 + x} \right]^{-1} dx \qquad (E)$$

Equations (B) and (E) can be solved numerically for the bed depth for any conversion. If the coefficient of dx in Eq. (E) is designated R,

$$\Delta z = R_{av} \Delta x \qquad (E')$$

At $z = 0$, $x = 0$, $T = 1616°R$ $(625°C)$

$$R_0 = \frac{21}{1{,}270{,}000} e^{-12.25} \frac{1}{1 - 0} = 3.30$$

If an increment Δx of 0.1 is chosen, the temperature at the end of the increment is, from Eq. (B),

$$T_1 = 1{,}616 - 248 \times 0.1$$
$$= 1591°R$$

† In the exponential term T has been converted to degrees Rankine.

Then at the end of the first increment

$$R_1 = \frac{21 + 0.1}{1,270,000} e^{12.43} \left[(1 - 0.1) - \frac{1.2}{0.28} \frac{0.1^2}{21 + 0.1} \right]^{-1} \tag{F)'}$$

$$R_1 = 4.18 \frac{1}{0.90 - 0.0020} = 4.65$$

The bed depth required for the first increment is given by Eq. (E'),

$$\Delta z = \frac{3.\overset{.}{3}0 + 4.65}{2} \times 0.1$$
$$= 0.40 \text{ ft}$$

Proceeding to the second increment,

$$T_2 = 1,616 - 248 \times 0.2$$
$$= 1566°R$$

$$R_2 = \frac{21 + 0.2}{1,270,000} e^{12.66} \left[(1 - 0.2) - \frac{1.2}{0.22} \frac{0.2^2}{21 + 0.2} \right]^{-1}$$
$$= 6.60$$

$$z_2 - z_1 = R_{av} \Delta x = \frac{R_1 + R_2}{2} \times 0.1 = \frac{4.65 + 6.60}{2} \times 0.1$$
$$= 0.56 \text{ ft}$$
$$z_2 = 0.40 + 0.56$$
$$= 0.96 \text{ ft}$$

The results of further calculations are shown in Table 11-1.

TABLE 11-1. STYRENE FROM ETHYL BENZENE: ADIABATIC REACTOR

Conversion, x	Temperature		Catalyst bed depth, ft
	°R	°C	
0	1616	625	0
0.10	1591	611	0.40
0.20	1566	597	0.96
0.30	1542	584	1.75
0.40	1517	570	2.93
0.50	1492	556	4.84
0.55	1480	549	6.3
0.60	1467	542	8.5
0.65	1455	536	13.2
0.69	1445	530	∞

[1] The value of K is estimated to be 0.28 at 1591°R from the tabulation of data given in the problem statement.

The rate of reaction becomes zero at a conversion of about $x = 0.69$ and a temperature of $1445°R$, as determined from Eqs. (B) and (D).

From Figure 11-5 it is found that a bed depth of 3.8 ft is required for a conversion of 45 per cent. The production of styrene from each reactor tube would be

$$\text{Production/tube} = 13.5 \times 0.45 \times 104 \times 24$$
$$= 15,200 \text{ lb/day} = 7.6 \text{ tons/day}$$

Hence two 4-ft-diameter reactor tubes packed with catalyst to a depth of at least 3.8 ft would be required to produce 15 tons/day of crude styrene.

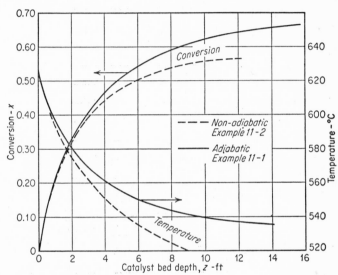

Fig. 11-5. Styrene from ethyl benzene; conversion vs. catalyst bed depth.

11-5. Nonadiabatic Operation, Simplified Procedure. The form of the radial temperature profile in a nonadiabatic fixed-bed reactor has been observed experimentally to have a parabolic shape. Data for the oxidation of sulfur dioxide with a platinum catalyst on $\frac{1}{8}$- by $\frac{1}{8}$-in. cylindrical pellets in a 2-in.-ID reactor are illustrated in Fig. 11-6.[1] Results are shown for several catalyst bed depths. The reactor wall was maintained at 197°C by a jacket of boiling water. This low temperature resulted in severe radial temperature gradients, more so than would exist in a commercial reactor, where the wall temperature would be higher. The longitudinal profiles are shown in Fig. 11-7 for the same experiment. These curves show the typical hot spots, or maxima, characteristic of exothermic reactions in a nonadiabatic reactor. The greatest increase above the reactants temperature entering the bed is at the center, $r/r_0 = 0$, as would

---

[1] R. W. Schuler, V. P. Stallings, and J. M. Smith, *Chem. Eng. Progr., Symposium Ser.* 4, **48**:19 (1952).

be expected.   This rise decreases as the wall is approached and actually disappears at a radial position of 0.9.   The temperature is so low here, even in the entering stream, that very little reaction occurs.   Hence the curve in Fig. 11-7 at $r/r_0 = 0.9$ is essentially a cooling curve, approaching 197°C as the bed depth increases.

A completely satisfactory design method for nonadiabatic reactors must predict the radial and longitudinal variations in temperature, such as

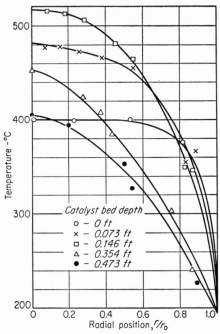

Fig. 11-6. Radial temperature profiles in a fixed-bed reactor for the oxidation of SO₂ with air.

those shown in Figs. 11-6 and 11-7, analogous concentration profiles, and the bulk mean conversion.   To do this, it is necessary to know the effective thermal conductivity and diffusivity for heat and mass transfer, as defined and presented in the preceding chapter.   The general procedure is one of solving differential equations similar to Eqs. 10-11 and 10-12.   However, at the beginning it is worthwhile to consider a simplified approach that eliminates the need for effective conductivities and diffusivities, but still gives a fairly reasonable approach to the actual temperature profile in the bed.

The parabolic shape of the radial temperature curves shown in Fig. 11-6 suggests that most of the resistance to heat transfer is near the wall of the reactor and only a small amount in the central core.   Carrying this idea further, if it were assumed that all the resistance to heat transfer were in a very thin layer next to the wall, the temperature profile would be as shown in Fig. 11-8 by the dotted lines. The solid line is the 0.146-ft bed-depth curve of Fig. 11-6. The horizontal dotted line represents the

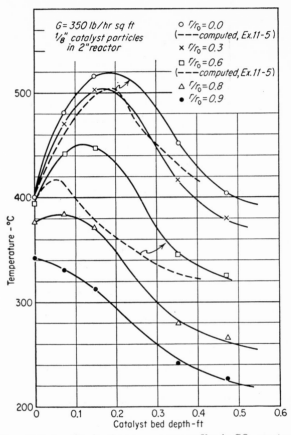

FIG. 11-7. Longitudinal temperature profiles in SO_2 reactor.

bulk mean temperature obtained by proper integration of the data on the solid line. If the actual situation is replaced by this approximate model, it would not be necessary to consider either heat or mass transfer within the bed. The only data necessary to establish the energy exchange with the surroundings would be the heat-transfer coefficient at the wall, based upon the bulk mean temperature of the reaction mixture, according to the equation

$$dQ'_s = h_w(t_m - t_w)A_R \, dz \qquad (11\text{-}1)$$

Under such conditions the design procedure would be the same as for nonadiabatic homogeneous tubular reactors, as illustrated in Example 6-5. The relationships required are:

1. The basic design equation (or mass balance),

$$r_c \, dW = F \, dx'$$

or $$A_c r_c \rho_B \, dz = F \, dx' = F y_0 \, dx \qquad (11\text{-}2)$$

where ρ_B is the bulk density of the catalyst, and y_0 is the mole fraction of limiting reactant in the feed

2. The rate equation,

$$r = f(\text{composition, temperature, pressure}) \qquad (11\text{-}3)$$

3. The energy balance, taking into account the heat transfer to the reactor wall,

$$F y_0 \, dx(-\Delta H) - h_w A_R(t_m - t_w) \, dz = \Sigma m_i c_{p_i} \, dt_m \qquad (11\text{-}4)$$

This simplified approach does not predict the true radial temperature profile, nor does it take into account concentration variations in the radial direction. However, it is useful as a rapid procedure for estimating the reactor size and predicting the effect of such variables as tube diameter. It is evident that as the tube diameter decreases, the ratio of the heat-transfer area to the reactor volume will increase. This means that the temperature rise of the reaction mixture as it passes through the bed will be less. It also means that the radial temperature variation within the bed will be less. Hence, where it is necessary not to exceed a certain temperature in the catalyst bed, small-diameter tubes are indicated. The problem of determining the size necessary for a given temperature can be solved approximately, using this simplified procedure. Problem 1 at the end of the chapter illustrates calculations for a phthalic anhydride reactor. The oxidation of naphthalene has a high ΔH value so that the size of the catalyst tubes is a critical point in the design.

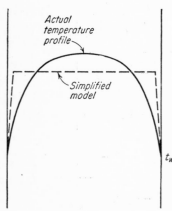

Actual temperature profile

Simplified model

t_w

FIG. 11-8. Comparison of simplified model of temperature profile with actual profile (fixed-bed reactor).

Examples 11-2 to 4 illustrate the simplified design method for different cases. The first is for the endothermic styrene reaction, where the temperature decreases continually with catalyst bed depth. Example 11-3 is for an exothermic reaction carried out under conditions where radial temperature gradients are not large. Example 11-4 is also for an exothermic case, but here the gradients are severe, and the simplified solution is not satisfactory.

Example 11-2. Under actual conditions the reactor described in Example 11-1 would not be truly adiabatic. Suppose that with reasonable insulation the heat loss would be that corresponding to a heat-transfer coefficient of 1.6 Btu/(hr)(sq ft of inside tube area)(°F). This value of U is based upon the difference in temperature between the reaction mixture and the surroundings at 70°F. Determine revised curves of temperature and conversion vs. catalyst bed depth for this nonadiabatic operation.

Solution. The design equation (C) and the rate expression (D) of Example 11-1 are applicable here, as is their combination, Eq. (E). The energy balance will be different and will follow the form of Eq. (11-4).

$$Fy_0 \, dx(-\Delta H) - h_w A_R(t_m - t_w) \, dz = \Sigma m_i c_{p_i} \, dT_m$$
$$13.5 \, dx(-60,000) - 1.6(\pi 4)(T_m - 530) \, dz = 3,270 \, dT_m$$
$$dT_m = -248 \, dx - 0.00615(T_m - 530) \, dz$$

Written in difference form, this becomes

$$\Delta T_m = -248 \, \Delta x - 0.00615(T_m - 530)_{\mathrm{av}} \, \Delta z \tag{G}$$

Equation (E′) of Example 11-1 and Eq. (G) of the present example provide the solution for the bed depth and temperature as a function of conversion. As in Example 11-1, it is convenient to choose an increment of conversion. However, in this nonadiabatic case it is necessary to assume a temperature at the end of the increment. Then Δz is computed from Eq. (E′) and the temperature assumption checked in Eq. (G).

Since the heat loss from the reactor will be small, assume the temperature at the end of the first increment, $\Delta x = 0.1$, to be the same as in Example 11-1, namely, $T_1 = 1591°R$.

From Example 11-1

$$R_0 = 3.30$$
$$R_1 = 4.65$$

Then from Eq. (E′)

$$\Delta z = \frac{3.30 + 4.65}{2} \times 0.1$$
$$= 0.40 \text{ ft}$$

Now, checking the assumed temperature in Eq. (G),

$$\Delta T_m = -248 \times 0.1 - 0.00615\left(\frac{1,616 + 1,591}{2} - 530\right) \times 0.40$$
$$= -24.8 - 2.6$$
$$= -27.4°F$$
$$T_{m_1} = 1,616 - 27$$
$$= 1589°R$$

At the end of the second increment, assume $T_2 = 1560°R$.

From Eq. (E), Example 11-1,

$$R_2 = \frac{21 + 0.2}{1,270,000} e^{12.70} \left[\frac{1}{(1 - 0.2) - \frac{1.2}{0.22} \frac{0.2^2}{21 + 0.2}} \right] = 5.51 \frac{1}{0.791} = 6.97$$

From Eq. (E'), Example 11-1

$$z_2 - z_1 = R_{av} \Delta x = \frac{4.65 + 6.97}{2} 0.1$$
$$= 0.58 \text{ ft}$$
$$z_2 = 0.40 + 0.58$$
$$= 0.98 \text{ ft}$$

Checking the temperature in Eq. (G),

$$\Delta T_m = -24.8 - 0.00615 \left(\frac{1,589 + 1,560}{2} - 530 \right) 0.58$$
$$= -24.8 - 3.7$$
$$= -28.5°R$$
$$T_{m_2} = 1,589 - 28.5$$
$$= 1560°R$$

This agrees with the assumption.
Proceeding with the calculations leads to the results shown in Table 11-2.

TABLE 11-2. STYRENE FROM ETHYL BENZENE: NONADIABATIC REACTOR

Conversion, x	Mean bulk temperature		Catalyst bed depth, ft
	°R	°C	
0	1616	625	0
10	1589	610	0.40
20	1560	594	0.98
30	1530	578	1.80
38	1505	564	2.80
45	1478	549	4.2
50	1456	537	5.8
55	1426	520	9.0
57	1412	512	∞

These results are also plotted in Fig. 11-5 and labeled nonadiabatic operation. As would be expected, the bed depth for a given conversion is greater in this case, because the temperature is less. For example, for a conversion of 50 per cent, 5.8 ft of catalyst is required in comparison with 4.8 ft in Example 11-1.

Example 11-3. A bench-scale study of the hydrogenation of nitrobenzene was published by Wilson[1] in connection with reactor-design studies. Nitrobenzene

[1] K. B. Wilson, *Trans. Inst. Chem. Engrs.* (*London*), **24**:77 (1946).

and hydrogen were fed at a rate of 65.9 g moles/hr to a 3.0-cm-ID reactor containing the granular catalyst. A thermocouple sheath, 0.9 cm in diameter, extended down the center of the tube. The void fraction was 0.424 and the pressure atmospheric.

The feed entered the reactor at 427.5°K, and the tube was immersed in an oil bath maintained at the same temperature. The heat-transfer coefficient from the mean reaction temperature to the oil bath was determined experimentally to be 8.67 cal/(hr)(sq cm)(°C). A large excess of hydrogen was used so that (1) the specific heat of the reaction mixture may be taken equal to that for hydrogen and (2) the change in total moles as a result of reaction may be neglected. The heat of reaction is approximately constant and equal to $-152,100$ cal/g mole.

The entering concentration of nitrobenzene was 5.0×10^{-7} g mole/cc. The rate of reaction was represented by the expression

$$r = 5.79 \times 10^4 C^{0.578} e^{-2,958/T}$$

where r = g moles nitrobenzene reacting/(cc)(hr), expressed in terms of void volume in reactor

C = concentration of nitrobenzene, g moles/cc

T = °K

The experimental-temperature vs. reactor-length results are shown in Fig. 11-9. From the data given, calculate temperatures up to a reactor length of 25 cm, and compare with the observed results.

Solution. The concentration C depends upon temperature as well as conversion. If V is the volumetric flow rate at a point in the reactor where the concentration is C and V_0 is the value at the entrance, the conversion of nitrobenzene is

$$x = \frac{C_0 V_0 - CV}{C_0 V_0} = 1 - \frac{C}{C_0} \frac{V}{V_0}$$

Since there is no change in pressure or number of moles, V changes only because of temperature changes. Hence, assuming perfect-gas behavior,

$$x = 1 - \frac{C}{C_0} \frac{T}{T_0}$$

or
$$C = (1 - x) \frac{C_0 T_0}{T} = (5 \times 10^{-7}) \frac{427.5}{T} (1 - x) \qquad (A)$$

Substituting this expression into the rate equation gives the rate in terms of the temperature and conversion

$$r = 439 \left(\frac{1 - x}{T}\right)^{0.578} e^{-2,958/T_m} \qquad (B)$$

The design equation, even though the reaction is catalytic, must be written in terms of the void volume because of the form in which the rate data are reported.

$$F \, dx = r \times 0.424 \, dV_R$$

The feed rate of nitrobenzene is

$$F = 65.9 \left(22{,}400 \, \frac{427.5}{273} \right) (5.0 \times 10^{-7})$$

$$= 1.15 \text{ g moles/hr}$$

$$1.15 \, dx = r \times 0.424 \, \frac{\pi}{4} \, (9 - 0.81) \, dz$$

or
$$dz = \frac{0.423}{r} \, dx \qquad\qquad\qquad (C)$$

The one additional relationship required is the energy balance.   For this non-adiabatic case, Eq. (11-4) is applicable,

$$-(-152{,}100)F \, dx - 8.67\pi \times 3(T_m - 427.5) \, dz = 65.9 \times 6.9 \, dT_m$$

where 6.9 cal/(g. mole)(°K) is the heat capacity of hydrogen at 427.5°K.   This equation may be simplified to become

$$dT_m = 385 \, dx - 0.180(T_m - 427.5) \, dz \qquad\qquad (D)$$

Equations (B), (C), and (D) are the rate, design, and energy-balance relationships necessary to solve the problem.   A numerical approach is indicated and may be carried out in the following way.[1]
1. Choose an incremental value of conversion, say, $\Delta x = 0.1$.
2. Calculate r at the beginning and end of the increment from Eq. (B) by assuming a temperature at the end of the increment.
3. Solve Eq. (C) for Δz.
4. Use Eq. (D) to check the assumed temperature.
Illustrating these calculations by starting with a conversion increment of $\Delta x = 0.10$, it is assumed that $T_{m_1} = 427.5 + 15 = 442.5°K$ at $x = 0.10$.

$$r_0 = 439 \left(\frac{1}{427.5} \right)^{0.578} e^{-2{,}958/427.5}$$

$$= 0.0130 \text{ g mole/(hr)(cc)}$$

$$r_1 = 439 \left(\frac{1 - 0.1}{442.5} \right)^{0.578} e^{-2{,}958/442.5} = 0.0152$$

From Eq. (C)

$$\Delta z = z_1 - 0 = 0.423 \left(\frac{1}{r} \right)_{\text{av}} \times 0.10$$

$$z_1 = 0.423 \left(\frac{1}{0.0130} + \frac{1}{0.0152} \right) \frac{1}{2} \times 0.10$$

$$z_1 = 3.02 \text{ cm}$$

From Eq. (D)

$$T_{m_1} - 427.5 = 385 \, \Delta x - 0.180(T - 427.5)_{\text{av}} \, \Delta z$$
$$T_{m_1} - 427.5 = 38.5 - 0.180 \times 7.5 \times 3.02$$
$$= 34.4°C$$

[1] Note that the method of solution is exactly the same as used in Example 6-5 for a homogeneous reaction.

This temperature rise of 34°C is much larger than the assumed value of 15°C. For the second trial, assume the temperature $T_{m_1} = 427.5 + 30 = 457.5°K$.

$$r_1 = 0.0186 \qquad \frac{1}{r_1} = 53.8$$

$$z = z_1 - 0 = 0.423 \times 65.4 \times 0.10$$
$$= 2.77 \text{ cm}$$
$$T_1 - 427.5 = 38.5 - 0.180 \times 15 \times 2.77$$
$$= 38.5 - 7.5$$
$$= 31°C$$

The assumed and calculated values are now close so that further calculations are unnecessary.   At the end of the first increment

$$x_1 = 0.10$$
$$z_1 = 2.8 \text{ cm}$$
$$T_{m_1} = 427.5 + 31$$
$$= 458.5°K$$

At the end of the second increment assume $T_{m_2} = 458.5 + 23 = 481.5°K$. Then from Eq. (B)

$$r_2 = 439 \left(\frac{1 - 0.2}{481.5} \right)^{0.578} e^{-2,958/481.5} = 0.0225$$

$$\frac{1}{r_2} = 44.4$$

Equation (C) gives the second increment of Δz,

$$\Delta z = 0.423 \frac{53.8 + 44.4}{2} \times 0.1$$
$$= 2.08 \text{ cm}$$

Checking the assumed value of T_2 in Eq. (D),

$$\Delta T_m = 38.5 - 0.180 \left(\frac{481.5 + 458.5}{2} - 427.5 \right) \times 2.08$$
$$= 38.5 - 15.9$$
$$= 22.6°C$$

(vs. the assumed value of 23°C).
   At the end of the second increment

$$x_2 = 0.20$$
$$z_2 = 2.77 + 2.08$$
$$= 4.85 \text{ cm}$$
$$T_{m_2} = 458.5 + 22.6$$
$$= 481°K$$

For T_{m_3} assume a value of $481 + 18 = 499°K$.

$$r_3 = 0.0260$$

$$\frac{1}{r_3} = 38.4$$

$$\Delta z = 0.423 \frac{44.4 + 38.4}{2} \times 0.1$$

$$= 1.75 \text{ cm}$$

$$z_3 = 6.6 \text{ cm}$$

$$\Delta T_m = 38.5 - 0.180 \left(\frac{481 + 499}{2} - 427.5 \right) \times 1.75$$

$$= 38.5 - 19.7$$

$$= 18.8°C$$

(vs. 18°C assumed).

It is apparent from the calculations thus far that the heat transfer to the reactor-tube wall is becoming larger as the conversion increases. This is due to the

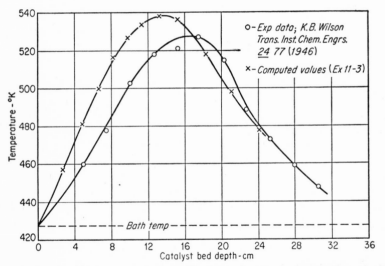

FIG. 11-9. Longitudinal temperature profile in reactor for hydrogenation of nitrobenzene.

increased temperature difference between reaction mixture and wall. The trend continues until the heat transferred to the oil bath is as large as that evolved as a result of reaction. The temperature reaches a maximum at this point, the so-called hot spot. The results of further calculations are summarized in Table 11-3 and Fig. 11-9 and show that the computed hot spot is reached at about 14 cm from the entrance to the reactor. This is 3 cm prior to the experimental hot spot. Also the temperature is 10°C less than the computed value at the maximum. Three points should be mentioned in making this comparison. First, the measured temperature corresponds to the center of the tube, while the computed results are for a bulk mean temperature. Second, the thermocouples were contained in a metal sheath entering down the center of the reactor. This sheath would reduce the observed temperatures, because of longitudinal conduction, and make them more nearly comparable with the bulk mean computed values. Third, using a specific heat of hydrogen for the whole reaction mixture results in a value that is too low. This would tend to make the calculated temperatures too high.

TABLE 11-3. TEMPERATURES AND CONVERSIONS IN NITROBENZENE
HYDROGENATION REACTOR (Ex. 11-3)

Conversion, x	Mean bulk temperature, °C	Catalyst bed depth, cm
0	427.5	0
0.1	458.5	2.8
0.2	481	4.85
0.3	500	6.6
0.4	516	8.2
0.5	527	9.8
0.6	534	11.4
0.7	538	13.1
0.8	536	15.1
0.9	518	18.3
0.95	498	21.1
0.97	478	24.1

Actually, the agreement shown in Fig. 11-9 is quite good, considering these three points and that the simplified method of approach, neglecting radial temperature gradients, has been employed. The fact that a heat-transfer coefficient determined experimentally in the same apparatus was available probably resulted in better agreement than otherwise. Unfortunately no information is available on the catalyst particle size so that a heat-transfer coefficient cannot be estimated from existing correlations [i.e., Eqs. (10-9) and (10-10)].

The simplified method of approach to the design of nonadiabatic reactors led to good results in Example 11-3, partly, at least, because radial temperature variations could not have been particularly large. This is so because the wall temperature was the same as the entering-reactants temperature. Thus at the entrance to the reactor radial variations in temperature were zero. At the hot spot the maximum difference in temperature between the center and wall was about 100°C. In Example 11-4 much larger radial temperature gradients exist, and the simplified method is not so suitable.

Example 11-4. Using the simplified method, compute curves for temperature and conversion vs. catalyst bed depth for comparison with the experimental data shown in Figs. 11-7 and 11-11 for the oxidation of sulfur dioxide.

The reactor consisted of a cylindrical tube, 2.06 in. ID. The superficial gas mass velocity was 350 lb/(hr)(sq ft), and its inlet composition 6.5 mole per cent sulfur dioxide and 93.5 mole per cent dry air. The catalyst was prepared from $\frac{1}{8}$-in. cylindrical pellets of alumina and contained a surface coating of platinum (0.2 per cent by weight of the pellet). The rate data in this case were not fitted to a kinetic equation but are shown as a function of temperature and conversion in Table 11-4 and Fig. 11-10. Since a fixed inlet gas composition to the reactor

TABLE 11-4. EXPERIMENTAL† RATE OF OXIDATION OF SO_2 USING A
0.2 PER CENT Pt ON Al_2O_3 CATALYST

Temp, °C.	Per cent conversion‡						
	0	10	20	30	40	50	60
350	0.011	0.0080	0.0049	0.0031			
360	0.0175	0.0121	0.00788	0.00471	0.00276	0.00181	
380	0.0325	0.0214	0.01433	0.00942	0.00607	0.00410	
400	0.0570	0.0355	0.02397	0.01631	0.0110	0.00749	0.00488
420	0.0830	0.0518	0.0344	0.02368	0.0163	0.0110	0.00745
440	0.1080	0.0752	0.0514	0.03516	0.0236	0.0159	0.0102
460	0.146	0.1000	0.0674	0.04667	0.0319	0.0215	0.0138
480	......	0.1278	0.0898	0.0642	0.0440	0.0279	0.0189
500	......	0.167	0.122	0.0895	0.0632	0.0394	0.0263

Rate = g moles SO_2 converted/(hr)(g of catalyst).
† R. W. Olson, R. W. Schuler, and J. M. Smith, *Chem. Eng. Progr.*, **46**:614 (1950).
‡ Conversion refers to a constant feed composition of 6.5 mole per cent SO_2 and 93.5 per cent air.

was used, independent variations of the partial pressures of oxygen, sulfur dioxide, and sulfur trioxide were not possible. Instead these pressures are all related to one variable, the extent of conversion. Hence the rate data shown in Table 11-4 as a function of conversion are sufficient for the calculations. The total pressure was essentially constant at 790 mm Hg.

The heat of reaction in this instance is nearly constant over a considerable temperature range and equal to $-22,700$ cal/g mole of sulfur dioxide reacted. The gas mixture is predominantly air so that its specific heat may be taken equal to that of air.

The bulk density of the catalyst as packed in the reactor was 64 lb/cu ft.

From Fig. 11-6 it is apparent that the entering temperature across the diameter is not constant but varies from a maximum value of about 400°C at the center down to the wall value of 197°C. Since the simplified method of solution to be used in this example is based upon a uniform temperature radially, use a mean value of 364°C. In the more rigorous methods considered in a later example the actual entering-temperature profile can be taken into account.

Solution. Before carrying out the reactor calculations it is necessary to estimate a wall heat-transfer coefficient. Leva's correlations [Eq. (10-10)] may be

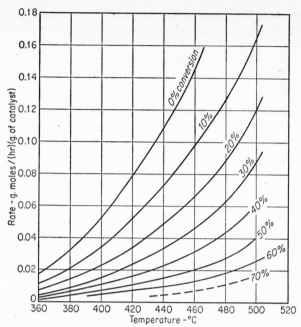

FIG. 11-10. Rate of oxidation of SO_2 on $\frac{1}{8}$-in. catalyst particles containing 0.2 per cent platinum. [Mass velocity = 350 lb/(hr)(sq ft).]

used for this purpose

$$\frac{d_p G}{\mu} = \frac{1}{8 \times 12} \frac{350}{0.08} = 46\dagger$$

$$\frac{d_p}{d_t} = \frac{1}{8 \times 2.06} = 0.0607$$

$$\frac{h d_t}{k} = (3.50)(46)^{0.7} e^{-4.6 \times 0.0607} = 38.7$$

$$h = \frac{12 \times 0.028}{2.06} \times 38.7$$

$$= 6.3 \text{ Btu/(hr)(sq ft)(°F)}$$

The energy balance for an element of reactor height dz is, according to Eq. (11-4),

$$F y_0 \, dx (+22{,}700) \times 1.8 - 6.3 \left(\pi \frac{2.06}{12} \right) (t_m - 197) 1.8 \, dz = \Sigma m_i c_{p_i} \, dt_m \times 1.8 \quad \text{(A)}$$

† The viscosity of 0.08 lb/(hr)(ft) at an estimated average bed temperature of 350°C is for air. An air value is a good approximation owing to the small concentration of SO_2.

In this expression the conversion factor of 1.8°F/°C has been introduced so that the temperature may be expressed in degrees centigrade

$$F = 350\pi \left(\frac{1.03}{12}\right)^2 \frac{1}{31.2}$$
$$= 0.26 \text{ lb mole/hr}$$

The number 31.2 is the molecular weight of the feed containing 6.5 mole per cent SO_2. The heat capacity of the reaction mixture, assumed to be that of air, at an average temperature of 350°C is 0.26 Btu/(lb)(°F). Hence

$$\Sigma m_i c_{p_i} = 350\pi \left(\frac{1.03}{12}\right)^2 \times 0.26$$
$$= 2.11 \text{ Btu/°F}$$

Substituting these values in Eq. (A),

$$0.26 \times 0.065\, dx \times 22{,}700 - 3.40(t_m - 197)\, dz = 2.11\, dt_m$$

or $\qquad\qquad dt_m = 182\, dx - 1.61(t_m - 197)\, dz \qquad\qquad$ (B)

The design equation [Eq. (11-2)] may be written

$$\pi \left(\frac{1.03}{12}\right)^2 r_c(\rho_B)\, dz = F y_0\, dx = 0.26 \times 0.065\, dx$$

The bulk density of the catalyst as packed is given as 64 lb/cu ft. Hence the design equation simplifies to the form

$$dz = 0.0112 \frac{dx}{r_c} \qquad\qquad (C)$$

In contrast to the previous examples the rate of reaction is not expressed in equation form but as a tabulation of experimental data. Actually a simple first- or second-order-type expression would not correlate the data for this reaction. Instead a Langmuir–Hougen and Watson type of equation, based upon adsorption of oxygen on the catalyst, was found necessary to explain the data. This equation was developed and tested in Example 9-4. The tabulation of rates is more convenient to use in this problem than the rate equation. The units of r_c in Eq. (C) should be pound moles reacted per hour per pound of catalyst, but numbers in these units are numerically equivalent to gram moles per hour per gram of catalyst so that the data in Table 11-4 can be used directly.

The method of solution is the same as in Examples 11-2 and 11-3:

1. An increment of conversion is chosen.
2. A temperature at the end of the increment is assumed.
3. The rates are obtained at the beginning and end of the increment from Table 11-4 or Fig. 11-10.
4. The increment of depth Δz is computed from Eq. (C).
5. The assumed temperature is checked in Eq. (B).

For the first increment choose $\Delta x = 0.05$.   From Fig. 11-4 the rate at the beginning of the increment, zero conversion and 364°C, is 0.020.   If the temperature at the end of the increment is assumed to be $364 + 1 = 365°C$, the rate at this temperature and $x = 0.05$ is 0.018.   Then in Eq. (C)

$$\Delta z = 0.0112 \left[\frac{1}{r}\right]_{av} \times 0.05$$

$$= 0.0112 \left(\frac{1}{0.02} + \frac{1}{0.018}\right) \times \frac{1}{2} \times 0.05$$

$$= 0.0294 \text{ ft}$$

Then in Eq. (B)

$$t_{m_1} - 364 = 182 \times 0.05 - 1.61(364 - 197) \times 0.0294$$
$$t_{m_1} - 364 = 9.1 - 8.0$$
$$= 1.1°C$$
$$t_{m_1} = 365.1°C$$

Continuing the computations gives the results summarized in Table 11-5 and shown in Fig. 11-11.   It is apparent that the mean computed temperature never rises appreciably above the entering value of 364°C.   Indeed, when a bed depth of about 0.2 ft is reached, the temperature is so low that the rate is no longer high enough to give a significant change in conversion.   The last calculation at a conversion of 24 per cent is estimated by extrapolating the tabulated rate data.

TABLE 11-5. CONVERSION AND TEMPERATURE IN SO₂ REACTOR:
SIMPLIFIED METHOD

Conversion, x	Temperature, °C	Catalyst bed depth, z, ft
0	364	0
0.05	365	0.029
0.10	364.5	0.065
0.15	361	0.112
0.18	357	0.149
0.21	347	0.210
0.24	(300)	(0.5)

In the experimental reactor used by Schuler et al.[1] the low wall temperature results in severe radial temperature gradients.   Hence the mean bulk temperature may be low, but the temperatures near the center of the bed may be high enough to cause a significant amount of reaction.   This is a major factor in the large difference between the experimental conversion curve and the results computed in this example, both shown in Fig. 11-11. A critical quantity in the simplified design method applied to this problem is the wall heat-transfer coefficient.   Small changes in h_w can cause large differences in the conversion.   The use of Leva's correlation [Eq.

[1] Schuler, Stallings, and Smith, *loc. cit.*

(10-10)] at a low Reynolds number is a questionable procedure here but is probably the best available.

In Example 11-5 an attempt is made to account for the effects of radial gradients by employing the semirigorous design method.

11-6. Nonadiabatic Operation, Semirigorous Procedure. In Chap. 10 the differential equations were developed relating temperature to position in a fixed bed in which no reaction occurred. Experimental data showed that the factor used to measure the rate of radial heat transfer, k_e, varied

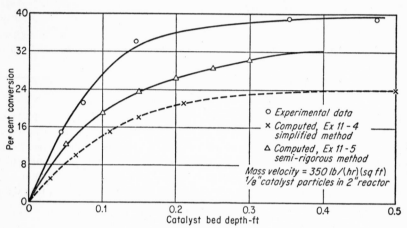

FIG. 11-11. Comparison of calculated and experimental conversions in SO_2 reactor.

with position. Taking this into account required a more complex differential equation [Eq. (10-12)] than for the assumption of a constant k_e [Eq. (10-11)]. It was also pointed out that there are data to indicate that the mass velocity of fluid through the reactor may vary with radial position. A rigorous solution of the temperature-distribution problem requires allowance for changes in k_e and G.

When the problem of reactor design is considered, the differential equations become even more complex because terms must be added to the equation for the energy and mass changes due to the reaction itself. Finally, it should be realized that even Eq. (10-12), and its counterpart for the concentration distribution, Eq. (10-49), involve a number of assumptions. These were mentioned in Chap. 10, but one of them deserves consideration here. When a reaction occurs on the surface of the catalyst pellet, the heat of reaction will be absorbed or released on the surface. This means that the mean temperature of the catalyst and the gas cannot be exactly the same. This assumption was made in developing Eq. (10-12).

Because of these complexities an entirely rigorous approach to the design of fixed-bed reactors is not practical. It then becomes important to decide which of the various assumptions can be made without undue loss in accuracy. The small number of experimental data available provide a partial answer to this question. The assumption of equality of the mean catalyst and gas temperatures eliminates half of the differential equations involved and appears to be satisfactory when the heat of reaction is not especially high. The variations in mass velocity and k_e in the radial direction change the form of the differential equation for the energy and mass balances, but not the procedures for the solution. Hence, for illustrating the method of design, it will be assumed that both k_e (and D_e for mass transfer) and G are constant across the reactor diameter. However, it should be realized that a closer approximation to experimental results can be made by taking into account the decreased values of these quantities near the wall of the reactor.

With these limitations the equations applicable for describing the temperature and concentration in a fixed-bed reactor are analogous to Eqs. (10-11) and (10-12) of Chap. 10. The differences are terms for: (1) the energy input per differential element of reactor, which is $(-\Delta H)r_c\rho_B(2\pi r \, dr \, dz)$;† (2) the mass input $-r_c(2\pi r \, dr \, dz)\rho_B$. If the first term is added to input terms in the development of Eq. (10-11) (Example 10-3), the energy balance becomes, after simplification,

$$-\frac{\partial t}{\partial z} + \frac{k_e}{Gc_p}\left(\frac{1}{r}\frac{\partial t}{\partial r} + \frac{\partial^2 t}{\partial r^2}\right) - \frac{\Delta H \, r_c\rho_B}{Gc_p} = 0 \qquad (11\text{-}5)$$

In a similar way, adding the mass-input term to Eq. (10-49) leads to the following equation for the mass balance during reaction:

$$-\frac{\partial(uC)}{\partial z} + \frac{D_e}{u}\left[\frac{1}{r}\frac{\partial(uC)}{\partial r} + \frac{\partial^2(uC)}{\partial r^2}\right] - r_c\rho_B = 0 \qquad (11\text{-}6)$$

It is generally more convenient to replace the concentration of limiting reactant C with the conversion x. This may be done by noting the definition of x (Chap. 4); i.e.,

$$x = \frac{\text{moles limiting reactant consumed}}{\text{moles limiting reactant in the feed}}$$

If C_0 and u_0 are the concentration and velocity entering the reactor,

$$x = \frac{C_0 u_0 - Cu}{C_0 u_0}$$

Solving for the product Cu yields

$$Cu = C_0 u_0(1 - x) \qquad (11\text{-}7)$$

† To distinguish between radial distance and rate of reaction, the latter is designated as r_c, the rate of the catalytic reaction.

Differentiating Eq. (11-7) with respect to r and z, noting that $C_0 u_0$ is constant,

$$\frac{\partial(uC)}{\partial r} = -C_0 u_0 \frac{\partial x}{\partial r} \tag{11-8}$$

$$\frac{\partial^2(uC)}{\partial r^2} = -C_0 u_0 \frac{\partial^2 x}{\partial r^2} \tag{11-9}$$

$$\frac{\partial(Cu)}{\partial z} = -C_0 u_0 \frac{\partial x}{\partial z} \tag{11-10}$$

Substituting Eqs. (11-8) to (11-10) into Eq. (11-6) gives the desired differential equation expressing the conversion x in terms of position, r and z,

$$\frac{\partial x}{\partial z} - \frac{D_e}{u}\left(\frac{1}{r}\frac{\partial x}{\partial r} + \frac{\partial^2 x}{\partial r^2}\right) - \frac{r_c \rho_B}{C_0 u_0} = 0 \tag{11-11}$$

If the mole fraction of the limiting component entering the reactor is y_0, then $C_0 u_0 = G y_0 / M_{av}$ and Eq. (11-11), like (11-5) for temperature, can be written in terms of mass velocity,

$$\frac{\partial x}{\partial z} - \frac{D_e}{u}\left(\frac{1}{r}\frac{\partial x}{\partial r} + \frac{\partial^2 x}{\partial r^2}\right) - \frac{r_c \rho_B M_{av}}{G y_0} = 0 \tag{11-12}$$

The design problem of computing the temperature and conversion at any point on the reactor can be solved by application of the energy-balance equation (11-5), the mass-balance or design equation (11-12), and the rate expression (11-3).

In comparing the simplified method with the more rigorous one, it is seen that the simple heat-balance [equation (11-4)] has been replaced by Eq. (11-5) and that the simple design equation (11-2) has been replaced by Eq. (11-12).

The similarity between Eqs. (10-11) and (11-5) and (10-49) and (11-12) suggests that the same numerical approach used in Chap. 10 can be used here where a reaction is involved.[1] Indeed, that is the case, and we may proceed immediately to the difference forms of Eqs. (11-5) and (11-12) by analogy to Eq. (10-42). Thus if the bed is divided into radial increments, Δr, and longitudinal increments, Δz, Eq. (11-5) may be written

$$t_{n,L+1} = t_{n,L} + \frac{\Delta z}{(\Delta r)^2}\frac{k_e}{G c_p}\left[\frac{1}{n}(t_{n+1,L} - t_{n,L}) + t_{n+1,L} - 2t_{n,L} + t_{n-1,L}\right]$$
$$- \frac{\Delta H (r_c)_a \rho_B}{G c_p}\Delta z \tag{11-13}$$

[1] T. Baron, *Chem. Eng. Progr.*, **48**:118 (1952), has developed an ingenious graphical method of solution which is applicable when the Peclet numbers for heat and mass transfer are assumed to be identical.

In a similar way, Eq. (11-12) may be written in difference form as follows:

$$x_{n,L+1} = x_{n,L} + \frac{\Delta z}{(\Delta r)^2} \frac{D_e}{u} \left[\frac{1}{n} (x_{n+1,L} - x_{n,L}) + x_{n+1,L} - 2x_{n,L} + x_{n-1,L} \right]$$
$$+ \frac{(r_c)_a \rho_B M_{\mathrm{av}}}{G y_0} \Delta z \qquad (11\text{-}14)$$

Provided the magnitude of the reaction terms involving r_c can be estimated, Eqs. (11-13) and (11-14) can be solved, step by step, to obtain the conversion. The first step is to compute values of t and x across the diameter, at $z = 1 \, \Delta z$, or $L = 1$, from known values at $L = 0$. Then continue to the next longitudinal increment, $L = 2$, etc. This procedure is just the same as that described in Example 10-7, where the reaction terms were not present. The difficulty in using Eqs. (11-13) and (11-14) at $n = 0$ can be avoided by using the special expressions

$$t_{0,L+1} = t_{0,L} + \frac{2 \, \Delta z}{(\Delta r)^2} \frac{k_e}{cG} (2t_{1,L} - 2t_{0,L}) - \frac{\Delta H \, (r_c)_a \rho_B \, \Delta z}{G c_p} \qquad (11\text{-}15)$$

$$x_{0,L+1} = x_{0,L} + \frac{2 \, \Delta z}{(\Delta r)^2} \frac{D_e}{u} (2x_{1,L} - 2x_{0,L}) + \frac{(r_c)_a \rho_B M_{\mathrm{av}} \, \Delta z}{G y_0} \qquad (11\text{-}16)$$

analogous to Eq. (10-45).

The effect of the reaction terms in Eqs. (11-13) and (11-14) is, for an exothermic reaction (ΔH negative), to increase both the temperature and the conversion. Since the rate depends upon the temperature and composition and the average value for the increment L to $L + 1$ is not known until Eqs. (11-13) and (11-14) are solved, a trial-and-error procedure is indicated. The calculations are illustrated in the following example, where the SO_2 reactor problem (Example 11-4) is recomputed, taking radial variations into account. The results of the two examples permit a comparison of the simplified and semirigorous design methods when radial temperature gradients are severe.

Example 11-5. Recompute the conversion vs. bed-depth curve for the SO_2 reactor of Example 11-4, using the semirigorous method and assuming k_e, D_e, and G are constant.

Experimental heat-transfer data for this case were presented in Example 10-4. However, to avoid reliance on experimental work as much as possible, predict the average value of k_e by the method described in Appendix B. Use the correlation presented in Fig. 10-4 to estimate the effective diffusivity D_e.

The temperature profile at the entrance to the reactor is as shown in Table 11-6. The reactants composition across the diameter may be assumed to be uniform.

Solution. EFFECTIVE THERMAL CONDUCTIVITY AND DIFFUSIVITY. The constant average value of D_e for the bed can be estimated from Fig. 10-4.

TABLE 11-6

Entering Gas Temperature, °C	Radial position, $\dfrac{r}{r_0}$
376.5	0.797
400.4	0.534
400.1	0.023
399.5	0.233
400.1	0.474
376.1	0.819
197	1.0

From Example 11-4

$$\frac{d_p}{d_t} = 0.0607$$

$$\mathrm{Re} = \frac{d_p G}{\mu} = 46$$

Then from Fig. 10-4

$$\mathrm{Pe}_m = \frac{u d_p}{D_e} = 9.0(1 + 19.4 \times 0.0607^2) = 9.6$$

For direct use in Eq. (11-14) the ratio D_e/μ is required.

$$\frac{D_e}{\mu} = \frac{d_p}{9.6} = \frac{1}{8 \times 12 \times 9.6}$$
$$= 0.00109 \text{ ft} \qquad (A)$$

The separate contributions to k_e are to be estimated by the procedure in Sec. 10-4 and illustrated in Example 10-6. Additional data for the packed bed are

Catalyst particle conductivity = 0.5 Btu/(hr)(ft)(°F)
Emissivity, $\epsilon = 0.5$
Void fraction, $\delta = 0.40$
Average bed temperature = 350°C (662°F)

1. Radiation contribution from Eq. (10-18)

$$k_r' = 4 \frac{0.5}{2 - 0.5} \frac{1}{8 \times 12} \frac{0.173(662 + 460)^3}{100^4} = 0.033$$

2. Point conductivity, Eq. (10-33)

$$\log k_p' = -1.76 + 0.0129 \frac{0.5}{0.4}$$
$$k_p' = 0.018$$

3. Coefficient h_c, Eq. (10-27)

$$\frac{h_c}{cG} = (1.95)(46)^{-0.51}(0.74)^{-\frac{2}{3}} = 0.338$$

$$h_c = 0.338 \times 350 \times 0.26$$
$$= 30 \text{ Btu}/(\text{hr})(\text{sq ft})(°F)$$

4. Coefficients h_r and h_p from Eqs. (10-31) and (10-32). Assume

$$h = h_c + h_p + h_r = 43$$

Then from Eq. (10-31)

$$h_r = \frac{0.033(2 \times 0.5 + 43 \times 0.0104)}{0.0104 \times 0.5} = 9.2$$

From Eq. (10-32)

$$h_p = \frac{0.018(2 \times 0.5 + 43 \times 0.0104)}{0.0104 \times 0.5} = 5.0$$

$$h = 30 + 9.2 + 5.0$$
$$= 44 \text{ Btu}/(\text{hr})(\text{sq ft})(°F)$$

This value agrees with the assumed h.

5. Series contribution from Eq. (10-25)

$$k'_{\text{series}} = \frac{43 \times 0.5 \times 0.0104}{2 \times 0.5 + 43 \times 0.0104} = 0.155$$

6. Turbulent-diffusion contribution, Eq. (10-17). The Peclet number for mass transfer has been estimated to be 9.6. Then, from Eq. (10-17),

$$k'_{td} = \frac{d_p cG}{\text{Pe}_m \delta} = \frac{0.0104 \times 0.26 \times 350}{9.6 \times 0.4} = 0.247$$

7. Molecular-conductivity contribution. The thermal conductivity of air at 350°C is approximately 0.028.

$$k'_c = 0.028$$

8. Total effective thermal conductivity and Pe_h, Eq. (10-16). Summing the individual contributions leads to a value of the average effective conductivity for the bed.

$$k_e = \delta(k'_c + k'_{td} + k'_r) + (1 - \delta)k'_{\text{series}}$$
$$k_e = 0.4(0.028 + 0.247 + 0.033) + (1 - 0.4) \times 0.155$$
$$= 0.123 + 0.093$$
$$= 0.216 \text{ Btu}/(\text{hr})(\text{ft})(°F)$$

The Peclet number for heat transfer is

$$\text{Pe}_h = \frac{d_p cG}{k_e} = \frac{0.0104 \times 0.26 \times 350}{0.216} = 4.4$$

These calculations indicate that, if single values of k_e and D_e are to be used for the entire bed, the Peclet numbers for heat and mass transfer are 4.4 and 9.6, respectively.

In Eq. (11-13) the quantity needed for the calculations is

$$\frac{k_e}{c_p G} = \frac{0.216}{0.26 \times 350}$$
$$= 0.00238 \text{ ft} \qquad (B)$$

Equations (A) and (B) provide the necessary heat- and mass-transfer information for the design. The next step is to carry out the stepwise calculations suggested by Eqs. (11-13) and (11-14).

TEMPERATURE AND CONVERSION EQUATIONS. It is convenient to divide the radius of the bed into five increments, so that

$$\Delta r = 0.2 r_0 = 0.2 \left(\frac{1.03}{12}\right) = 0.0172 \text{ ft}$$

If Δz is chosen to be 0.05 ft,

$$\frac{\Delta z}{(\Delta r)^2} = \frac{0.05}{(0.0172)^2}$$
$$= 170 \text{ ft}^{-1}$$

Then the coefficients in Eqs. (11-13) and (11-14) are as follows:

$$\frac{k_e}{c_p G} \frac{\Delta z}{(\Delta r)^2} = 0.00238 \times 170 = 0.404 \qquad \text{dimensionless}$$

$$\frac{D_e}{\mu} \frac{\Delta z}{(\Delta r)^2} = 0.00109 \times 170 = 0.185 \qquad \text{dimensionless}$$

$$\frac{\Delta H \, \rho_B \, \Delta z \, r_c}{G c_p} = \frac{(-22{,}700 \times 64 \times 0.05) r_c}{350 \times 0.26} = -798 r_c \qquad °C$$

$$\frac{r_c \rho_B M_{av} \, \Delta z}{G y_0} = \frac{64 \times 31.2 \times 0.05 r_c}{350 \times 0.065} = 4.38 r_c \qquad \text{dimensionless}$$

Substituting these values in Eqs. (11-13) and (11-14) gives working expressions for calculating the temperature and conversion at a bed depth $L + 1$, from data at the previous bed depth, L.

$$t_{n,L+1} = t_{n,L} + 0.404 \left[\frac{1}{n} (t_{n+1,L} - t_{n,L}) + t_{n+1,L} - 2t_{n,L} + t_{n-1,L} \right]$$
$$+ 798(r_c)_a \qquad (C)$$

$$x_{n,L+1} = x_{n,L} + 0.185 \left[\frac{1}{n} (x_{n+1,L} - x_{n,L}) + x_{n+1,L} - 2x_{n,L} + x_{n-1,L} \right]$$
$$+ 4.38(r_c)_a \qquad (D)$$

CALCULATIONS FOR THE FIRST BED-DEPTH INCREMENT $(L = 1)$. The entering-temperature distribution is known and plotted in Fig. 11-12, and the entering conversion will be zero at all radial positions.   Starting at $n = 1$, the temperatures $t_{0,0}$, $t_{1,0}$, and $t_{2,0}$, as read from Fig. 11-12, are all 400°C.

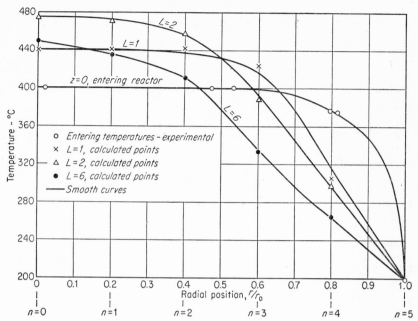

FIG. 11-12. Calculated temperatures in SO_2 reactor (Example 11-5).

Substituting these values into Eq. (C) gives $t_{1,1}$ in terms of the average rate, $(r_c)_a$, over the increment of bed depth from 0 to $L = 1$ ($z = 0.05$ ft).

$$t_{1,1} = t_{1,0} + 0.404[\tfrac{1}{1}(t_{2,0} - t_{1,0}) + t_{2,0} - 2t_{1,0} + t_{0,0}] + 798(r_c)_a$$
$$t_{1,1} = 400 + 0.404 \times 0 + 798(r_c)_a = 400 + 798(r_c)_a \qquad \text{(E)}$$

Since $x_{0,0}$, $x_{1,0}$, and $x_{2,0}$ are all 0, Eq. (D) gives, for the conversion at $n = 1$, $L = 1$,

$$x_{1,1} = 0 + 0.185 \times 0 + 4.38(r_c)_a = 4.38(r_c)_a \qquad \text{(F)}$$

Equations (E), (F), and the rate data, Table 11-4 or Fig. 11-10, constitute three relationships between the unknown quantities $t_{1,1}$, $x_{1,1}$, and $(r_c)_a$.   A method of solution is to follow a four-step process.

1. Assume a value of $(r_c)_a$, after obtaining $r_{1,0}$ from Fig. 11-10.
2. Compute $t_{1,1}$ and $x_{1,1}$ from Eqs. (E) and (F).
3. Evaluate the rate $r_{1,1}$ at the end of the increment from Fig. 11-10.
4. Average $r_{1,1}$ and $r_{1,0}$, and compare with the assumed $(r_c)_a$.   If agreement is not obtained, repeat the sequence with a revised value of $(r_c)_a$.
Carrying out these steps,

1:            $r_{1,0} = 0.0550$ at 400°C and zero conversion

Assume $(r_c)_a = 0.051$.

2:                      $t_{1,1} = 400 + 798 \times 0.051$
                              $= 441°C$

3:                      $x_{1,1} = 4.38 \times 0.051 = 0.223$

From Fig. (11-10) at 441°C and 22.3 per cent conversion $r_{1,1} = 0.046$.

4:                      $(r_c)_a = \dfrac{0.055 + 0.046}{2} = 0.0505$

This result is close to the assumed value of 0.051. Hence the calculated temperature and conversion at $n = 1$, $L = 1$ may be taken as 441°C and 22.3 per cent.

The same result would apply at $n = 0$, and 2. This is because the entering temperature is 400°C up to a radial position of $n = 3$ ($r/r_0 = 0.6$) as noted in Fig. 11-12. At $n = 3$ the situation will change because $t_{4,0} = 376°C$. Making the stepwise calculations at this radial position,

1:                      $r_{3,0} = 0.055$

Assume $(r_c)_a = 0.046$.
From Eq. (C)

2: $t_{3,1} = 400 + 0.404[\tfrac{1}{3}(376 - 400) + 376 - 2 \times 400 + 400] + 798 \times 0.046$
          $= 400 - 13 + 37$
          $= 424°C$
$x_{3,1} = 0 + 4.38 \times 0.046 = 0.201$

From Fig. 11-10 at 424°C and 20.1 per cent conversion

3:                      $r_{3,1} = 0.037$

4:                      $(r_c)_a = \dfrac{0.055 + 0.037}{2} = 0.046$

Continuing the calculations at $n = 4$ ($r/r_0 = 0.8$), where $t_{4,0} = 376°$ and $x_{4,0} = 0$,

1:                      $r_{4,0} = 0.029$

Assume $(r_c)_a = 0.015$.

2: $t_{4,1} = 376 + 0.404[\tfrac{1}{4}(197 - 376) + 197 - 2 \times 376 + 400] + 798 \times 0.015$
          $= 376 - 83 + 12$
          $= 305°C$

3. From Fig. 11-10 at 305°C and $x = 0.066$ it is evident that the rate is close to zero.

4:                      $(r_c)_a = \dfrac{0.029 + 0}{2} = 0.015$

which agrees with the assumed value. Hence at $n = 4$ and $L = 1$ the calculated temperature will be 305°C and the conversion 6.6 per cent.

Since at $n = 5$ the wall is reached, the temperature remains 197°C. The rate is zero at this temperature; so there will be no conversion due to reaction. Hence $t_{5,1} = 197°C$, and $x_{5,1} = 0$. At higher bed depths the conversion at the wall will not be zero, not because of reaction, but because of diffusion of the product SO_3 from the center of the tube. This problem of the conversion at the wall will be considered in the calculations for the second bed depth.

The computations have now been made across the radius of the reactor at $L = 1, z = 0.05$ ft. The temperature results are indicated by the points marked

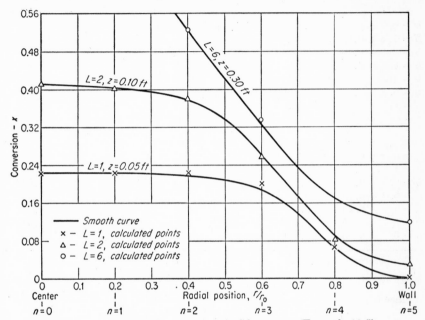

FIG. 11-13. Calculated conversions in SO_2 reactor (Example 11-5).

$\times$ in Fig. 11-12. As in Example 10-7, where no reaction occurred, the results computed by this stepwise procedure do not form a smooth curve at low bed depths. Hence it is desirable before proceeding to the next increment to draw a smooth curve for this bed depth as indicated in Fig. 11-12. The computed values and corresponding smooth curve for conversion are shown in Fig. 11-13. The temperatures and conversions read from the smoothed curves, and to be used in the calculations at $L = 2$, are given in Table 11-7.

CALCULATIONS FOR SECOND BED-DEPTH INCREMENT $(L = 2)$. In the calculations for the first increment it was not necessary to use the special equations for the center, $n = 0$, because the conversions and temperatures up to $n = 3$ were the same at $L = 0$. This situation does not exist for the second increment, and the results at $n = 1$ and $n = 0$ will differ. Thus Eqs. (11-15) and (11-16) for $n = 0$ and $L = 2$ become

$$t_{0,2} = t_{0,1} + 2 \times 0.404(2t_{1,1} - 2t_{0,1}) + 798(r_c)_a \qquad (G)$$
$$x_{0,2} = x_{0,1} + 2 \times 0.185(2x_{1,1} - 2x_{0,1}) + 4.38(r_c)_a \qquad (H)$$

TABLE 11-7. CONVERSIONS AND TEMPERATURES FOR SO_2 OXIDATION BY THE
SEMIRIGOROUS METHOD

Bed depth	Radial position, $\dfrac{r}{r_0}$					
	(Center) $n = 0$	0.2 $n = 1$	0.4 $n = 2$	0.6 $n = 3$	0.8 $n = 4$	1.0 (wall) $n = 5$
$L = 0, z = 0$	400	400	400	400	376	197
$L = 1, z = 0.05$ ft	441	441	437	418	315	197
$L = 2, z = 0.10$	475	471	458	390	298	197
$L = 3, z = 0.15$	496	488	443	378	285	197
$L = 4, z = 0.20$	504	476	437	360	278	197
$L = 5, z = 0.25$	470	466	415	350	269	197
$L = 6, z = 0.30$	451	435	412	334	265	197
Conversion, x						
$L = 0, z = 0$	0	0	0	0	0	0
$L = 1, z = 0.05$ ft	0.223	0.223	0.216	0.186	0.066	0
$L = 2, z = 0.10$	0.411	0.402	0.380	0.258	0.090	0.027
$L = 3, z = 0.15$	0.557	0.540	0.464	0.293	0.110	0.053
$L = 4, z = 0.20$	0.658	0.607	0.510	0.311	0.130	0.072
$L = 5, z = 0.25$	0.686	0.638	0.527	0.318	0.150	0.096
$L = 6, z = 0.30$	0.684	0.650	0.525	0.337	0.173	0.122

Temperatures $= °C$.

Since $t_{1,1} = t_{0,1} = 441°C$ and $x_{1,1} = x_{0,1} = 0.223$, these expressions become

$$t_{0,2} = 441 + 798(r_c)_a$$
$$x_{0,2} = 0.223 + 4.38(r_c)_a$$

Assume the average rate to be 0.043 for $n = 0$ and from $L = 1$ to $L = 2$.
Then

$$t_{0,2} = 441 + 798 \times 0.043 = 441 + 34$$
$$= 475°C$$
$$x_{0,2} = 0.223 + 4.38 \times 0.045 = 0.223 + 0.188 = 0.411$$
$$(r_c)_a = \frac{0.046 + 0.039}{2} = 0.0425$$

(This agrees well with the assumed value.)
At radial position 1, Eqs. (C) and (D) become

$$t_{1,2} = t_{1,1} + 0.404[\tfrac{1}{1}(t_{2,1} - t_{1,1}) + t_{2,1} - 2t_{1,1} + t_{0,1}] + 798(r_c)_a$$
$$x_{1,2} = x_{1,1} + 0.185[\tfrac{1}{1}(x_{2,1} - x_{1,1}) + x_{2,1} - 2x_{1,1} + x_{0,1}] + 4.38(r_c)_a$$

Substituting numerical values,

$t_{1,2} = 441 + 0.404[\frac{1}{1}(437 - 441) + 437 - 2 \times 441 + 441] + 798(r_c)_a$
$\quad = 441 - 3.2 + 798(r_c)_a$
$x_{1,2} = 0.223 + 0.18[\frac{1}{1}(0.216 - 0.223) + 0.216 - 2 \times 0.223 + 0.223] + 4.38r_c$
$\quad = 0.223 - 0.003 + 4.38(r_c)_a$

If $(r_c)_a$ is assumed to be 0.042,

$$t_{1,2} = 441 - 3.2 + 33.5$$
$$\quad = 471°C$$
$$x_{1,2} = 0.220 + 0.184 = 0.404$$
$$(r_c)_a = \frac{0.046 + 0.038}{2} = 0.042$$

This is a satisfactory check on $(r_c)_a$, so that $t_{1,2} = 471°C$ and $x_{1,2} = 0.402$. Calculations at $n = 2$, 3, and 4 proceed in a similar fashion. At the wall, $n = 5$, application of Eq. (D) is not clear-cut because $x_{n+1,L}$ is at $n = 6$, or beyond the reactor wall. However, it is known that the concentration gradient at the wall must be zero; i.e., no mass can diffuse through the reactor wall. One way of achieving this condition is to make the conversion curve symmetrical about the wall, i.e., to take $x_{6,L} = x_{4,L}$. Following this procedure for $L = 2$, Eq. (D) becomes

$$x_{5,2} = x_{5,1} + 0.185[\frac{1}{5}(x_{4,1} - x_{5,1}) + x_{4,1} - 2x_{5,1} + x_{4,1}] + 798(r_c)_a$$
$$x_{5,2} = 0 + 0.185[\frac{1}{5}(0.066 - 0) + 0.066 - 2 \times 0 + 0.066] + 4.38(r_c)_a$$
$$x_{5,2} = 0.027 + 4.38(r_c)_a$$

The wall temperature is fixed at 197°C. Hence $t_{5,2} = 197°C$, and it is not necessary to apply Eq. (C) at $n = 5$. Since r_c is essentially zero at 197°C, the preceding equation becomes

$$x_{5,2} = 0.027 + 4.38 \times 0 = 0.027$$

This result states that sufficient SO_3 has diffused from the center to the wall in the increment $L = 1$ to $L = 2$, to give a conversion of 2.7 per cent at the wall. The results of the calculations at $L = 2$ are also plotted in Figs. 11-12 and 11-13. The computed values fall more nearly on a smooth curve than those at $L = 1$. The quantities at $L = 2$ shown in Table 11-7 were read from the smooth curves. These rather than the computed points are used in the calculations for the next bed depth. At higher bed depths the tabulated values are those directly computed from the equations. This procedure for additional increments of bed depth are exactly the same as for $L = 1$ to 2. Equations (G) and (H) are used for $n = 0$ and Eqs. (C) and (D) for $n = 2$, 3, 4, and 5. At $n = 5$ the value of $x_{6,L}$ is taken equal to $x_{4,L}$ in Eq. (D). The results are tabulated in Table 11-7 up to a bed depth of 0.30 ft. It is seen that a conversion of 68 per cent is reached at the center, while almost 12 per cent is obtained at the wall. The temperature reaches a maximum value of 504°C at $z = 0.20$ ft and then decreases at higher bed depths. The decrease is due to the radial transfer of heat toward the wall exceeding the heat evolved due to reaction. The temperature and conversion profiles at $z = 0.30$ are also plotted on Figs. 11-12 and 11-13.

MEAN CONVERSION AND TEMPERATURE. The bulk mean conversions and temperatures at any bed depth are obtained by graphical integration of the radial temperature and conversion profiles such as shown in Figs. 11-12 and 11-13. The bulk mean temperature is the value resulting when the stream through the reactor is completely mixed in the radial direction. Hence the product of the heat capacity and the temperature at each radial position should be averaged. For an element dr the heat capacity of the flowing stream will be $(G2\pi r\, dr)c_p$. Hence the bulk mean temperature is given by the equation

$$t_m = \frac{\int_0^{r_0} G(2\pi r\, dr)c_p t}{\pi G r_0^2 c_{p_m}} = \frac{2\int_0^{r_0} t c_p r\, dr}{r_0^2 c_{p_m}}$$

If the variable $n = r/r_0$ is used to replace r, this expression becomes

$$t_m = \frac{2}{c_{p_m}} \int_0^1 t c_p n\, dn \tag{I}$$

In Eq. (I) c_p is the specific heat at the temperature t, and c_{p_m} is that at the bulk mean temperature t_m. Equation (I) can be integrated by plotting the product $t c_p n$ vs. n and evaluating the area under the curve.

Similarly, the bulk mean conversion corresponds to complete radial mixing of the flow through the reactor. The moles of SO_2 converted in an element of thickness dr are $x(G/M_a)y_0 2\pi r\, dr$, where G/M_a represents the total moles per unit area entering the reactor and y_0 is the mole fraction SO_2 in the feed. M_a is the average molecular weight of the feed.

Integrating over all radial elements,

$$\frac{\pi G r_0^2 y_0 x_m}{M_a} = \int_0^{r_0} x \frac{G}{M_a} y_0 2\pi r\, dr$$

or
$$x_m = \frac{2\int_0^{r_0} xr\, dr}{r_0^2}$$

If r/r_0 is replaced by n,

$$x_m = 2\int_0^1 xn\, dn \tag{J}[1]$$

From the data in Table 11-7 graphs can be made of $t c_p n$ and xn vs. n. The areas of such graphs represent the values of the integrals in Eqs. (I) and (J). Actually, the mean conversion is the quantity of interest. Table 11-8 shows xn at a bed depth of $z = 0.30$ ft. These data are plotted in Fig. 11-14, and the area is as follows:

$$\int_0^1 xn\, dn = 0.150$$

Then from Eq. (J)

$$x_m = 2 \times 0.150 = 0.300, \text{ or } 30\% \text{ conversion}$$

[1] The velocity does not appear in Eq. (I) or (J) because it is assumed that G is constant across the diameter of the reactor.

TABLE 11-8. CALCULATION OF MEAN CONVERSION AT $L = 6$, $z = 0.30$ FT

n	x	nx
0	0.684	0
0.2	0.650	0.130
0.4	0.525	0.210
0.5	0.422	0.211
0.6	0.337	0.202
0.8	0.173	0.139
1.0	0.122	0.122

Similar evaluations of the mean conversion have been made at the other bed depths. The results are plotted on Fig. 11-11, which also shows the measured conversions and those calculated by the simplified method in Example 11-4.

It is evident that the semirigorous method has resulted in improved agreement over the simplified approach but that the computed conversions are still less than the experimental results. In view of the problems in estimating the radial heat- and mass-transfer rates, and possible uncertainties in kinetic-rate data, the comparison is reasonably good. The net effect of allowing for radial heat and mass transfer is to increase the conversion. The computed results are sensitive to rather small variations in the effective thermal conductivities and diffusivities and emphasize the need for the best possible information concerning these quantities.

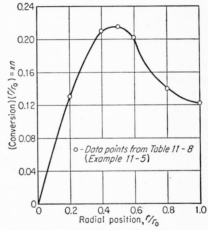

FIG. 11-14. Graph for obtaining mean conversion.

The temperatures shown in Fig. 11-7 represent experimental data for the conditions of this example. The computed values for r/r_0 of 0.0 and 0.6 have been taken from Table 11-7 and plotted as dotted lines on the figure for comparison. Referring to the center data ($r/r_0 = 0$), it is seen that the computed results are about 10 to 20°C below the experimental values, although the location of the hot spot is predicted accurately. The comparison at $r/r_0 = 0.6$ is not so good.

DESIGN OF FLUIDIZED-BED REACTORS

11-7. General Design Features. A description of fluidized-bed reactors and some of their operating characteristics has been given in Chap. 4 and Sec. 11-2 of the present chapter. Heat transfer between the reactor and surroundings was discussed in Chap. 10. The significance of these factors in relation to design will be briefly considered in this section, and then attention devoted to interpreting laboratory rate data and to actual design procedures.

In contrast to fixed-bed operation the mass velocity of fluid through the fluidized-bed reactor cannot be chosen predominantly on the basis of the kinetic requirements. There is a fairly narrow range of velocities within which stable fluidization is possible. These velocities are low, in magnitude of the order of 1 ft/sec. Leva and coworkers[1] have prepared correlations for predicting the minimum mass velocity necessary to attain fluidization in terms of the size and density of the solid particles, density of the fluid stream, and void fraction at the onset of fluidization. This restriction on fluid velocity means that it is not possible to vary the space velocity or residence time in a fluidized bed over so wide a range as in fixed-bed operation.

On the basis of experimental data[2-5] it appears that the rapid mixing of solids results in a nearly uniform temperature throughout the fluidized reactor. This simplifies the problems of design and interpretation of kinetic data, because the rate of reaction then is dependent only on the concentrations of reactants and products. From the temperature standpoint the behavior is similar to that of a well-agitated tank-type reactor.

With regard to mixing of the fluid stream the picture is not so clear. From experimental measurements on mixing of tracer gases Gilliland and Mason[5] concluded that complete radial mixing, along with no longitudinal mixing, approximated the performance of reactors with a large bed height-to-diameter ratio. In large-diameter short beds mixing in the direction of flow (longitudinal direction) is significant. Unless suitable mixing data are available, it appears best to consider a fluidized reactor as a fixed-bed unit so far as mixing in the fluid stream is concerned and as a tank-type reactor with respect to uniformity of temperature. Or to put the case in another way, the fluidized-bed unit behaves like an isothermal fixed-bed reactor.

Most experimental studies[6,7] have found no resistance to external diffusion. The turbulent motion of the solid particles seemingly prevents these diffusional resistances from being significant with respect to those of the surface processes on the catalyst particles.

[1] M. Leva, M. Weintraub, M. Grummer, and H. H. Storch, *Chem. Eng. Progr.*, **44**: 619 (1948).

[2] H. S. Mickley and C. A. Trilling, *Ind. Eng. Chem.*, **41**:1135 (1949).

[3] M. Leva, M. Weintraub, and M. Grummer, *Chem. Eng. Progr.*, **45**:563 (1949).

[4] M. Leva, M. Weintraub, M. Grummer, and M. Pollchik, *Ind. Eng. Chem.*, **41**:1207 (1949).

[5] E. R. Gilliland and E. A. Mason, *Ind. Eng. Chem.*, **41**:1191 (1949).

[6] W. K. Lewis, E. R. Gilliland, and W. A. Reed, *Ind. Eng. Chem.*, **41**:1227 (1949).

[7] W. K. Lewis, E. R. Gilliland, and G. T. McBride, *Ind. Eng. Chem.*, **41**:1213 (1949).

Similarly the resistance to internal, or pore, diffusion is unimportant. The small sizes used for catalyst particles reduce the pore length to such a low value that the effectiveness factor (Sec. 9-11) will be close to unity.

11-8. Interpretation of Laboratory Rate Data. The treatment of kinetic data in fluidized beds follows the same procedure as that for homogeneous and solid catalytic tubular flow reactors, as described in Chaps. 6 and 9. Analysis of integral-reactor data to determine a satisfactory rate equation is possible because of the uniformity of temperature throughout the bed. In fact it is frequently difficult to operate a fluidized-bed unit on a differential basis.

The proposed rate equations should, in principle at least, be based upon the Langmuir-Hinshelwood concepts described in Chap. 9, since processes on solid surfaces are involved. The following example is taken from a study of the reaction between powdered coal and carbon dioxide carried out by Lewis, Gilliland, and McBride.[1] It is a noncatalytic heterogeneous case, but the amount of carbon in the bed was essentially constant during any run. Hence the reactor operated at steady-state conditions and behaved the same as a gas-solid catalytic type.

Example 11-6. On the basis of previous and current work Lewis *et al.*[1] proposed the following rate equation for the reaction

$$C + CO_2 \rightarrow 2CO$$

in a fluidized-bed reactor,

$$r_c = \frac{k_1 p_{co_2}}{1 + k_2 p_{co} + k_3 p_{co_2}} \tag{A}$$

where k_2, k_3 = constants at a fixed temperature, per atm
r_c = rate of decomposition of carbon dioxide, lb moles/(min)(lb of carbon in bed)
p = partial pressure, atm
k_1 = a constant involving the specific-reaction rate, lb moles/(min)(atm)(lb of carbon)

From the concepts developed in Chap. 9 it is apparent that this equation could be developed on the basis of adsorption of carbon monoxide and dioxide on the surface of the carbon. With this interpretation k_1 would include a specific-reaction rate for the controlling process and properties of the carbon surface, while k_2 and k_3 are analogous to adsorption equilibrium constants for carbon monoxide and dioxide.

Lewis and coworkers tested this equation by determining the constancy of k_1, k_2, and k_3 for different feed consumptions. All their experimental data were obtained in a steel reactor which was 1.78 in. ID and 7 ft high. To illustrate the methods employed, compute a single set of constants from the data of Table 11-9 for three runs on anthracite coal.

[1] *Ibid.*

TABLE 11-9

	Run		
	W21	W13	W15
Inlet flow rates, lb moles/min			
CO_2	4.843×10^{-4}	0.657×10^{-4}	2.693×10^{-4}
CO	0.366×10^{-4}	4.41×10^{-4}	2.333×10^{-4}
N_2	0.013×10^{-4}	0.156×10^{-4}	0.082×10^{-4}
Exit gas			
Total rate, lb moles/min........	8.02×10^{-4}	6.05×10^{-4}	6.83×10^{-4}
Mole % CO_2.................	34.7	6.2	22.2
Weight of carbon in bed, lb.......	2.54	2.90	2.78
Temperature, °F................	1775	1775	1775
Total pressure (mean), atm.......	1.12	1.12	1.12

Solution. The conversion of carbon dioxide leaving the fluidized bed can be computed for each run. For the first

$$x_1 = \frac{4.843 - 8.02 \times 0.347}{4.843} = 0.427$$

Results for the other runs are 0.430 and 0.438. These conversions indicate that integral operation is attained. Hence the design equation will have to be integrated to take into account the significant variations in partial pressures.

If W represents the mass of carbon in the bed, the usual design equation for catalytic reactors is applicable,

$$F \, dx = r_c \, dW \qquad (B)$$

where F = feed rate of carbon dioxide

x = the conversion

Equation (B) assumes no mixing longitudinally in the bed. Errors due to this assumption for fluidized reactors are considered in Sec. 11-9.

In order to integrate Eq. (B), the rate equation must be expressed in terms of x. Suppose the molal flow rate of CO_2 is N_{CO_2}, that for CO is N_{CO}, and nitrogen N_N. If the rate entering the reactor is designated with the subscript zero, the molal rate at any position will be

$$N_{CO_2} = (N_0)_{CO_2}(1 - x) = F(1 - x)$$
$$N_{CO} = (N_0)_{CO} + 2Fx$$
$$N_N = (N_0)_N$$
$$\text{Total } N_t = [(N_0)_{CO_2} + (N_0)_{CO} + (N_0)_N] + Fx = (N_0)_t + Fx$$

Then each partial pressure in terms of x will be given by

$$p_{CO_2} = \frac{F(1 - x)}{(N_0)_t + Fx} p_t$$
$$p_{CO} = \frac{(N_0)_{CO} + 2Fx}{(N_0)_t + Fx} p_t$$

Employing these values in the rate equation (A), and simplifying, yields

$$r_c = \frac{k_1 F(1 - x)p_t}{[(N_0)_t + Fx] + k_2[(N_0)_{CO} + 2Fx]p_t + k_3 F(1 - x)p_t} \qquad (C)$$

This result can now be substituted in the design equation to obtain an expression which contains only x and W as variables.

$$F \, dx = \frac{k_1 F(1 - x)p_t \, dW}{[(N_0)_t + Fx] + k_2[(N_0)_{CO} + 2Fx]p_t + k_3 F(1 - x)p_t}$$

Rearranging for integration gives the form

$$dW = \alpha \frac{dx}{1 - x} + \beta \frac{x \, dx}{1 - x} \qquad (D)$$

where
$$\alpha = \frac{(N_0)_t + k_2(N_0)_{CO}p_t + k_3 F p_t}{k_1 p_t} \qquad (E)$$

$$\beta = \frac{F + 2k_2 p_t F - k_3 F p_t}{k_1 p_t} \qquad (F)$$

Integrating Eq. (D) and applying the boundary condition, $x = 0$ at $W = 0$ and $x = x_1$ at $W = W_1$, yield

$$W_1 = -(\alpha + \beta) \ln (1 - x_1) - \beta x_1 \qquad (G)$$

Since values of W_1 and x_1 are known for each run, three equations of the form of (G) can be written, one for each run. Along with the definitions of α and β from Eqs. (F) and (E), the three equations may be solved for k_1, k_2, and k_3. For run $W21$, Eq. (G) becomes

$$2.54 = -(\alpha_1 + \beta_1) \ln (1 - 0.427) - \beta_1 \times 0.427 \qquad (H)$$

From Eqs. (E) and (F) α and β for this run are

$$\alpha_1 = \frac{(4.843 + 0.366 + 0.013) + 0.366 \times 1.12 \times k_2 + 4.843 \times 1.12 \times k_3}{1.12 k_1}$$
$$\times 10^{-4} \qquad (I)$$

$$\beta_1 = \frac{4.843 + 2 \times 1.12 \times 4.843 \times k_2 - 4.843 \times 1.12 \times k_3}{1.12 k_1} \times 10^{-4} \qquad (J)$$

Equations (H), (I), and (J) constitute one relationship between k_1, k_2, and k_3. Runs $W13$ and $W15$ each provides a similar relationship, obtained by substituting the appropriate numbers from Table 11-9 in Eqs. (G), (E), and (F).

Solving these three relationships simultaneously gives the following approximate results:

$$k_1 = 3.8 \times 10^{-4} \text{ lb mole/(min)(atm)(lb of carbon)}$$
$$k_2 = 3.6 \text{ atm}^{-1}$$
$$k_3 = 0.8 \text{ atm}^{-1}$$

11-9. Design Procedures. Except for the possibility of longitudinal mixing, the design methods outlined in Sec. 11-4 for isothermal, fixed-bed reactors are applicable to fluidized systems. The rate of reaction is a function of composition only, and the design equation relating the mass of catalyst particles to the exit conversion can frequently be integrated analytically. The problem is simply the variation of Example 11-6 for which the rate equation is known and the exit conversion the required quantity.

If the rate of reaction is high, particularly in short reactors with large diameters, longitudinal mixing can invalidate the simple analogy to a fixed-bed reactor. Provided effective diffusivity data are available, the design equation can be modified to take such mixing into account. For a first-order rate equation the results can be obtained in analytical form, while for more complex rate expressions numerical integration is necessary.

Gilliland and Mason[1] measured effective diffusivities in tubes 1 to 4 in. ID and 3.3 to 6 ft long. Air was used to fluidize (in batch operation, as far as the solid flow was concerned) microspheres[2] and glass beads covering a size range of 65- to 200-mesh. Their preliminary results were correlated by the expression

$$\frac{u}{D_L} = 2.6 \left(\frac{1}{u}\right)^{0.61} \qquad (11\text{-}17)$$

where u = superficial velocity, ft/sec
D_L = effective longitudinal diffusivity, sq ft/sec

If an element of reactor of length dz is chosen, a mass balance for steady-state operation requires

(Input by diffusion and mass velocity)
     − (output by diffusion and mass velocity)
         = (removal by reaction)   (11-18)

Suppose the reaction is first-order and may be represented by the equation

$$A \rightarrow B$$

The rate expression, in terms of concentration, is

$$r_c = k_1 C = \text{(moles reacting)(time)}^{-1}\text{(mass of catalyst)}^{-1}$$
$$C = \text{concentration of } A, \text{ (moles)(volume)}^{-1}$$

The rate of diffusion in terms of the effective diffusivity is

$$\text{(Moles)(time)}^{-1}\text{(cross-sectional area)}^{-1} = -D_L \frac{dC}{dz}$$

---

[1] *Loc. cit.*
[2] Silica-alumina petroleum cracking catalyst.

The mass balance for component A, per unit cross-sectional area, may be written mathematically in the following form:

$$\left(-D_L \frac{dC}{dz} + uC \right) - \left[-D_L \left(\frac{dC}{dz} + \frac{d^2C}{dz^2} \, dz \right) + u \left(C + \frac{dC}{dz} \, dz \right) \right]$$
$$= (k_1 C) \rho_B \, dz$$

Simplifying this expression yields

$$D_L \frac{d^2C}{dz^2} - u \frac{dC}{dz} - k_1 \rho_B C = 0 \tag{11-19}$$

where ρ_B = bulk density of fluidized solid
u = velocity of reaction gas through bed
Equation (11-19) is based upon the assumption of a constant velocity, u, and diffusivity, D_L.
The boundary conditions on this differential equation are

$$\begin{aligned} z &= 0 \text{ (bottom of bed)} & C &= C_0 \\ z &= \infty & C &= 0 \text{ (irreversible reaction)} \end{aligned} \tag{11-20}$$

Solving Eq. (11-19) and applying the boundary conditions lead to the result

$$C = C_0 e^{\gamma z} \tag{11-21}$$

where
$$\gamma = \frac{1}{2} \frac{u}{D_L} \left(1 - \sqrt{1 + \frac{4k_1 \rho_B D_L}{u^2}} \right) \tag{11-22}$$

If the total length of the reactor is L and the exit concentration is C_1, Eq. (11-21) may be written

$$C_1 = C_0 e^{\gamma L} \tag{11-23}$$

The exit conversion x_1 is given by the expression

$$x_1 = \frac{u(C_0 - C_1)}{uC_0} = 1 - \frac{C_1}{C_0} \tag{11-24}$$

Then combining Eqs. (11-23) and (11-24) gives x_1 in terms of the length of reactor, diffusivity, and specific-reaction rate k_1.

$$x_1 = 1 - e^{\gamma L} \tag{11-25}$$

It is interesting to compare this result with that for the case of no longitudinal mixing. In this case $D_L = 0$, and the solution of Eq. (11-19) is

$$C_1 = C_0 e^{-k_1 \rho_B L/u} \tag{11-26}$$

The conversion according to Eq. (11-24) will become

$$(x_1)_{\text{ideal}} = 1 - e^{-k_1 \rho_B L/u} \tag{11-27}$$

Equations (11-25) and (11-27) permit a comparison between the results for no mixing and those based upon a finite value of D_L.

More data for the diffusivity are desirable, particularly on the effect of the dimensions of the reactor, in order to clarify the importance of mixing in fluidized-bed reactors.

Example 11-7. Suppose the first-order reaction $A \rightarrow B$ has a value of $k_1 = 0.076$ cu ft/(sec)(lb of catalyst) at the operating temperature in a fluidized reactor. The superficial velocity is 1.0 ft/sec, the bulk density of the catalyst 5.25 lb/cu ft, and the bed length 5 ft.

Assuming that the diffusivity correlation of Eq. (11-17) is applicable, calculate the exit conversion.

What error would be made if longitudinal mixing were neglected?

Solution. To apply Eq. (11-25), γ must be evaluated.

From Eq. (11-17)

$$\frac{u}{D_L} = 2.6 \left(\frac{1}{1}\right)^{0.61}$$
$$= 2.6 \text{ ft}^{-1}$$

$$\frac{k_1 \rho_B D_L}{u^2} = \frac{0.076 \times 5.25}{2.6 \times 1} = 0.154 \text{ (dimensionless)}$$

Then from Eq. (11-22)

$$\gamma = \tfrac{1}{2} \times 2.6(1 - \sqrt{1 + 4 \times 0.154})$$
$$= -0.35 \text{ ft}^{-1}$$

Now the conversion can be obtained from Eq. (11-25),

$$x_1 = 1 - e^{-0.35 \times 5} = 1 - 0.174$$
$$= 0.826, \text{ or } 82.6\%$$

If longitudinal diffusion were neglected, the conversion is obtained from Eq. (11-27).

$$\frac{k_1 \rho_B L}{u} = \frac{0.076 \times 5.25 \times 5}{1} = 2$$

$$(x_1)_{\text{ideal}} = 1 - e^{-2} = 1 - 0.136$$
$$= 0.864, \text{ or } 86.4\%$$

The effect of diffusion is to reduce the conversion. This reduction results because mixing lowers the reactant concentration, and hence the rate of reaction, in the bottom of the reactor, where most of the conversion takes place.

NOMENCLATURE

A_c Cross-sectional area
A_R Wall heat-transfer area/per unit length of reactor
C Concentration, (moles)(volume)$^{-1}$
c_p Specific heat at constant pressure

c_{p_m} Mean specific heat
D_e Effective diffusivity in radial direction
D_L Effective diffusivity in longitudinal direction
d_p Catalyst particle diameter
F Feed rate
G Superficial mass velocity, lb/(hr)(sq ft)
ΔH Heat of reaction
h_w Heat-transfer coefficient at wall of reactor
k_e Effective thermal conductivity
L Number of longitudinal increments of size Δz
M_m Mean molecular weight
n Number of radial increments of size Δr
N_i Molal rate of flow of component i
M_m Mean molecular weight
Pe_m Peclet number for mass transfer, $d_p u / D_e$
Pe_h Peclet number for heat transfer, $d_p c_p G / k_e$
Q'_s Heat-transfer rate from reactor to surroundings
r Radial distance measured from center of reactor tube
r_0 Radius of reactor
r_c Catalytic rate of reaction, (moles)(time)$^{-1}$(mass of catalyst)$^{-1}$
T Absolute temperature
t_m Bulk mean temperature of reaction mixture
t_w Wall temperature
u Superficial velocity in longitudinal direction in reactor
W Mass of catalyst in reactor
x Conversion, fraction of a reactant converted
y Mole fraction of a component in a gaseous mixture
y_0 Mole fraction in feed stream
m_i Weight rate of flow of component i
z Longitudinal distance in reactor
δ Bulk void fraction in a catalytic reactor
ϵ Emissivity of solid particles in packed-bed reactor
ρ_B Bulk density of solid catalyst in reactor

PROBLEMS

1. Suppose that it were possible to operate an ethyl benzene dehydrogenation reactor under approximately isothermal conditions. If the temperature is 650°C, prepare a conversion vs. catalyst-bed-depth curve which extends to the equilibrium conversion. The catalyst to be used is that for which rate data were presented in Example 11-1. Additional data are as follows:

Diameter of catalyst tube = 3 ft
Feed rate per tube
    Ethyl benzene = 8.0 lb moles/hr
    Steam = 225 lb moles/hr
Bulk density of catalyst as packed = 90 lb/cu ft
Equilibrium-constant data are given in Example 11-1.

2. In this case assume that the reactor in Prob. 1 operates adiabatically and that the entrance temperature is 650°C. If the heat of reaction is $\Delta H = 60,000$ Btu/lb mole, compare the conversion vs. bed-depth curve with that obtained in Prob. 1.

3. In the German phthalic anhydride process,[1-3] naphthalene is passed over a vanadium pentoxide (on silica gel) catalyst at a temperature of about 350°C. Analysis of the available data indicates that the rate of reaction (r = pound moles of naphthalene reacted to phthalic anhydride per hour per pound of catalyst) can be empirically represented by the expression

$$r_c = 305 \times 10^5 p^{0.38} e^{-28,000/RT}$$

where p = partial pressure of naphthalene, atm

T = °K

The reactants consist of 0.90 mole per cent naphthalene vapor and 99.1 per cent air. Although there will be some complete oxidation to carbon dioxide and water vapor, it will be satisfactory to assume that the only reaction is the following one, as long as the temperature does not exceed 400°C:

$$C_{10}H_8 + 4.5O_2 \rightarrow C_8H_4O_3 + 2H_2O + 2CO_2$$

The heat of this reaction is $\Delta H = -6300$ Btu/lb of naphthalene, but use a value of -7300 Btu/lb in order to take into account the increased heat release due to the small amount of complete oxidation. (The properties of the reaction mixture may be taken equivalent to those for air.)

It is desired to determine how large the reactor tubes can be and still not exceed the maximum temperature of 400°C. The reactor will be designed to operate at a conversion of 80 per cent and have a production rate of 6,000 lb/day of phthalic anhydride. It will be a multitube type (illustrated in Fig. 11-1) with heat-transfer salt (HTS) circulated through the jacket. The temperature of the entering reactants will be raised to 340°C by preheating, and the circulating HTS will maintain the inside of the reactor-tube walls at 340°C.

Determine temperature vs. catalyst-bed-depth curves, using tubes of three different sizes, 1.0, 2.0, and 3.0 in. ID, and in so doing ascertain how large the tubes can be and still not exceed the maximum permissible temperature of 400°C (i.e., the temperature at which complete oxidation becomes excessive).

The catalyst will consist of 0.20- by 0.20-in. cylinders, and the bulk density of the packed bed may be taken as 50 lb/cu ft for each size tube.[4]

The superficial mass velocity of gases through each tube will be 400 lb/(hr)(sq ft of tube area).

Use the simplified design procedure, neglecting radial gradients in the catalyst tubes.

4. In order to compare different batches of catalysts for fixed-bed cracking operations, it is desired to develop a numerical catalyst activity. This is to be accomplished by comparing each batch with a so-called standard catalyst for which the x vs. W/F curve is known.

If the activity of a batch is defined as the rate of reaction of that batch divided by the rate for the standard catalyst at the same conditions, which of the following two procedures would be a true measure of the catalyst activity?

a. Determine from the curves the values of W/F required to obtain the same conversion x, and call the activity the ratio

$$\frac{(W/F)_{\text{standard}}}{(W/F)_{\text{actual}}}$$

---

[1] FIAT report 984,649.

[2] BIOS reports 1597, 957, 753, and 666.

[3] CIOS report XXVIII 29, XXVII 80 and 89.

[4] This represents an approximation, since the bulk density will depend to some extent upon the tube size, especially in the small-diameter cases.

b. Determine from the curves the values of x at the same W/F, and call the activity the ratio

$$\frac{x_{\text{actual}}}{x_{\text{standard}}}$$

Also, sketch the x vs. W/F curves for a standard catalyst and a curve for a catalyst with an activity less than unity.

5. It is necessary to design a reactor system to produce styrene by the vapor-phase catalytic dehydrogenation of ethyl benzene. The reaction is endothermic, and hence operation must be carried out at elevated temperatures in order to obtain reasonable conversions.

The plant capacity is to be 20 tons of crude styrene (styrene, benzene, and toluene) per day. Determine the bulk volume of catalyst and the number of tubes in the reactor by the simplified method. Assume that two reactors will be necessary in order to obtain continuous production of 20 tons/day, one reactor being in operation while the catalyst is being regenerated in the other. Determine also the composition of the crude styrene product from the reactors.

With the catalyst proposed for the plant, three reactions may be significant. These are as follows:

1: $\qquad\qquad$ $C_6H_5C_2H_5 \rightarrow C_6H_5CH{=}CH_2 + H_2$
2: $\qquad\qquad$ $C_6H_5C_2H_5 \rightarrow C_6H_6 + C_2H_4$
3: $\qquad\qquad$ $H_2 + C_6H_5C_2H_5 \rightarrow C_6H_5CH_3 + CH_4$

The mechanism of each reaction can be considered to follow the stoichiometry indicated by the preceding reactions just as though they were homogeneous and no catalyst was involved. The specific-reaction velocity constants determined for the different catalyst by Wenner and Dybdal[1] are as follows:

$$\log k_1 = \frac{-11{,}370}{4.575T} + 0.883$$

$$\log k_2 = \frac{-50{,}800}{4.575T} + 9.13$$

$$\log k_3 = \frac{-21{,}800}{4.575T} + 2.78$$

where $T = {}^\circ K$

k_1 = lb moles styrene produced/(hr)(atm)(lb of catalyst)
k_2 = lb moles benzene produced/(hr)(atm)(lb of catalyst)
k_3 = lb moles toluene produced/(hr)(atm)^2(lb of catalyst)

The over-all equilibrium constants for the three reactions are as follows:

Temp, °C	K		
	Reaction 1	Reaction 2	Reaction 3
400	1.7×10^{-3}	2.7×10^{-2}	5.6×10^4
500	2.5×10^{-2}	3.1×10^{-1}	1.4×10^4
600	2.3×10^{-1}	2.0	4.4×10^3
700	1.4	8.0	1.8×10^3

[1] *Loc. cit.* This problem is taken from an example suggested by these authors.

The reactor will be heated by flue gas passed countercurrent (outside the tubes) to the reaction mixture in the reactor tubes. The reactant stream entering the reactor will be entirely ethyl benzene. Additional design data and assumptions are as follows:

Reactor tubes: ID 4.03 in.
          OD 4.50 in.
          Length 15 ft

Feed: 425 lb of ethyl benzene/(hr)(tube)
      Feed temperature = 550°C $= 1022°$ *Entering* $= 823°K$

Catalyst: Pellet size = 0.0167 ft
        Bulk density = 61 lb/cu ft

Flue gas: Rate = 6,520 lb/(hr)(tube)
        Temperature leaving reactor = 1600°F

Pressure: Entering reactor = 44 psia
        Leaving reactor = 29 psia

Heat-transfer coefficient between reaction mixture and flue gas = 9.0 Btu/(hr)(sq ft) (°F) (based on outside area).

THERMODYNAMIC DATA

    Average sp heat of reaction mixture = 0.63 Btu/(lb)(°F)
    Average sp heat of flue gas = 0.28 Btu/(lb)(°F)
    Average heat of reaction 1, ΔH_1 = 53,600 Btu/lb mole
    Average heat of reaction 2, ΔH_2 = 43,900 Btu/lb mole
    Average heat of reaction 3, ΔH_3 = −27,700 Btu/lb mole

To simplify the calculations assume that the pressure drop is directly proportional to the length of catalyst tube. Point out the reasons for error in this assumption, and describe a more accurate approach.

6. A pilot plant for the hydrogenation of nitrobenzene is to be designed, using the rate data of Wilson (see Example 11-3).

The reactor will consist of a 1-in.-I.D. tube packed with catalyst. The feed, 2.0 mole per cent nitrobenzene and 98 per cent hydrogen, will enter at 150°C at a rate of 0.25 lb mole/hr. To reduce temperature variations, the wall temperature of the tube will be maintained at 150°C by a constant-temperature bath. The heat-transfer coefficient between reaction mixture and wall may be taken equal to 20 Btu/(hr) (sq ft)(°F).

Determine the temperature and conversion as a function of catalyst bed depth to cover a conversion range of 0 to 90 per cent. Convert the rate equation in Example 11-3 to a form where r_c is expressed in pound moles of nitrobenzene reacting per hour per pound of catalyst by taking the void fraction equal to 0.424 and the bulk density of catalyst as 60 lb/cu ft.

The heat of reaction is a constant value of − 274,000 Btu/lb mole. The properties of the reaction mixture may be assumed to be the same as those for hydrogen.

7. Using the semirigorous method, compute the conversion for bed depths up to 0.30 ft for the oxidation of sulfur dioxide under conditions similar to those described in Examples 11-4 and 11-5.

The same reactor conditions apply except for (1) the superficial mass velocity, which in the present case is 147 lb/(hr)(sq ft) and (2) the temperature profile at the entrance to the reactor. For this lower mass velocity the temperatures are as shown in Table 11-10.

TABLE 11-10. ENTRANCE-TEMPERATURE PROFILE

t, °C	r/r_0
352.0	0.797
397.5	0.534
400.4	0.248
401.5	0.023
401.2	0.233
397.4	0.474
361.2	0.819
197	1.00

For comparison purposes the experimentally measured conversions are as shown in Table 11-11.

TABLE 11-11

Catalyst bed, in.	% SO_2 converted
0	0
0.531	26.9
0.875	30.7
1.76	37.8
4.23	41.2
5.68	42.1

8. Using the results of Example 11-6, determine the fraction of the carbon dioxide decomposed by a fluidized bed of carbon for the following conditions:
Inlet flow rates, lb moles/min

$$CO_2 = 2.654 \times 10^{-4}$$
$$CO = 2.333 \times 10^{-4}$$
$$N_2 = 0.082 \times 10^{-4}$$
$$\text{Weight of carbon in bed, lb} = 2.76$$
$$\text{Temperature, °F} = 1775$$
$$\text{Total pressure, atm} = 1.12$$

The reactor is 1.78 in. ID and 7 ft high as in Example 11-6.

9. A first-order, gaseous reaction

$$A \rightarrow B$$

is carried out in a fluidized bed at 500°F and 2 atm pressure. At this temperature $k_1 = 0.05$ cu ft/(sec)(lb of catalyst). The bulk density of the catalyst bed is 3 lb/cu ft at a superficial mass velocity of 0.15 lb/(sec)(sq ft). If the bed height is 10 ft, what will be the exit conversion? The molecular weight of component A is 44.

10. Repeat Prob. 9 for case of a reversible reaction for which the equilibrium constant is 0.6.

11. A reaction

$$2A \rightarrow B$$

is being studied in a fluidized reactor at atmospheric pressure and 200°F. It appears that the rate of reaction may be approximated by a second-order irreversible equation

$$r_c = k_2 p_A^2$$

where k_2 = lb moles/(sec)(atm)^2(lb of catalyst).

At the operating temperature $k_2 = 4.0 \times 10^{-6}$. The linear velocity in the reactor is 1.0 ft/sec, and the bulk density of the fluidized catalyst 4.0 lb/cu ft.

    a. Calculate the conversion of A, neglecting longitudinal diffusion, for bed heights of 5, 10, and 15 ft.

    b. Correct for the effect of longitudinal diffusion, using the diffusivity data expressed by Eq. (11-17).

APPENDIX A

SECTIONS 3-9 TO 3-12

3-9. Application of Absolute Rate Theory. *Atomic Reactions.* If in the reaction

$$A + B \rightarrow C + D$$

A and B are atoms, the absolute rate theory leads to a result that is identical with the collision-theory prediction. In this case the reactants each possess three translational and no rotational or vibrational contributions to their total partition function. The activated complex will have three translational, two rotational (linear molecule), and one vibrational contribution. The one vibrational degree of freedom will be along the path of decomposition. These facts may be represented mathematically by the expressions

$$Q_A = Q_{t_a}^3 = \frac{(2\pi m_A k_B T)^{\frac{3}{2}}}{h^3} \tag{3-47}$$

$$Q_B = Q_{t_B}^3 = \frac{(2\pi m_B k_B T)^{\frac{3}{2}}}{h^3} \tag{3-48}$$

The partition function of the activated complex, without its vibrational contribution, will be

$$Q_{AB}^* \text{ (activated complex)} = (Q_t^*)^3 (Q_r^*)^2 \tag{3-49}$$

or

$$Q_{AB}^* = \frac{[2\pi(m_A + m_B)k_B T]^{\frac{3}{2}}}{h^3} \frac{8\pi^2 k_B T}{h^2} I^* \tag{3-50}$$

where m_A, m_B = masses of atoms of atoms A and B
I = moment of inertia of linear complex
The specific-reaction rate for such a reaction is given by Eq. (3-46).

$$k = \frac{k_B T}{h} e^{-\Delta E_0/RT} \frac{Q_{AB}^*}{Q_A Q_B} = k_B T e^{-\Delta E_0/RT} \frac{[2\pi(m_A + m_B)k_B T]^{\frac{3}{2}} 8\pi^2 k_B T I^*}{(2\pi k_B T m_A)^{\frac{3}{2}} (2\pi k_B T m_B)^{\frac{3}{2}}} \tag{3-51}$$

This expression may be simplified to the following form:

$$k = 2\sqrt{2}\,(\pi k_B T)^{\frac{1}{2}} \left(\frac{m_A + m_B}{m_A m_B}\right)^{\frac{3}{2}} I^* e^{-\Delta E_0/RT} \tag{3-52}$$

373

The moment of inertia I^* is given by the equation

$$I^* = \sigma_{AB}^2 \frac{m_A m_B}{m_A + m_B} \tag{3-53}$$

Substitution of Eq. (3-53) into Eq. (3-52) yields the final expression for the specific-reaction rate,

$$k = \sigma_{AB}^2 (8\pi k_B T)^{\frac{1}{2}} \left(\frac{m_A + m_B}{m_A m_B} \right)^{\frac{1}{2}} e^{-\Delta E_0/RT} \tag{3-54}$$

It will be observed that this result is the same as predicted by the collision theory. This is as it should be, since for an atomic reaction the only energy contributions available are either translational or rotational. Similarly the classical treatment used to obtain the expression for the number of collisions included only translation and rotational possibilities for energy absorption (hard-sphere concept).

Molecular Reactions. For molecular reactions the possibility of vibrational degrees of freedom leads to an expression considerably different from Eq. (3-54). For example, consider the second order gas-phase decomposition of hydrogen iodide.

$$2HI \rightarrow H\!-\!I \rightarrow I_2 + H_2$$
$$\begin{matrix} | & | \\ H\!-\!I & \end{matrix}$$

where the intermediate step represents the activated complex. In this case the HI molecule possesses $3n - 5 = 1$ vibrational degree of freedom and the activated complex $3 \times 4 - 6$, or 6 vibrational degrees of freedom. Of these six, one is along the path of decomposition. Hence the partition functions for reactant and activated complex are

$$Q_{HI} = \frac{(2\pi m_{HI} k_B T)^{\frac{3}{2}}}{h^3} \frac{8\pi^2 k_B T I_{HI}}{h^2} (1 - e^{-h v_{HI}/k_B T})^{-1} \tag{3-55}$$

and $$Q^* = \frac{(4\pi m_{HI} k_B T)^{\frac{3}{2}}}{h^3} \frac{8\pi^2 (8\pi^3 A^* B^* C^*)^{\frac{1}{2}} (k_B T)^{\frac{3}{2}}}{h^3} \prod_{i=1}^{5} (1 - e^{-h v_i/k_B T})^{-1} \tag{3-56}$$

In the first equation I_{HI} is the moment of inertia of the molecule HI and v_{HI} the vibration frequency of HI. In the second $A^* B^* C^*$ represents the product of the three principal moments of inertia of the nonlinear activated complex, and the last factor on the right represents the product of the five vibration contributions, one for each of the five stable fundamental vibration frequencies v_i.

The specific-reaction rate is given by substitution of Eqs. (3-55) and (3-56) into Eq. (3-46).

It is apparent that the result will be very complex in comparison with the result for atomic reactions and that the complexity increases with the number of atoms involved in the reactants. Also the problem of assigning the most probable structure for the activated complex becomes extremely difficult. Assignment of this structure is necessary before the evaluation of the principal moments of inertia and the fundamental vibration frequencies can be made. On the other hand the flexibility of the final equation for k is much greater than possible from the simple collision concept. Hence such theoretical expressions are in line with the great variation in rates, from one reaction to another, observed experimentally.

The theory of absolute reaction rates is capable of predicting that the rate between complex molecules may be of the order of 10^{-5} of that between atoms. This result can be shown in a semiquantitative manner[1] by making the assumption that the partition functions for vibration, rotation, and translation have constant values. While individual vibrational partition functions may differ from each other by a large amount percentagewise, they are all of the same order of magnitude in comparison with rotational and translational partition functions. Thus vibrational contributions are generally near unity, rotational ones about 10, and translational about 10^8.

The equation for the partition functions for each reactant in the reaction

$$A + B \rightarrow A \cdot B$$

can be written

$$Q_A = Q_t^3 Q_r^3 Q_v^{3n_A - 6}$$
$$Q_B = Q_t^3 Q_r^3 Q_v^{3n_B - 6}$$

assuming that A contains n_A atoms and B contains n_B atoms. Similarly the activated-complex partition function will be

$$Q_{AB}^* = Q_t^3 Q_r^3 Q_v^{3(n_A + n_B) - 7}$$

Hence the specific-reaction rate is

$$k = \frac{k_B T}{h} \frac{Q_v^{3(n_A + n_B) - 7}}{Q_t^3 Q_r^3 Q_v^{3(n_A + n_B) - 12}} e^{-\Delta E_0 / RT} = \frac{k_B T}{h} \frac{Q_v^5}{Q_t^3 Q_r^3} e^{-\Delta E_0 / RT} \qquad (3\text{-}57)$$

For an atomic reaction

$$k = \frac{k_B T}{h} \frac{Q_t^3 Q_r^2}{Q_t^3 Q_t^3} e^{-\Delta E_0 / RT} = \frac{k_B T}{h} \frac{Q_r^2}{Q_t^3} e^{-\Delta E_0 / RT} \qquad (3\text{-}58)$$

[1] Following the development of K. J. Laidler, "Chemical Kinetics," p. 72, McGraw-Hill Book Company, Inc., New York, 1950.

Then the ratio of k for the complex reaction from Eq. (3-57) to k for the simple atomic reaction from Eq. (3-58) is given, approximately, by the expression

$$\frac{k_{\text{complex}}}{k_{\text{atomic}}} = \frac{Q_v^5/Q_i^3 Q_r^3}{Q_r^2/Q_t^3} = \left(\frac{Q_v}{Q_r}\right)^5 \tag{3-59}$$

Taking $Q_v = 1.0$ and $Q_r = 10$, this ratio is 10^{-5}. The k for an atomic reaction computed by the absolute theory is the same as that predicted by the collision theory. Hence 10^{-5} is also a possible value for the ratio of k (absolute theory) to k (collision theory) for a complex reaction.

3-10. Thermodynamic Representation of the Absolute Reaction Rate Theory. Equation (3-46) can be written in terms of the equilibrium constant K^* of the activated complex shorn of its decomposition vibration contribution. This is accomplished by utilizing the relationship between the equilibrium constant and the partition function, for this form of the activated complex,

$$K^* = \frac{Q_{AB}^*}{Q_A Q_B} e^{-\Delta E_0/RT} \tag{3-60}[1]$$

Combining this result with Eq. (3-46) gives

$$k = \frac{k_B T}{h} K^* \tag{3-61}$$

From the thermodynamic expression for the equilibrium constant, K^* can be expressed in terms of an enthalpy and entropy change for the activation step. Thus the equilibrium constant is related to ΔF^* as follows:

$$\Delta F^* = -RT \ln K^*$$

At constant temperature

$$\Delta F^* = \Delta H^* - T \,\Delta S^*$$
So
$$K^* = e^{-\Delta F^*/RT} = e^{\Delta S^*/R - \Delta H^*/RT} \tag{3-62}$$

Substituting this result into Eq. (3-61) yields

$$k = \frac{k_B T}{h} e^{\Delta S^*/R - \Delta H^*/RT} \tag{3-63}$$

Equation (3-63) provides a method of predicting the rate of reaction from the thermodynamic properties of the reactants and activated complex. If the structure of the activated complex can be predicted, its enthalpy of formation and absolute entropy can be estimated. Then the

[1] Note that at zero temperature the vibration contribution to ΔE_0 due to the decomposition degree of freedom would be zero, so that ΔE_0 is the same as in Eq. (3-38).

entropy and enthalpy of activation are

$$\Delta S^* = S^* - S_R$$
$$\Delta H^* = \Delta H^* - \Delta H_R$$

where S_R and ΔH_R refer to the reactants and S^* and ΔH^* refer to the activated complex. One method of estimating these thermodynamic properties is through evaluation of the partition functions. Using this approach leads directly back to the other form of the specific-reaction-rate equation, namely, Eq. (3-46). In some cases other means of estimating the entropy and enthalpy of activation can be used, such as illustrated in Example 3-8.

3-11. Units. In Eq. (3-61) the units of the group $k_B T/h$ are per second (i.e., frequency units). For a unimolecular reaction the equilibrium constant is dimensionless, and the units of k are reciprocal seconds. However, for a multiple-order reaction K^* is not dimensionless, and the units of k will depend upon the units of the equilibrium constant. In the development of Eq. (3-61), K^* was expressed as $C_{AB*}/C_A C_B$ and would have the units liters per gram mole or cubic centimeters per molecule. The specific-reaction rate k is then given in terms of liters per gram mole per second or cubic centimeters per molecule per second. For a gaseous reaction the equilibrium constant could also be expressed in pressure units (i.e., atmospheres). In this case the specific-reaction velocity k_p would have the units per atmosphere per second (for a second-order reaction).

3-12. Enthalpy and Energy of Activation. In the thermodynamic representation of the specific-reaction rate [Eq. (3-63)] the enthalpy of activation ΔH^* is not exactly equal to the energy of activation E, determined experimentally from the Arrhenius equation. The relationship between the two quantities is different for gas- and liquid-phase reactions and will be considered for each case separately.

The true-equilibrium constant K in terms of activities is related to the enthalpy change by the equation

$$\frac{d \ln K}{dT} = \frac{\Delta H}{RT^2} \tag{3-64}$$

For a liquid-phase reaction the standard state is normally a 1-molal solution. If the liquid is an ideal solution, the equilibrium constant expressed in terms of concentrations K_c is equal to K. Hence for the formation of the activated complex under ideal-solution conditions,

$$\frac{d \ln K_c^*}{dT} = \frac{\Delta H^*}{RT^2}$$

Differentiating the equation for k in terms of K^* [Eq. (3-61)] with respect to temperature,

$$\frac{d \ln k_c}{dT} = \frac{1}{T} + \frac{d \ln K_c^*}{dT} \qquad (3\text{-}65)[1]$$

and combining this result with the enthalpy relationship gives

$$\frac{d \ln k_c}{dT} = \frac{1}{T} + \frac{\Delta H^*}{RT^2} \qquad (3\text{-}66)$$

The activation energy is determined experimentally from the Arrhenius equation (3-24) by plotting $\ln k$ vs. $1/T$. If the experimental data are interpreted in terms of a rate constant in concentration units, the activation energy will be E_c, according to the equation

$$\ln k_c = \ln A - \frac{E_c}{RT} \qquad (3\text{-}67)$$

Combining Eqs. (3-67) and (3-66) gives

$$E_c = RT + \Delta H^* \qquad (3\text{-}68)$$

which is the desired relationship between the enthalpy of activation and the experimental energy of activation.

It is sometimes desirable to write the thermodynamic expression for the specific-reaction rate in terms of the energy of activation. This can be done by substituting ΔH^* from Eq. (3-68) into Eq. (3-63). The result is

$$k_c = e \frac{k_B T}{h} e^{\Delta S^*/R} e^{-E_c/RT} \qquad (3\text{-}69)$$

It is apparent from this equation that the frequency factor A in the Arrhenius theory is related to the entropy of activation as follows:

$$A = e \frac{k_B T}{h} e^{\Delta S^*/R} \qquad (3\text{-}70)$$

For a gaseous reaction the situation is different. The standard state of each component is not a concentration of 1 mole/liter, but instead unit fugacity, or 1 atm pressure in the case of perfect gases. Hence the equilibrium constant in Eq. (3-64) is not equal to K_c but instead to K_p. If as before the rate constant is in concentration units (that is, k_c), Eqs. (3-68) and (3-69) are not correct. It is necessary to develop new equations based upon the relationship between K_c and K_p. Since the concentration is related to the partial pressure by the expression $p = CRT$, the two equilibrium constants are related in the following way,

$$K_p = \frac{p_C^c p_D^d}{p_A^a p_B^b} = K_c (RT)^{c+d-(a+b)} = K_c (RT)^{+\Delta n}$$

where Δn represents the change in number of moles as a result of reaction.

<hr>

[1] The subscript c is employed to indicate that concentration units are used.

Then according to Eq. (3-64)

$$\frac{d \ln K_p^*}{dT} = \frac{d \ln [K_c^*(RT)^{\Delta n}]}{dT} = \frac{d \ln K_c^*}{dT} + \frac{d \ln (RT)^{\Delta n}}{dT} = \frac{\Delta H^*}{RT^2} \quad (3\text{-}71)$$

If k is in concentration units Eq. (3-71) may be solved for $(d \ln K_c^*)/dT$ and substituted in Eq. (3-65). This yields

$$\frac{d \ln k_c}{dT} = \frac{1}{T} + \frac{\Delta H^*}{RT^2} - \frac{d \ln (RT)^{\Delta n}}{dT} = \frac{1 - \Delta n}{T} + \frac{\Delta H^*}{RT^2} \quad (3\text{-}72)$$

Comparison with the activation energy from the Arrhenius equation (3-67) gives

$$E_c = (1 - \Delta n)RT + \Delta H^* \quad (3\text{-}73)$$

This is the relationship between E_c and ΔH^* for a gas-phase reaction in analogy to Eq. (3-68) for liquid-phase reactions.

The value of E_c determined experimentally by plotting $\ln k_c$ vs. $1/T$ is not equivalent to that for E_p, obtained from $\ln k_p$ vs. $1/T$. Hence Eq. (3-73) does not provide a relationship between E_p and ΔH^* for a gaseous reaction. This point is illustrated in Example 3-8.

Example 3-8. The homogeneous dimerization of ethylene in the gas phase has been studied by pressure measurements by Jahn[1] and Pease[2] and found to have an experimental activation energy of 35,000 cal/g mole determined from data for k_p at different temperatures.

As an approximation the structure of the activated complex may be assumed to be 1-butene.

From this information and the group-contribution method (Chap. 2) estimate the specific-reaction rate (in terms of disappearance of ethylene, per atmosphere, per hour) at 623 and 723°K from the theory of absolute reaction rates. Use the group-contribution method to obtain ΔS^* and the activation energy to obtain ΔH^*.

Also estimate the k values at these two temperatures from the collision theory, taking $\sigma = 3.78 \times 10^{-8}$ cm.

Compare both results with the experimental values of 0.0056 and 0.243 atm^{-1} hr^{-1} for the rate of conversion of ethylene determined by measuring the rate of change of pressure with time in a constant-volume static apparatus. Also make the comparison of the k values in terms of liters per gram mole per second.

Solution 1. The collision theory will be used first to estimate the k values. The values of M_A and M_B in Eq. (3-31) are the same and equal to 28 g/mole. Taking $\sigma = 3.78 \times 10^{-8}$ cm, noting that $R = k_B$ (6.02 $\times$ 10^{23}), and working at 623°K,

$$k = (3.78 \times 10^{-8})^2 \left[\frac{8\pi k_B(6.02 \times 10^{23}) \times 623 \times 2}{28} \right]^{\frac{1}{2}} e^{-E_c/RT}$$

$$= (3.78 \times 10^{-8})^2 (3.0 \times 10^5) e^{-E/RT} = 4.4 \times 10^{-10} e^{-E_c/RT} \quad \text{cc/(molecule)(sec)}$$

[1] F. P. Jahn, *J. Am. Chem. Soc.*, **61**:798 (1939).

[2] R. N. Pease, *J. Am. Chem. Soc.*, **53**:613 (1931).

In units of liters per gram mole per sec

$$k_c = 4.4 \times 10^{-10} \frac{6.02 \times 10^{23}}{1,000} e^{-E_c/RT} = 2.7 \times 10^{11} e^{-E_c/RT}$$

Before this result can be compared with the experimental result, E_c must be related to the experimental E_p of 35,000 cal/mole and k_c must be converted to k_p. The experimental activation energy is based upon plotting $\ln k_p$ vs. $1/T$. Hence k_p (per atmosphere, per second) is defined by the equation

$$\frac{dp_D}{d\theta} = k_p p_E^2 \qquad (A)$$

and related to the activation energy by the expression

$$k_p = A e^{-E_p/RT} \qquad (B)$$

where p_D and p_E are the partial pressures of dimer and ethylene.

On the other hand, the equation for k_c from the collision theory involves an activation energy determined by plotting $\ln k_c$ (liters per gram mole per sec) vs. $1/T$. To find the relationship between the two activation energies, the definition of k_p from Eq. (A) must be compared with the following defining equation for k_c:

$$\frac{dC_D}{d\theta} = k_c C_E^2 \qquad (C)$$

$$k_c = A e^{-E_c/RT} \qquad (D)$$

If the gases are ideal, $p = CRT$ and $dp_E/d\theta = RT(dC_E/d\theta)$. Using these relations, Eq. (A) becomes

$$RT \frac{dc_D}{d\theta} = k_p C_E^2 (RT)^2$$

Comparison with Eq. (C) gives the following relationship between k_c and k_p:

$$k_c C_E^2 = k_p C_E^2 RT$$

or

$$k_p = \frac{k_c}{RT} \qquad (E)$$

Taking the logarithm of Eqs. (B) and (D) and differentiating the result with respect to temperature give an expression for each activation energy,

$$\ln k_p = \ln A - \frac{E_p}{RT}$$

$$RT^2 \frac{d \ln k_p}{dT} = E_p \qquad (F)$$

Similarly

$$RT^2 \frac{d \ln k_c}{dT} = E_c \qquad (G)$$

Using Eq. (E) to eliminate k_c from Eq. (G),

$$E_c = RT^2 \frac{d \ln k_p RT}{dT} = RT^2 \frac{d \ln k_p}{dT} + RT$$

Finally, eliminating k_p with Eq. (F) yields the desired relationship between E_c and E_p,

$$E_c = E_p + RT = 35,000 + RT \tag{H}$$

This value for E_c can now be substituted in the collision-theory expression for k_c, yielding

$$k_c = 2.7 \times 10^{11} e^{-35,000/RT-1} = 2.7 \times 10^{11} e^{-1} e^{-35,000/RT}$$
$$k_c = (2.7 \times 10^{11}) e^{-1} e^{-35,000/RT} \quad \text{liters/(g mole)(sec)}$$
$$= 0.052 \text{ liter/(g mole)(sec)} \quad \text{at } 623°K$$

Using Eq. (E) to convert k_c to k_p,

$$k_p = \frac{k_c}{RT} = \frac{0.052 \times 3,600}{0.082 \times 623}$$
$$= 3.7 \text{ atm}^{-1} \text{ hr}^{-1}$$

(in comparison with the experimental value of 0.0056).

The value of k_p at 723°K can be obtained by noting that the collision theory proposes that k is proportional to $T^{\frac{1}{2}} e^{-E/RT}$,

$$k_p = 3.7 \left(\tfrac{7\,2\,3}{6\,2\,3}\right)^{\frac{1}{2}} \frac{e^{-35,000/723R}}{e^{-35,000/623R}}$$
$$= 205 \text{ atm}^{-1} \text{ hr}^{-1}$$

2. Now proceeding to the theory of absolute reaction rates, the specific-reaction rate is given by the expression [Eq. (3-63)]

$$k = \frac{k_B T}{h} e^{\Delta S^*/R - \Delta H^*/RT}$$

If the complex is assumed to be 1-butene, the activation step is the conversion of 2 moles of ethylene to 1 of 1-butene according to the reaction

$$2C_2H_4 \rightarrow H_2C\!\!=\!\!CH\!-\!CH_2\!-\!CH_3$$

The entropy change for this process can be estimated using the group-contribution method, described in Chap. 2. Table 3-12 summarizes the calculations. The values for the various contributions were taken from tables published by Hougen and Watson.[1]

Using this information,

$$\Delta S^*_{298} = 74.1 - (2 \times 52.8)$$
$$= -31.5 \text{ cal/(g mole)(°K)}$$

The difference between the heat capacities of the activated complex and the reactants is

$$\Delta c_p = (a^* - 2a_E) + (b^* - 2b_E) \times 10^{-3} T + (c^* - 2c_C) \times 10^{-6} T^2$$
$$\Delta c_p = -0.26 + 5.60 \times 10^{-3} T - 3.24 \times 10^{-6} T^2$$

[1] O. A. Hougen and K. M. Watson, "Chemical Process Principles," vol. 2, Thermodynamics, p. 759, John Wiley & Sons, Inc., New York, 1947.

TABLE 3-12

	$S_{298°K},$ cal/(g mole)(°K)	a	$b \times 10^3$	$c \times 10^6$
CH_4	44.5	3.42	17.85	−4.16
CH_3—CH_3	10.4	−2.04	24.00	−9.67
Double bond	−2.1	1.33	−12.69	4.77
Ethylene	52.8	2.71	29.16	−9.06
CH_4	44.5	3.42	17.85	−4.16
CH_3CH_3	10.4	−2.04	24.00	−9.07
CH_3—CH_2—CH_3	9.2	1.11	18.47	−6.85
CH_3—CH_2—CH_2CH_3	9.2	1.11	18.47	−6.85
Double bond	0.8	1.56	−14.87	5.57
1-butene	74.1	5.16	63.92	−21.36

Hence the activation entropy at 623°K is given by the expression

$$\Delta S^*_{623} = \Delta S^*_{298} + \int_{298}^{623} \frac{\Delta C_p}{T} \, dT$$

$$\Delta S^*_{623} = -31.5 - 0.26 \ln \frac{623}{298} + 5.60 \times 10^{-3}(623 - 298)$$

$$- \frac{3.24 \times 10^{-6}}{2} (623^2 - 298^2)$$

$$= -31.5 - 0.2 + 1.8 - 0.5$$
$$= -30.4 \text{ cal/(g mole)(°K)}$$

By a similar calculation,

$$\Delta S^*_{723} = -31.5 - 0.2 + 2.4 - 0.7 = -30.0$$

The enthalpy of activation is related to the energy of activation E_c by Eq. (3-73) for a gaseous reaction in which the standard states are unit fugacity. The relationship between E_c and E_p was developed in part 1 of this solution. Hence from Eq. (3-73)

$$\Delta H^* = E_c - (1 - \Delta n)RT = E_c - 2RT$$

Using Eq. (H)

$$\Delta H^* = (E_p + RT) - 2RT$$
$$\Delta H^* = E_p - RT = 35,000 - RT$$
$$\Delta H^*_{623} = 35,000 - 2 \times 623$$
$$= 33,800 \text{ cal/g mole}$$
$$\Delta H^*_{723} = 35,000 - 2 \times 723 = 33,600$$

These results can now be used in Eq. (3-63) to evaluate the rate constant. Since ΔS^* has been determined from group-contribution data based upon a standard state of unit fugacity, the k value will come out directly in pressure units. Another way of explaining this point is to note that K^* is measured in pressure units if the preceding entropy values are used (that is, $K^* = K_p$, for ideal gases). Since k is given by $(k_B T/h)K^*$, the units of k will be per second per atmosphere. Substituting into Eq. (3-63), at 623°K

$$k_p = \frac{(1.38 \times 10^{-16}) \times 623}{6.62 \times 10^{-27}} e^{-30.4/R} e^{-33,800/(R \times 623)}$$

$$= 13 \times 10^{12} \frac{1}{4.5 \times 10^6} \frac{1}{7 \times 10^{11}}$$

$$= 4.1 \times 10^{-6} \text{ atm}^{-1} \text{ sec}^{-1}$$

In hour units

$$k_p = 4.1 \times 10^{-6} \times 3,600 = 1.5 \times 10^{-2}$$
$$= 0.015 \text{ atm}^{-1} \text{ hr}^{-1}$$

This result, unlike that obtained from the collision theory, refers to the rate of formation of dimer and must be doubled to give the specific-reaction rate for the disappearance of ethylene. Hence the computed value for comparison with the experimental result is 0.030.

At 723°K,

$$k_p = 15 \times 10^{12} \frac{1}{3.6 \times 10^6} \frac{1}{1.4 \times 10^{10}} \times 3,600 \times 2$$

$$= 2.1 \text{ atm}^{-1} \text{ hr}^{-1}$$

The results for both temperatures are summarized in Table 3-13.

TABLE 3-13

Temp, °K	k_p, atm^{-1} hr^{-1}		
	Experimental	Collision theory	Absolute reaction rate theory
623	0.0056	3.7	0.03
723	0.243	205	2.1

As is frequently the case for reactions involving complex molecules, the values of k computed by the collision theory are too high. On the other hand, the theory of absolute reaction rates possesses the flexibility to predict lower specific-reaction rates for reactions between complex molecules. In the present instance the agreement with the experimental results is reasonably good.

It should be emphasized that the experimental activation energy has been used to estimate the enthalpy of activation ΔH^*. The theory of absolute reaction rates as developed by Eyring can be used to predict ΔH^* as well as ΔS^*. However, this prediction depends upon a complete and accurate knowledge of the structure of the activated complex. The results are generally much less precise for a complex reaction than when ΔH^* is determined through an experimental activation energy.

The k values in the units of liters per gram mole per second can be obtained from Eq. (E). This simply involves multiplying k_p by RT.

APPENDIX B

A CONTINUATION OF SECTION 10-4

Quantitative Prediction of the Effective Thermal Conductivity.[1] At steady-state conditions the heat-transfer rate through a cylindrical plane parallel to the center line of a packed cylindrical bed will be the sum of the part passing through the void space and the part passing through the solid material. If q is this total rate of heat flow per unit area of the plane, the point effective thermal conductivity k_e per unit of plane area is defined by the expression

$$q = -k_e \frac{\partial t}{\partial r} = q_{\text{void}} + q_{\text{solid}} \qquad (10\text{-}13)^2$$

This concept is illustrated in the upper half of Fig. 10-2. The temperature gradient in Eq. (10-13) applies to the bed as a whole and deserves some explanation because of the possibility of temperature differences between the solid and fluid phases in a packed bed. Bunnell[3] measured temperatures at the same radial position both in the gas and in the center of the solid particle and found no significant difference. The solid particles were activated alumina, a material of relatively low conductivity. On the basis of these data it will be assumed that the average temperature of the particle is the same as that of the gas at the same radial position. This does not require that the temperature gradient within a single solid particle coincide with that of the fluid phase. As an illustration, Bunnell measured effective thermal conductivities of the order of 0.10 to 0.30 Btu/(hr)(ft)(°F), while the conductivity of his alumina pellets is estimated to be about 0.5. Clearly the solid particles are not conducting heat under the gross radial gradient observed for the bed as a whole. For solid packings with thermal conductivities of 0.5 or greater, the gradients within the pellets would normally be less than those for the

---

[1] W. B. Argo and J. M. Smith, *Chem. Eng. Progr.*, **49**:443 (1953).

[2] Note that q_{void} is the heat-transfer rate through the void space per unit of void plus nonvoid area. It is not based upon a unit of void area. Similarly q_{solid} is not per unit of solid area, but per unit of void plus solid area.

[3] D. G. Bunnell, H. G. Irvin, R. W. Olson, and J. M. Smith, *Ind. Eng. Chem.*, **41**: 1977 (1948).

whole bed.   This situation is shown graphically in the lower portion of Fig. 10-2.   The higher the true thermal conductivity of the solid, the less the temperature change in the solid phase, so that with metallic pellets the temperature within a single particle would be expected to approach a constant value.   The gradient in Eq. (10-13) is the value for the bed as a whole and is designated as the "observed gradient" in Fig. 10-2.   It is the same as that in the continuous fluid phase.

As shown in Fig. 10-2, there may exist a considerable difference in temperature between gas and particle. This results in heat transfer to the particle on one side and from the particle back to the gas stream on the other side.   The temperature gradient within the particle would then be just sufficient to transfer this heat from one side to the other.

The heat passing across the plane in the void space is the sum of that due to molecular conduction (c), turbulent diffusion (td), and radiation (r). Since these paths are in parallel,

$$q_{\text{void}} = -\delta(k_c' + k_{td}' + k_r') \frac{\partial t}{\partial r} \quad (10\text{-}14)$$

where δ is the void fraction and the prime superscript indicates that the conductivity is based upon a unit of void area.[1]

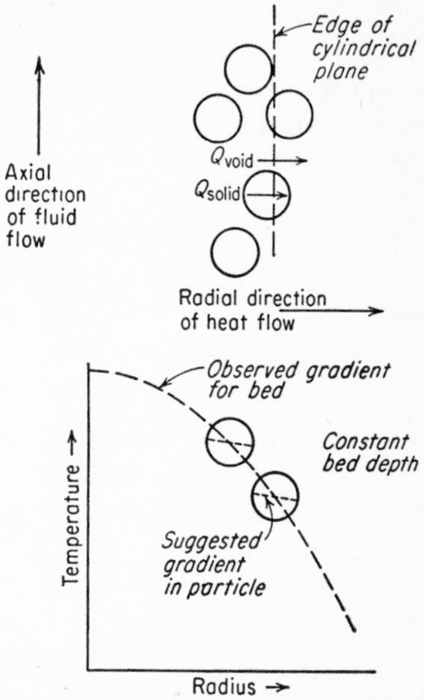

FIG. 10-2. Heat flow through packed beds.

The precise evaluation of the heat transfer through the particle presents a mathematically complex problem.   This complexity arises both from the geometry of the bed and from the several mechanisms by which heat can enter and leave the pellet.   To solve this problem, no simplification will be made concerning the heat-transfer mechanisms, but an ideal model of the packed bed will be employed in order to avoid geometrical difficulties.   The methods by which heat can enter a particle from its inner side are radiation, convection from the gas stream, and conduction through point contacts and stagnant fillets, as indicated in Fig. 10-3.   Heat is transferred through the particle and leaves the other side by the same three mechanisms.   The three processes are in series, and the whole will be designated as the series mechanism.   Hence

[1] Conductivities based upon a unit of void plus nonvoid area are related to the primed values by equations like this: $k_r = k_r'\delta$ etc.

$$q_{\text{solid}} = -k'_{\text{series}} (1 - \delta) \frac{\partial t}{\partial r} \tag{10-15}$$

Combining Eqs. (10-13) to (10-15) gives an expression for the point effective thermal conductivity in terms of contributions for each mechanism responsible for radial heat transfer.

$$k_e = \delta(k'_c + k'_{td} + k'_r) + (1 - \delta)k'_{\text{series}} \tag{10-16}$$
$$= k_c + k_{td} + k_r + k_{\text{series}}$$

FLUID-PHASE CONDUCTION. The value of k'_c in Eq. (10-16) is the molecular conductivity of the fluid. Its value will change with radial

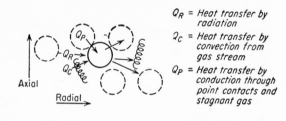

Q_R = Heat transfer by radiation

Q_C = Heat transfer by convection from gas stream

Q_P = Heat transfer by conduction through point contacts and stagnant gas

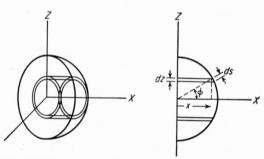

FIG. 10-3. Heat transfer in a single spherical particle.

position in the bed because of temperature variations. For gases k'_c is so low that it is not an important contribution to k_e, while for liquids this may not be true.

TURBULENT DIFFUSION. The contribution of turbulent diffusion k_{td} is a measure of heat transfer as a result of turbulent mixing of portions of the gas stream at different temperatures. As Singer and Wilhelm[1] have pointed out, its value can be advantageously estimated from measurements of mass transfer radially by the same mechanism. The advantage of using mass-transfer data is due to the fact that the transfer of mass radially in a packed bed does not involve the series or radiation mecha-

---

[1] E. Singer and R. H. Wilhelm, *Ind. Eng. Chem.*, **46**:343 (1950).

nisms but is caused only by molecular conduction and turbulent diffusion. In addition the contribution of molecular conduction is small. On this basis

$$k_{td} = \delta k'_{td} = \rho c_p D_e$$

where D_e is the effective diffusivity.

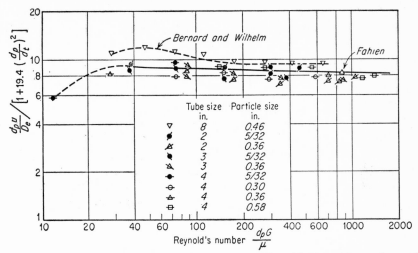

FIG. 10-4. Correlation of average Peclet number, $d_p u/D_e$, with Reynolds number and d_p/d_t.

In terms of modified Peclet numbers ($\text{Pe}_m = d_p u/D_e$) determined from mass-transfer data the turbulent-diffusion contribution is

$$k'_{td} = \frac{\rho c_p d_p u}{\delta(\text{Pe}_m)} = \frac{d_p c_p G}{\delta(\text{Pe}_m)} \tag{10-17}$$

Bernard and Wilhelm[1] have presented data for mass-transfer Peclet numbers for one gas system—air flowing through packed beds of $\frac{3}{8}$-in. spheres in an 8-in. pipe. At high velocities Baron[2] has shown on theoretical grounds that the Peclet number for mass transfer should be independent of particle size. Recently Fahien and Smith[3] have studied radial mass transfer for air in pipes from 2 to 4 in. in diameter and for a range of packing sizes. The correlation of their data and those of Bernard and Wilhelm is given in Fig. 10-4. This chart may be used to estimate the turbulent-diffusion contribution to heat transfer through Eq. (10-17).

The value of k'_{td} may vary significantly with radial position, especially near the pipe wall, where the void fraction and velocity are rapidly

[1] R. A. Bernard and R. H. Wilhelm, *Chem. Eng. Progr.*, **46**:233 (1950).
[2] T. Baron, *Chem. Eng. Progr.*, **48**:118 (1952).
[3] R. W. Fahien and J. M. Smith, *AIChE J.*, **1**: 28 (1955).

changing. The results in Fig. 10-4 are average figures determined for the bed as a whole but of course do not include the wall resistance that is associated with over-all effective thermal conductivities.

RADIATION CONTRIBUTION. The value of k_r' depends upon the temperature level and gradient. If the temperature gradient is large, it will vary with radial position. An accurate evaluation of the radiation contribution requires experimental temperature measurements. Schuler, Stallings, and Smith,[1] using measured temperature gradients, found (1) that k_r' reached a maximum at 0.4 to 0.6 of the distance from the center to the wall and (2) that the temperature level was more important in establishing k_r' than the temperature gradient. Thus Damkoehler's[2] simplified expression for radiation (corrected for emissivities, ϵ, less than 1.0)

$$k_r' = 4 \frac{\epsilon}{2 - \epsilon} d_p \, 0.173 \frac{T_a^3}{100^4} \tag{10-18}$$

was found to agree well with more elaborate methods, even though it included only the bulk mean temperature of the bed, T_a [in degrees Rankine in Eq. (10-18)].

Schuler's investigations were made at temperatures as high as 400°C and with large temperature gradients. At low mass velocities the radiation contribution to k_e was of the order of 10 to 15 per cent. Hence an approximate equation such as Eq. (10-18) is satisfactory for estimating k_r', except for reactions at very high temperatures.

SERIES MECHANISM. The mathematical problems encountered in evaluating the series mechanism in a packed bed with its nonuniform arrangement of solid particles have been mentioned. In order to obtain a useful solution to the problem of radial heat transfer through the pellet, the following assumptions will be made:

1. A constant temperature gradient exists in the fluid phase for a radial distance of one pellet diameter.

2. A constant temperature gradient exists in the solid particle.

3. Heat flow in the particle is radial in direction.

4. The mean temperature of the particle is equal to the temperature of the surrounding fluid at the center line of the particle.

5. An average heat-transfer coefficient may be considered applicable to the entire surface of the particle.

Assumption 3 permits the heat transfer in the particle to be summed over elements normal to the direction of flow. One-half of such a spherical particle with the normal element is illustrated in the lower half of

---

[1] R. W. Schuler, V. P. Stallings, and J. M. Smith, *Chem. Eng. Progr., Symposium Ser.* 4, **48**:19 (1952).

[2] G. Damkoehler, "Der Chemie Ingemeur," Euken Jacob 3, pt. I, p. 44, Akademische Verlagsgesellschaft m.b.H, Leipzig, 1937.

Fig. (10-3). An energy balance on the element leads to the expression

$$dQ' = k_s(2\pi z\, dz)\frac{t - t_p}{x} = h2\pi z(t_p - t_g)\, ds \qquad (10\text{-}19)$$

where dQ' = rate of heat flow through element of solid particle
k_s = molecular thermal conductivity of solid particle, based upon a unit area of solid
z = coordinate normal to heat flow (parallel to axis of bed)
x = coordinate in direction of heat flow
t = temperature at center plane of particle = temperature of fluid phase at same radial position
t_p = temperature of surface of particle at a distance x
$t_g = t + x\, dt/dx$ = temperature of fluid at a distance x
ds = element of surface through which heat is transferred to gas stream or to other particles
h = total heat-transfer coefficient from surface of particle to fluid or to other particles.

The element of surface area available for heat transfer to the gas stream may be related to dz as follows,

$$ds = \frac{dz}{\cos\phi} = \frac{d_p\, dz}{2x} \qquad (10\text{-}20)$$

where d_p is the diameter of the spherical particle.

Combining Eqs. (10-20) and (10-19) gives the following expression for t_p:

$$t_p = \frac{2k_s t + h d_p t_g}{2k_s + h d_p}$$

Using the fact that $t_g = t + x\, dt/dx$, this equation becomes

$$\frac{t - t_p}{x} = \frac{-h d_p}{2k + h d_p}\frac{dt}{dx} \qquad (10\text{-}21)$$

This value of $(t - t_p)/x$ may now be substituted into the second member of Eq. (10-19) to obtain an expression for dQ' in terms of the constant gradient dt/dx. This can be integrated directly from 0 to z, to obtain the total heat flow through the particle at a vertical plane a distance x from the center. The result is

$$Q' = -\frac{h k_s d_p}{2k_s + h d_p}\pi z^2 \frac{dt}{dx} \qquad (10\text{-}22)$$

In as much as πz^2 is the cross-sectional area of the solid at this point, and since dt/dx is the radial temperature gradient in the fluid phase, Eq.

(10-22) may be written

$$Q' = -\frac{hk_s(d_p/2)}{k_s + hd_p/2} A \frac{dt}{dr} \tag{10-23}$$

Here Q' is the heat transferred through the solid, based on the temperature gradient of the bed.

Since q_{solid} is based upon a unit area of normal plane, including both void and nonvoid surface,

$$q_{\text{solid}} = \frac{Q'}{A}(1 - \delta) = -\frac{hk_s(d_p/2)}{k_s + hd_p/2}(1 - \delta)\frac{\partial t}{\partial r} \tag{10-24}$$

Comparison of Eqs. (10-15) and (10-24) gives the desired expression for k'_{series},

$$k'_{\text{series}} = \frac{hk_s d_p}{2k_s + hd_p} \tag{10-25}$$

Similar derivations for cylindrical particles, oriented in the bed with the cylindrical axis either parallel or normal to the axis cf the pipe, yield the same result as Eq. (10-25) provided d_p is equal to the length of the cylinder.

The evaluation of k'_{series} requires a knowledge of the total heat-transfer coefficient h. This will be the sum of the convection coefficient from the fluid surrounding the particle, the radiation contribution from adjacent particles, and a conduction contribution from pellets in contact with each other. Thus h may be defined as follows:

$$h = \frac{Q'}{A(\Delta t)_m} = \frac{q'_c + q'_r + q'_p}{A(\Delta t)_m} = h_c + h_r + h_p \tag{10-26}$$

The convection coefficient h_c can be predicted from the data on heat transfer between solids and fluids in packed beds, such as the work of Hougen and Wilkie[1] and Hougen, Gamson, and Thodos.[2] Their correlations are

$$\left(\frac{h_c}{c_p G}\right)\left(\frac{c_p \mu}{k}\right)^{\frac{2}{3}} = 1.95 \left(\frac{d_p G}{\mu}\right)^{-0.51} \qquad \text{Re} < 350 \tag{10-27}$$

$$\left(\frac{h_c}{c_p G}\right)\left(\frac{c_p}{k}\right)^{\frac{2}{3}} = 1.06 \left(\frac{d_p G}{\mu}\right)^{-0.41} \qquad \text{Re} > 350 \tag{10-28}$$

The radiation and conduction coefficients, h_r and h_p, depend upon the value of $(\Delta t)_m$ defined by Eq. (10-26). A derivation based upon the same assumptions as employed in obtaining Eq. (10-25) leads to the results

$$(\Delta t)_m = -\frac{d_p k_s}{2(2k_s + hd_p)}\frac{dt}{dr} \tag{10-29}$$

[1] O. A. Hougen and C. R. Wilkie, *Trans. AIChE*, **41**:445 (1945).

[2] O. A. Hougen, B. Gamson, and G. Thodos, *Trans. AIChE*, **39**:1 (1943).

Since Eq. (10-18) gives the radiation contribution in terms of k'_r, h_r must be expressed in terms of k'_r,

$$h_r = -k'_r \frac{A'}{A} \frac{dt/dr}{(\Delta t)_m} \qquad (10\text{-}30)$$

where A' = projected area of one-half of spherical particle = $d_p^2/4$
    A = area of one-half of spherical particle = $d_p^2/2$
Combination of Eqs. (10-29) and (10-30) to eliminate $(\Delta t)_m$ gives for h_r

$$h_r = \frac{k'_r(2k_s + hd_p)}{d_p k_s} \qquad (10\text{-}31)$$

Equation (10-31) permits the evaluation of h_r by employing Eq. (10-18) for k'_r. The analogous expression for h_p is

$$h_p = \frac{k'_p(2k_s + hd_p)}{d_p k_s} \qquad (10\text{-}32)$$

The conductivity k'_p determines the heat transfer through the pellet by solid contact with an adjacent pellet, and through stagnant gas fillets surrounding the contact points. The correlation of Wilhelm, Johnson, Wynkoop, and Collier,[1] summarized by Eq. (10-33), may be used with Eq. (10-32) to determine h_p.

$$\log k'_p = -1.76 + 0.0129 \frac{k_s}{\delta} \qquad (10\text{-}33)$$

COMBINATION OF SEPARATE CONTRIBUTIONS. Summation of the expressions for each mechanism in accordance with Eq. (10-16) results in a composite equation for the effective thermal conductivity,

$$k_e = \delta \left(k'_c + \frac{d_p c_p G}{\mathrm{Pe}_m \delta} + 4 \frac{\epsilon}{2 - \epsilon} d_p \times 0.173 \frac{T_a^3}{100^4} \right) + (1 - \delta) \frac{hk_s d_p}{2k_s + hd_p} \qquad (10\text{-}34)$$

In this expression the heat-transfer coefficient h is given by Eqs. (10-26), (10-27), (10-31), and (10-32). Equation (10-34) predicts the effect of a number of the basic variable upon k_e. Since Pe_m is relatively insensitive to particle diameter, the second, third, and fourth terms in the equation require that k_e increase with particle diameter. Since h increases with mass velocity G, the equation predicts that k_e will increase with G. It is also expected that k_e will increase with the conductivity of the solid particle, although the increase will be slight, because k_s occurs in both numerator and denominator of the last term.

When the temperature in the bed is less than 300°C, the radiation contributions to k_e may be neglected. Under these circumstances, Eq.

[1] R. H. Wilhelm, W. C. Johnson, R. Wynkoop, and D. W. Collier, *Chem. Eng. Progr.*, **44**:105 (1948).

(10-34) can be simplified to the following form,

$$k_e = \delta(k_c' + k_{td}') + (1 - \delta)k_s \frac{d_p h_c + 2k_p'}{d_p h_c + 2k_s} \qquad (10\text{-}35)$$

where k_p' is the conductivity between solid particles in contact and is given by Eq. (10-33). If the Peclet number for heat transfer is introduced through the relation $Pe_h = d_p c_p G / k_e$ and Eq. (10-27) is used for h_c, Eq. (10-35) may be written,

$$\frac{1}{Pe_h} = \delta \left[\frac{1}{(Pr)(Re)} + \frac{1}{Pe_m} \right] + (1 - \delta) \frac{k_s}{Re \, \mu c_p} \frac{1 + \dfrac{k_p'(Re)^{-0.49}(Pr)^{\frac{2}{3}}}{c_p \mu}}{1 + \dfrac{k_s(Re)^{-0.49}(Pr)^{\frac{2}{3}}}{c_p \mu}}$$

$$(10\text{-}36)$$

Example 10-6. Using the procedure proposed by Argo, estimate the value of k_e for a packed bed through which air is flowing at the following conditions:

Pipe diameter = 2.0 in. ID
Particle = $\frac{1}{8}$- by $\frac{1}{8}$-in. cylindrical alumina pellets; $k_s = 0.5$ Btu/(hr)(ft)(°F)
Void fraction = 0.40
Mass velocity of air,
Case I = 147 lb/(hr)(sq ft of total pipe cross section)
Case II = 493 lb/(hr)(sq ft)
Emissivity of particles = 0.9

Solution. Schuler *et al.*[1] determined k_e from experimental temperature data for these conditions. The mean bed temperatures were 455 and 536°F for cases I and II, and these values will be used in order to be able to compare the computed results with their experimental values.

The computations are summarized in Table 10-7 for both cases. The detailed calculations are given for case I.

1. RADIATION CONTRIBUTION. Equation (10-18) can be used to estimate k_r' for case I.

$$k_r' = 4 \frac{0.9}{2 - 0.9} \frac{1}{8 \times 12} \times 0.173 \frac{(455 + 460)^3}{100^4} = 0.044$$

At the higher temperature level in case II, $k_r' = 0.056$.

2. POINT-CONTACT CONDUCTIVITY (EQ. 10-33)

$$\log k_p' = -1.76 + 0.0129 \frac{k_s}{\delta}$$

$$= -1.76 + 0.0129 \frac{0.5}{0.4}$$

$$k_p' = 0.018$$

This value is the same for both case I and case II.

3. COEFFICIENT h_c BETWEEN PELLET AND GAS (EQ. 10-27). The Reynolds numbers for the two conditions are

[1] Schuler, Stallings, and Smith, *loc. cit.*

For case I

$$\frac{d_p G}{\mu} = \frac{1}{8 \times 12} \frac{147}{0.061} = 25$$

For case II

$$\text{Re} = \frac{493}{(8 \times 12) \times 0.066} = 78$$

For both conditions Eq. (10-27) is applicable,

$$\frac{h_c}{cG} = (1.95)(25)^{-0.51}(0.74)^{-\frac{2}{3}} = 0.462$$

For case I

$$h_c = 0.462 \times 147 \times 0.255 = 17.3$$

4. COEFFICIENTS h_r AND h_p. The calculation of the radiation and point-to-point contact coefficients from Eqs. (10-31) and (10-32) is a trial-and-error procedure, since both expressions involve the summation coefficient h.

If, for case I, h is estimated to be 33, the value of h_r is, by Eq. (10-31),

$$h_r = \frac{0.044(2 \times 0.5 + 33 \times 0.0104)}{0.0104 \times 0.5} = 11.3$$

From Eq. (10-32)

$$h_p = \frac{0.018(2 \times 0.5 + 33 \times 0.0104)}{0.0104 \times 0.5} = 4.6$$

Since the sum of $h_c + h_r + h_p = 17.3 + 11.3 + 4.6 = 33.2$, the original assumption of 33 for h is satisfactory.

For Case II similar trial-and-error calculations give

$$h_r = 17$$
$$h_p = 5.2$$
$$h = 33 + 17 + 5.2 = 55$$

5. THE SERIES CONTRIBUTION. Knowing the coefficient h at the surface of the particle, the series contribution to k_e can be evaluated from Eq. (10-25). For case I

$$k'_{series} = \frac{h k_s d_p}{2k_s + h d_p} = \frac{33 \times 0.5 \times 0.0104}{2 \times 0.5 + 33 \times 0.0104} = 0.129$$

6. TURBULENT-DIFFUSION CONTRIBUTION. The ratio of diameters of particle to tube is

$$\frac{d_p}{d_t} = \frac{\frac{1}{8}}{2.06} = 0.0607$$

From Fig. 10-4, at a Reynolds number of 25,

$$\frac{\text{Pe}_m}{1 + 19.4 \left(\frac{d_p}{d_t}\right)^2} = 8.7$$

$$\text{Pe}_m = 8.7 \, (1 + 19.4 \times 0.0607^2) = 9.3$$

Similarly, at Re = 78,

$$\text{Pe}_m = 9.0 \times 1.07 = 9.7$$

The turbulent-diffusion contributions can then be evaluated from Eq. (10-17).

For case I

$$k'_{td} = \frac{d_p cG}{(\text{Pe}_m)\delta} = \frac{0.0104 \times 0.255 \times 147}{9.3 \times 0.4} = 0.105$$

7. MOLECULAR-CONDUCTIVITY CONTRIBUTION. The thermal conductivity of air at 455°F is approximately 0.024 and 0.026 at 536°F. Hence

For case I

$$k'_c = 0.024$$

For case II

$$k'_c = 0.026$$

8. EFFECTIVE THERMAL CONDUCTIVITY. The value of k_e now can be ascertained by summing the several contributions according to Eq. (10-16).

$$k_e = \delta(k'_c + k'_{td} + k'_r) + (1 - \delta)k'_{\text{series}}$$

For case I

$$k_e = 0.4(0.024 + 0.105 + 0.044) + (1 - 0.4) \times 0.129$$
$$= 0.146$$

The value determined from experimental temperature data by Schuler *et al.* is 0.113 at these conditions.

The results for case II are shown in Table 10-7.

TABLE 10-7. CALCULATION OF EFFECTIVE THERMAL CONDUCTIVITIES

	Case I	Case II
Mass velocity, lb/(hr)(sq ft)	147	493
d_p, ft	0.0104	0.0104
Reynolds number	25	78
1. k'_r [Eq. (10-18)]	0.044	0.056
2. k'_p [Eq. (10-33)]	0.018	0.018
3. h_c [Eq. (10-27)]	17	33
4. h_r [Eq. (10-31)]	11.3	17
h_p [Eq. (10-32)]	4.6	5.2
$h = h_c + h_p + h_r$	33	55
5. Series contribution, k'_{series} [Eq. (10-25)]	0.129	0.182
6. Turbulent-diffusion contribution, k'_{td} [Eq. (10-17)]	0.105	0.339
7. Molecular-conductivity contribution. k'_c	0.024	0.026
8. Effective thermal conductivity, k_e [Eq. (10-16)]	0.146	0.277
Experimental values	0.113	0.276

NAME INDEX

Allgood, H. Y., 321
Amis, E. S., 88
Argo, W. B., 300, 384
Askey, P. J., 87

Baars, G. M., 281
Baron, S., 278
Baron, T., 348, 387
Beeck, O., 210
Begley, J. W., 316
Berkman, S., 225
Bernard, R. A., 387
Berzelius, J. J., 202
Blue, R. W., 279
Bodenstein, M., 56, 76
Brown, C. L., 325
Brown, R. W., 283
Brunauer, S., 215, 216, 218
Bunnell, D. G., 384

Cheney, H. A., 162
Cherniavsky, A. J., 162
Chilton, T. H., 283
Clark, E. L., 289
Coberly, C. A., 293
Colburn, A. P., 289
Collier, D. W., 391
Conn, A. L., 325
Cummings, G. H., 283

Damkoeler, G., 291, 388
Daniels, Farrington, 46, 87, 88
Denbigh, K. G., 174
Dow, W. M., 310
Downs, C. R., 105, 320
Drake, L. C., 223
Drew, T. B., 283, 308
Dybdal, F. C., 327

Egloff, G., 225
Emmett, P. H., 210, 212, 216, 222, 226, 228

Ergun, S., 235, 309
Eyring, Henry, 3, 78

Fahien, R. W., 387
Fairbairn, A. W., 162
Farkas, A., 88
Fast, E., 279
Felix, J. R., 293
Fisher, R. A., 111
Freundlich, H., 211
Frost, A. A., 87, 88

Gaffney, G. B., 308
Gamson, B. W., 235, 308, 390
Gilliland, E. R., 237, 360, 364
Glasstone, Samuel, 78, 79
Goba, E. J., 325
Gooch, D. B., 106
Gretton, A. T., 315
Griffith, R. H., 226
Groll, H. P. A., 162
Grummer, M., 310, 360

Hall, R. E., 292
Harkness, J. B., 86
Hearne, G., 162
Heckelsberg, L., 279
Hinshelwood, C. N., 47, 87
Hobson, M., 308
Hohnig, C. E., 325
Holm, V. C. F., 279
Hoogschagen, J., 269
Hougen, J. O., 293
Hougen, O. A., 14, 150, 231, 235, 236, 255, 308, 381, 390
Hurt, D. M., 234, 261, 308

Innes, W. B., 227, 228
Irvin, H. B., 291, 384

Jahn, F. P., 379
Jakob, M., 310

395

SUBJECT INDEX